CLASSICS Appreciation SOCIETY

THE THREE MUSKETEERS
by Alexandre Dumas

LIVES OF THE POETS
by Samuel Johnson

ETHICS
by Baruch Spinoza

THE CLOUDS
by Aristophanes

and

WANDERING WILLIE'S TALE
by Sir Walter Scott

Harriet Beecher Stowe TELLS
WHAT SORT OF WOMAN SHE IS

Martin Luther REFUSES TO RECANT
BEFORE THE DIET OF WORMS

CLASSICS Appreciation SOCIETY

CONDENSATIONS

Standard Book Number: 7172–1400–1

Library of Congress Catalog Card Number: 55–12250

CONTENTS

Each Home Course Appreciation precedes its work.

ILLUSTRATED BY WILLIAM SHARP

THE
THREE
MUSKETEERS

by

Alexandre Dumas

TRANSLATED BY
W. Robson

A CONDENSATION

NOTE: *The editor's summaries of various omitted passages*
appear italicized and in brackets throughout the text.

HOME COURSE APPRECIATION

ALEXANDRE DUMAS was not a man who was given to moderation. When he indulged his appetites, he did so always with gusto; and when he worked, he likewise exceeded the bounds of ordinary endurance. For forty years he was writing at least two or three works at one time—historical romances, plays, travel books and entire newspapers. The reader who starts through his works is daunted by their sheer numbers.

Dumas' masterpiece is *The Three Musketeers*. It was, as it is today, a fresh and vivid piece of historical romancing, humorous and exciting. Yet it was written in collaboration with another man, in a very short period of time, with several other volumes and hundreds of other responsibilities demanding the time of the author. Moreover, he had been writing professionally for almost twenty years; yet *The Three Musketeers* is as fresh and shining as a new-minted coin. Dumas' novels are remarkable productions, but even more remarkable than any of the novels was the character of Alexandre Dumas *père*—as he is called to distinguish him from his illegitimate son, Alexandre Dumas *fils,* the dramatist and author of *Camille.*

VITALITY: THE HEREDITARY TRAIT OF THE DUMAS

Prodigious energies and immense activities ran in the Dumas family. The father of Alexandre Dumas *père* was born in the West Indies, the natural son of an enslaved Negro mother and an aristocratic French father. He went to France as a young man and promptly enlisted as a private in the army. At the request of his father, who feared that the aristocratic family name of de la Pailleterie might be soiled by association with a common soldier, he assumed his mother's name of Dumas. He was a young man of great strength, mild in temper. The story is told that he could insert the four fingers of one

3

Alexandre Dumas the Elder (1803–1870).

hand into the barrels of four muskets and hold them straight before him. He was as fearless as he was strong, and more than ordinarily intelligent. As long as the old régime lasted, his chances to display these qualities were limited, and he remained a private. But as soon as the Revolution broke out, his advancement was quick; he was successively lieutenant, lieutenant colonel, and then, under Napoleon, a major general in command of three armies—all before he was thirty-three years old.

As one would expect, he was a valiant general. Some of his exploits read like those of the Musketeers whom his son made famous. He always charged at the head of his troops, unmindful of hazards. On one occasion he scaled a mountain and captured a fortified point by tossing his men, one at a time, over a palisade, where they slaughtered the bewildered enemy. Yet he was not vengeful or bloodthirsty; and by abolishing the death penalty and the system of political commissars in his armies, this splendid giant won from his troops the nickname of "Monsieur Humanity."

POVERTY AND HUMILIATION

GENERAL DUMAS' FREE AND INDEPENDENT WAYS, however, led to trouble with Napoleon. Sickness forced his retirement from the service, and he died, penniless and forgotten, barely forty years old. He left his widow, daughter and four-year-old son with no property of any sort and few friends, for Napoleon refused even to speak with the widow of the impertinent General Dumas, and few friends were brave enough to cause the displeasure of the emperor.

Alexandre had a very scrappy and haphazard education, severely limited by his mother's poverty and by the careless disposition which he inherited from his father. Born in 1803, he was just old enough to feel the full force of the reaction which followed Napoleon's final defeat at Waterloo in 1815. As he came into his young manhood, Alexandre Dumas could have been pardoned for thinking regretfully that the exciting, heroic days of the Revolution and of the Napoleonic conquests were gone forever. He shrank from a career in the priesthood; he could not hope for a military career like his father's; he had salvaged nothing from his intermittent schooling save a handsome and impressive handwriting. To all appearances, the best prospect confronting him when he came to Paris in 1822 was a dull, routine clerk's job in a government office. And, in fact, this was the first job that Alexandre Dumas undertook.

5

But Dumas became a clerk only so that he might continue to eat while making his way in the world of literature. For already at the age of twenty, and despite the fact that he had no visible qualifications, this handsome youth fancied himself a poet, or perhaps a playwright—in any case, a man with a mark to make, and preferably in literature. He did not know the first thing about the craft of writing, but he was a natural storyteller and dramatist, and made his way quickly in the world of letters.

His early plays (*Christina, Henry III and His Court* and *Antony*) could not possibly hold the stage today. They are wildly melodramatic and often absurdly rhetorical; they are carelessly written and loosely constructed. But, somehow or other, the breath of life is in them, as it was in everything that Dumas wrote. He struck out for himself, shocking some people, amusing others, always catching the interest of the public and always putting something of his own dynamic personality into his work. He worked prodigiously, and soon established himself as a playwright. He was never particular about the source of his plots. Whatever incident he happened to pick out of a casual volume, whatever half-formed idea some "collaborator" offered him, he was capable of turning into a gripping piece of theater or an attention-getting novel. What if he sometimes turned out more books in a year than any single man could possibly have written? He never denied using collaborators; they profited from the fact that a "Dumas story" —any Dumas story—sold for four times the price an unknown author could command. They profited also from the touches of life, wit, vivacity, and action which Dumas never failed to provide in any story which left his hands. The truth is that none of his collaborators ever published an independent work half so good as the things they turned out with Dumas.

THE BEGINNING OF "THE THREE MUSKETEERS"

THUS "THE THREE MUSKETEERS," though it is a work of multiple collaboration, is nonetheless stamped unmistakably with the genius of Alexandre Dumas. The first of his collaborators in this book was a young man named Auguste Maquet, with whom Dumas had previously done a play and a novel. Sometime in the year 1843, Maquet proposed to Dumas a novel dealing with the age of Louis XIII and Cardinal Richelieu. Dumas was enthusiastic about the idea, particularly when one or the other of the two collaborators (no one has ever been quite sure which one) discovered a rare eighteenth-century book called *The Memoirs of Monsieur d'Artagnan, Captain-Lieutenant in the First Company of the King's Musketeers.* The author of this book was a certain Gatien de Courtilz de Sandras; he published his volume at least thirty years after the death of the man he was describing, and nearly seventy years after the events of *The Three Musketeers* are supposed to have taken place.

THE BRIGHT LIGHT OF DUMAS' IMAGINATION

Indubitably, *The Memoirs of M. d'Artagnan* contain the kernel of *The Three Musketeers,* but it is a dry and unpromising kernel. Some of the incidents of Dumas' novel are reported here, in a flat, unimaginative way. We have young d'Artagnan leaving home for Paris, quarreling at Meung, meeting with Athos, Porthos and Aramis, and coming into the sphere of the terrible Milady. Courtilz de Sandras probably tried to describe events pretty much as they happened; his d'Artagnan is a rough and ready young Gascon, and his Musketeers are not disguised noblemen, but plain, rowdy soldiers. And when Maquet submitted to his famous collaborator a first scenario for their novel, he too proposed very little in the way of a transformation. He had a costume romance in mind, a little, picturesque fable about unremembered seventeenth-century figures. He wanted to prettify the *Memoirs,* not to rework them from the bottom up.

But Dumas tore up the scenario and rewrote it on a grand scale. To satisfy him, the novel must be a tale of intrigue and passion and heroic gambling with empires for the stakes. The obedient collaborator went back to the memoirs, diaries, and scandal sheets of the seventeenth century. There he dug up a story about Anne of Austria's love for the Duke of Buckingham, and a fantastic tale about twelve misplaced diamond studs. With Dumas doing the dialogues and Maquet the description, the book flowed forth with ease.

TROUBLE WITH A TITLE

The novel finally lacked only one thing: a title. Dumas originally proposed to call it "Athos, Porthos, and Aramis," but the newspaper in which it was advertised to appear reported a deluge of inquiries about this title, half serious and half mocking. Was M. Dumas proposing to write a new history of Clotho, Lachesis, and Atropos, the Three Fates of tradition? Clearly, the title was troublesome; so the editor suggested that they call the new novel *The Three Musketeers*. Dumas was delighted, the more so because the title, inaccurate though it was in tallying the musketeers, augured the greatest possible success for the novel.

A FORMULA FOR FICTION

THERE WERE MANY REASONS why *The Three Musketeers* should have been the immense publishing success which it at once became. Dumas had fallen on a story in which he could display many facets of his own character. He was a headstrong man who went out of his way to seek or create difficulties, and who bore a charmed life in the midst of them. The Musketeers he imagined bore themselves with all the dash and gallantry of their inexhaustible creator.

There were social reasons for the novel's success. After the defeat of Napoleon, the future of France had seemed to many an inglorious prospect. The effort that had gone to make the triumphs of Napoleon had ended in the bloodless middle-class banalities of Louis-Philippe. To the lowered national pride Dumas' swashbuckling heroics and theatrical speeches came as a tonic. A generation accustomed to the timid voice of prudence and moderation was thrilled by the recollection of ancestors heroic and proud whom nothing dismayed.

Finally, there was the art of the story itself. It matters little that details are often unclear, that Planchet is forgotten in London and then miraculously returned to France, that bullets always conveniently miss the heroes, and confidential conversations are always fortuitously overheard by them. The important thing is that the headlong movement is never allowed to falter. We are propelled from crisis to crisis, never sure about what is going to happen in the next few pages. Dumas had discovered a wonderful device in this historical romance; by mixing up two distinct conflicts (the Cardinal versus the throne, and England versus France), he insured his heroes against any deadly pauses. They are always teetering on the edge of one danger or another, ever more careless and courageous, and, in their audacity, more enthralling to read about.

PORTRAIT OF THE ARTIST AND FRANCE

Above all, Dumas excelled in his character drawing. The Musketeers themselves are distinct, not only as a group but as individuals. Aramis, with his penchant for theology, his reticence and his hair-trigger temper, is one aspect of the French character. Athos is the

French aristocracy at its best—graceful, cool, resourceful and unflustered in the presence of incarnate evil. Porthos, the vain and kindly giant who resembles his creator, is strong with a peasant strength. There is a story that, when he was writing a sequel to *The Three Musketeers,* Dumas was found crying by a friend who asked what was the matter. "It's Porthos," said the author disconsolately, "I'm killing him off. Ah, Monsieur, you have no idea how fond I was of him. . . ."

But it is the young Gascon, d'Artagnan, who shows Dumas' mastering of the art of character portrayal. He is far from an ideal character; some of his love affairs are distinctly on the sordid side; he is often foolish and always rash. His good intentions are frequently offset by his touchy pride. Yet, from the minute he appears, straddling his melancholy yellow nag, the reader is drawn to his side. In d'Artagnan one sees most clearly the image of invincibility which Dumas had formed of himself. D'Artagnan is a thoroughly quixotic hero—an innocent who must prove himself in the great world, but one who has something to teach the world, too. Along with the sinister and unenchanted Cardinal, even the most cynical reader falls under the spell of d'Artagnan and his dashing comrades.

SCALE OF PAY AS A DETERMINANT OF STYLE

GRIMAUD, THE LACONIC LACKEY who serves Aramis, was created by Dumas as a matter of business. The newspapers which first printed Dumas' novels paid by the line, and a single word of dialogue counted as a line. Nothing pleased Dumas more than to beat the penny-a-liners' game by spinning out dialogue like this parody:

"Have you seen him?"
"Whom?"
"Him."
"Whom?"
"Dumas."
"Père?"
"Yes."
"What a man!"
"No doubt."
"How mad!"
"Surely."
"How prolific!"
"Rather!"

9

All for one, one for all—Athos, Porthos, Aramis, d'Artagnan.

The monosyllabic Grimaud is simply a line thief fattening the author's purse. Originally, he appeared on many pages, but in the middle of the novel the newspapers decided that only half a line or more of actual type would count as a full line, and Dumas dropped pages of staccato dialogue from his novel.

A TRIUMPH OF ENERGY

More often than not, the man who writes with one eye on the cash register and the other on his characters is doomed to failure. But with Alexandre Dumas, this was not the case. Not only did he make *The Three Musketeers* one of the finest cloak-and-dagger romances ever written, but he also made it a story which for sheer vitality and excitement is the envy of many more polished craftsmen. Hugo and Balzac subscribed to the paper which printed Dumas' novel, and followed the story with frank enthusiasm. Sworn enemies of the journal which serialized the novel sent in their subscriptions, doubling and tripling the circulation while the novel was appearing. When the final installment was published, Dumas was, by general acclaim, the lion of the Paris literary world.

The energies of this amazing man were far from exhausted by his achievement. Before he finished writing *The Three Musketeers,* he had embarked on another work, *The Count of Monte Cristo.* And before that novel was finished, he had three or four others in progress. In the course of his lifetime, Dumas *père* probably turned out more than a thousand volumes. In *Twenty Years After* (1845) and *The Vicomte de Bragelonne* (1847), Dumas concluded the story of d'Artagnan, to the last unflagging in inspiration and unfailing of invention. He came to consider *The Three Musketeers* merely the first unit of an enormous project of novels which would cover all the history of France. The project was never completed. In 1860, when he was fifty-eight years old, Dumas rushed off to fight with Garibaldi for the freedom of Italy. Ten years later the lion-hearted old man, so childish in his vanities, so careless and disorderly in his habits, harassed by creditors and domineering women, died at his son's house near Dieppe.

The Three Presents of M. D'Artagnan the Elder

ON THE FIRST MONDAY of the month of April, 1625, the town of Meung, in which the author of the *Romance of the Rose* was born, appeared to be in as perfect a state of revolution as if the Huguenots had just made a second Rochelle of it. Many citizens, seeing the women flying toward High Street, and hearing the children crying on the doorsteps, hastened to don their cuirasses, and, supporting their somewhat uncertain courage with a musket or a partisan, directed their steps toward the hostelry of the Franc-Meunier, before which was gathered a compact, vociferous, and curious group, increasing in numbers every minute.

In those times panics were common, and every few days some city registered in its archives an event of this kind. There were nobles who made war against each other; there was the King, who made war against the Cardinal; there was Spain, which made war against the King. Then, in addition to these concealed or public, official or unofficial wars, there were robbers, mendicants, Huguenots, wolves and the servants of nobles, who made war upon everybody. The citizens always took up arms readily against thieves, wolves and servants—often against nobles and Huguenots—sometimes against the King—but never against the Cardinal or Spain. It resulted, then, from this habit, that on the said first Monday of the month of April 1625, the citizens, on hearing the clamor, and seeing neither the red and yellow standard nor the livery of the Duke de Richelieu, rushed toward the hostel of the Franc-Meunier.

13

On their arrival the cause of this hubbub was apparent to all.

It was a young man, whose portrait we can sketch in a few lines. Imagine to yourself Don Quixote at eighteen; Don Quixote without his corselet, his coat of mail, and his pedantic foolishness; Don Quixote clothed in a woolen doublet, the blue color of which had faded into a nameless shade between lees of wine and a heavenly azure. Imagine to yourself, further, a long, brown face, with high cheek bones (a sign of cunning) and enormously developed maxillary muscles, an infallible sign by which a Gascon may always be known, even without his beret. But our young man wore a beret, set off with a sort of feather. He had an open and intelligent eye and a hooked but finely chiseled nose. Too big for a youth, too small for a grown man, an inexperienced eye might have taken him for a farmer's son upon a journey, had it not been for the long sword, which, dangling from a leather baldric, hit against the calves of its owner as he walked and against the rough side of his steed when he was on horseback.

For our young man had a mount which was the observed of all observers. It was a Béarn pony, from twelve to fourteen years old, of a yellow color, without a hair in its tail, but not without windgalls on its legs. This pony, though going with its head lower than its knees, rendering a martingale quite unnecessary, contrived, nevertheless, to traverse eight leagues a day. Unfortunately, the good qualities of this steed were so well concealed by its strange-colored hide and unaccountable gait that, at a time when everybody was a connoisseur in horseflesh, its appearance at Meung, which place it had entered about a quarter of an hour before by the gate of Beaugency, produced an unfavorable feeling that extended to its master.

And this feeling had been the more painful to young d'Artagnan —for so was the Don Quixote of this second Rosinante named—because he did not in the least conceal from himself the ridiculous appearance that such a steed gave him, good horseman as he was. He had sighed deeply, therefore, on accepting the gift of the pony from M. d'Artagnan the elder. He was not ignorant of the fact that such a beast was worth the munificent sum of at least twenty whole livres; but the words which had accompanied the present were above all price.

"My son," said the old Gascon nobleman—in that pure Béarn patois of which Henry IV could never rid himself—"my son, this horse was born in the house of your father, about thirteen years ago, and has remained in it ever since, which ought to make you love it.

Never sell it—allow it to die tranquilly and honorably of old age; and if you make a campaign with it, take as much care of it as you would of an old servant. At court, provided you ever have the honor to go there," continued M. d'Artagnan the elder, "an honor to which your ancient nobility gives you right, sustain worthily your name of nobleman, which has been worthily borne by your ancestors during five hundred years; sustain it both for your own sake and for those who belong to you. By these I mean your relations and friends. Endure nothing from anyone but the Cardinal and the King. It is by his courage, understand me well, by his courage alone, that a nobleman can make his way nowadays. Whoever trembles for a second, perhaps lets the bait escape him which, during that exact second, fortune held out to him. You are young; you ought to be brave for two reasons—the first is that you are a Gascon and the second is that you are my son. Be ever ready for the occasion, and seek adventures. I have taught you how to handle a sword; you have sinews of iron, a wrist of steel: fight on all occasions; fight the more because duels are forbidden, since, in consequence, there is twice as much courage in fighting. I have nothing to give you, my son, but fifteen crowns, my horse and the counsels you have just heard. Your mother will add to them a recipe for a certain balsam, which she had from a Bohemian and which has the miraculous virtue of curing all wounds that do not reach the heart. Take advantage of all and live happily and long. I have but one word to add and that is to propose an example to you—not mine, for I myself have never appeared at court and have only taken part in religious wars as a volunteer. I speak of M. de Tréville, who was formerly my neighbor, and who had the honor to be as a child the playfellow of our King, Louis XIII, whom God preserve! Sometimes their play degenerated into battles, and in these battles the King was not always the stronger. The blows he received gave him a great esteem and friendship for M. de Tréville. Afterwards M. de Tréville fought with others: on his first journey to Paris, five times; from the death of the late King to the majority of the young one, without reckoning wars and sieges, seven times; and from that majority up to the present day, perhaps a hundred times! So that in spite of edicts, ordinances, and decrees, he is today captain of the Musketeers—that is to say, leader of a legion of Caesars, whom the King holds in great esteem, and whom the Cardinal dreads—he who dreads next to nothing, as we all know. In addition, M. de Tréville gains ten thousand crowns a year; he is, therefore, a great noble. He began as you begin; go to him with this letter and make him your model, that you may do as he has done."

Whereupon M. d'Artagnan the elder girded his own sword around his son, kissed him tenderly on both cheeks and gave him his benediction.

On leaving the paternal chamber, the young man found his mother, who was waiting for him with the famous recipe, of which the counsels we have just repeated would necessitate a frequent employment. The adieux on this side of the house were longer and more tender than they had been on the other. Not that M d'Artagnan did not love his son, who was his only offspring, but he was a man and would have considered it unworthy of a man to give way to his feelings; whereas Madame d'Artagnan was a woman and, still more, a mother. She wept abundantly and, let us speak it to the praise of M. d'Artagnan the younger, notwithstanding his efforts to be as firm as a future Musketeer should be, nature prevailed, and he shed many tears, of which he succeeded with great difficulty in concealing half.

That same day the young man set forth on his journey, furnished with the three paternal presents, which consisted, as we have said, of fifteen crowns, the horse and the letter for M. de Tréville, the counsels being thrown into the bargain.

With such trappings, d'Artagnan was, morally and physically, an exact copy of the hero of Cervantes, to whom we compared him so happily when the duty of an historian placed us under the necessity of sketching his portrait. Don Quixote took windmills for giants and sheep for armies; d'Artagnan took every smile for an insult and every look as a provocation; whence it resulted that from Tarbes to Meung his fist was constantly doubled, or his hand on the hilt of his sword, and yet the fist did not descend upon any jaw, nor did the sword issue from its scabbard. This was not because the sight of the wretched pony did not excite numerous smiles on the countenances of passers-by, but, as against the side of this pony rattled a sword of respectable length, and as over this sword gleamed an eye ferocious rather than haughty, the said passers-by repressed their hilarity, or, if hilarity prevailed over prudence, they endeavored to laugh only on one side, like the masks of the ancients. D'Artagnan, then, remained majestic and intact in his susceptibility till he came to this unlucky city of Meung.

But there, as he alighted from his horse at the gate of the Franc-Meunier, without anyone, host, waiter, or hostler, coming to hold his stirrup or take his horse, d'Artagnan spied, through an open window on the ground floor, a gentleman, well-made and of good carriage, although of rather a stern countenance, talking with two persons who appeared to listen to him with respect. D'Artagnan fancied quite naturally, according to his custom, that he must be the object of their conversation and listened. This time he was only in part mistaken: he himself was not in question, but his horse was. The gentleman appeared to be enumerating all its qualities to his auditors, and the auditors, seeming, as I have said, to have great deference for the narrator, every moment burst into fits of laughter. Now, as half a smile was sufficient to awaken the irascibility of the young man, the effect produced upon him by this vociferous mirth may be easily imagined.

However, d'Artagnan was desirous of first examining the appearance of this impertinent personage who was laughing at him. He fixed his haughty eye upon the stranger, and perceived a man of from forty to forty-five years of age, with black and piercing eyes, a pale complexion, a strongly marked nose and a black and well-shaped mustache. He was dressed in a violet doublet and hose, with shoulder-knots of the same color, but without any ornaments besides the customary slashes through which the shirt appeared. This doublet and hose, though new, looked creased, like traveling clothes for a long time packed up in a portmanteau. D'Artagnan took in these details with the rapidity of a most minute observer and, doubtless, from an instinctive feeling that this unknown was destined to have a great influence over his future life.

Now, as at the very moment in which d'Artagnan fixed his eyes upon the gentleman in the violet doublet, that gentleman made one of his most knowing and profound remarks respecting the Béarnese pony, his two auditors laughed even louder than before and he himself, though contrary to his custom, allowed a pale smile (if we may be allowed to use such an expression) to flit over his countenance. This time there could be no doubt: d'Artagnan was really insulted. Full, then, of this conviction, he pulled his cap down over his eyes and, endeavoring to copy some of the court airs he had picked up in Gascony among young traveling nobles, he advanced, one hand resting on the hilt of his sword and the other on his hip. Unfortunately, as he advanced, his anger increased at every step and, instead of the proper and lofty speech he had prepared as a prelude to his challenge, he found nothing at the tip of his tongue but a gross personality, which he accompanied with a furious gesture.

"I say, sir—you, sir, who are hiding yourself behind that shutter! —yes, you, sir, tell me what you are laughing at and we will laugh together."

The gentleman withdrew his eyes slowly from the nag to its master, as if he required some time to ascertain whether it could be to him that such strange reproaches were addressed; then, when he could not possibly entertain any doubt of the matter, he contracted his eyebrows slightly and, with an accent of irony and insolence that it is impossible to describe, replied to d'Artagnan—

"I am not speaking to you, sir!"

"But I am speaking to you!" shouted the young man, still more exasperated by this mixture of insolence and good manners, politeness and scorn.

The unknown looked at him again with a slight smile and, retiring from the window, came out of the hostelry with a slow step and placed himself before the horse within two paces of d'Artagnan. His quiet manner and the ironical expression of his countenance redoubled the mirth of the persons with whom he had been talking and who still remained at the window.

D'Artagnan, seeing him approach, drew his sword a foot out of the scabbard.

"This horse is decidedly, or rather has been in his youth, a buttercup," resumed the unknown, continuing the remarks he had begun and addressing himself to his auditors at the window, without paying the least attention to the exasperation of d'Artagnan, who, however, placed himself between him and them. "It is a color very well known in botany, but till the present time very rare among horses."

"There are people who laugh at a horse that would not dare to laugh at its master," cried the young emulator of the terrible Tréville.

"I do not often laugh, sir," replied the unknown, "as you may perceive by the air of my countenance; but I claim, nevertheless, the privilege of laughing when I please."

"And I," cried d'Artagnan, "will allow no man to laugh when it displeases me!"

"Indeed, sir," continued the unknown, more calm than ever, "well! that is perfectly right!" and, turning on his heel, he was about to re-enter the hostelry by the front gate, under which d'Artagnan, on arriving, had observed a saddled horse.

But d'Artagnan was not of a character to allow a man who had had the insolence to laugh at him to escape him in this way. He drew his sword entirely from the scabbard, and followed him, crying:

"Turn, turn, Master Joker, lest I strike you from behind!"

"Strike me!" said the other, turning sharply around and surveying the young man with as much astonishment as contempt. "Why, my good fellow, you must be mad!" Then, in a suppressed tone, as if speaking to himself: "This is annoying. What a godsend this would be for his Majesty, who is seeking everywhere for brave fellows to recruit his Musketeers!"

He had scarcely finished, when d'Artagnan made such a furious lunge at him, that if he had not sprung nimbly backward, he would have jested for the last time. The unknown, perceiving that the matter had gone beyond a joke, then drew his sword, saluted his adversary and placed himself on his guard. But at the same moment his two auditors, accompanied by the host, fell upon d'Artagnan with sticks, shovels and tongs. This caused so rapid and complete a diversion to the attack, that d'Artagnan's adversary, while the latter turned around to face this shower of blows, sheathed his sword with the same precision and from an actor, which he had nearly been, became a spectator of the fight, a part in which he acquitted himself with his usual impassibility, muttering nevertheless:

"A plague upon these Gascons! Put him on his orange horse again and let him begone!"

"Not before I have killed you, poltroon!" cried d'Artagnan, facing his three assailants as well as possible and never retreating one step before the blows they continued to shower upon him.

"Another Gasconade!" murmured the nobleman. "Upon my honor, these Gascons are incorrigible! Keep up the dance, then, since he will have it so. When he is tired he will tell us perhaps that he has enough of it."

But the unknown did not know the headstrong personage he had to deal with; d'Artagnan was not the man ever to cry for quarter. The fight was consequently prolonged for some seconds; but at length d'Artagnan's sword was struck from his hand by the blow of a stick and broken into two pieces. At the same moment another blow, full upon his forehead, brought him to the ground, covered with blood and almost fainting.

It was at this moment that people came flocking to the scene of action from all sides. Fearful of consequences, the host, with the help of his servants, carried the wounded man into the kitchen, where some trifling attention was bestowed upon him.

As to the nobleman, he resumed his place at the window and surveyed the crowd with a certain air of impatience, evidently annoyed by its continued presence.

"Well, how is it with this madman?" he exclaimed, turning around as the opening of the door announced the entrance of the host, who came to inquire if he was unhurt.

"Your excellency is safe and sound?" asked the host.

"Oh, yes! perfectly safe and sound, my good host, and wishing to know what has become of our young man."

"He is better," said the host; "he has fainted quite away."

"Indeed!" said the gentleman.

"But before he fainted, he collected all his strength to call you, and to defy you while calling you."

"Why, this fellow must be the devil in person!" cried the unknown.

"Oh, no, your excellency!" replied the host, with a grin of contempt; "he is not the devil, for during his fainting we rummaged his valise and found nothing but a clean shirt and twelve crowns, which, however, did not prevent his saying, as he was fainting, that if such a thing had happened in Paris you should have instantly repented it, while here you would only have cause to repent it at a later period."

"Then," said the unknown coldly, "he must be some prince in disguise."

"I have told you this, good sir," resumed the host, "in order that you may be on your guard."

"Did he name no one in his passion?"

"Yes! he struck his pocket and said, 'We shall see what M. de Tréville will think of this insult offered to his protégé.' "

"M. de Tréville?" said the unknown, becoming attentive. "He put his hand upon his pocket while pronouncing the name of M. de Tréville? Now, my dear host! while your young man was insensible, you did not fail, I am quite sure, to ascertain what that pocket contained. What was in it?"

"A letter addressed to M. de Tréville, captain of the Musketeers."

"Indeed!"

"Exactly as I have the honor to tell your excellency."

The host, who was not endowed with great perspicacity, did not

20

observe the expression which his words had called forth on the physiognomy of the unknown. The latter rose from before the window, upon the sill of which he had leaned with his elbow and knitted his brows like a man suddenly rendered uneasy.

"The devil!" he murmured, between his teeth. "Can Tréville have set this Gascon upon me? He is very young, but a sword-thrust is a sword-thrust, whatever the age of him who gives it, and a youth is less likely to be suspected than an older man. A weak obstacle is sometimes sufficient to overthrow a great design."

And the unknown fell into a reverie which lasted some minutes.

"Host," said he, "could you not contrive to get rid of this frantic boy for me? In conscience, I cannot kill him; and yet," he added, with a coldly menacing expression, "and yet, he annoys me. Where is he?"

"In my wife's room, where they are dressing his hurts, on the first floor."

"His things and his bag are with him? Has he taken off his doublet?"

"On the contrary, everything is in the kitchen. But if he annoys you, this young fool——"

"To be sure he does. He causes a disturbance in your hostelry, which respectable people cannot put up with. Go, make out my bill and call my servant."

"What, sir! do you mean to leave us already?"

"You know I was going, as I ordered you to have my horse saddled. Has my order not been carried out?"

"Yes, sir; and as your excellency may have observed, your horse is in the great gateway, ready for your departure."

"That is well; then do as I have directed you."

"The devil!" said the host to himself, "can he be afraid of this boy?" But an imperious glance from the unknown stopped him short; he bowed humbly and retired.

"Milady must see nothing of this fellow," continued the stranger. "She will soon pass—she is already late. I had better get on horseback and go to meet her. I should like, however, to know what this letter addressed to Tréville contains!"

And the unknown, muttering to himself, directed his steps toward the kitchen.

In the meantime, the host, who entertained no doubt that it was the presence of the young man that drove the unknown from his

21

hostelry, reascended to his wife's chamber and found d'Artagnan just recovering his senses. Giving him to understand that the police would deal with him pretty severely for having sought a quarrel with a great lord (for, in the opinion of the host, the unknown could be nothing less than a great lord), he insisted that, notwithstanding his weakness, he should get up and depart as quickly as possible. Thereupon d'Artagnan, half stupefied, without his doublet and with his head bound up in a linen cloth, arose and, urged forward by the host, began to descend the stairs; but, on arriving in the kitchen, the first thing he saw was his antagonist, talking calmly at the step of a heavy carriage, drawn by two large Norman horses.

His interlocutor, whose head appeared through the carriage window, was a woman of from twenty to twenty-two years of age. We have already observed with what rapidity d'Artagnan seized the expression of a countenance: he perceived at a glance that this woman was young and beautiful, and her style of beauty struck him the more forcibly because it was totally different from that of the southern countries in which he had hitherto resided. She was pale and fair, with long, blonde curls falling in profusion over her shoulders; she had large, blue, languishing eyes, rosy lips and hands of alabaster. She was talking with great animation to the unknown.

"His eminence, then, orders me——" said the lady.

"To return instantly to England and to inform him immediately should the duke leave London."

"And my other instructions?" asked the fair traveler.

"They are contained in this box, which you will not open until you are on the other side of the Channel."

"Very well; and you, what are you going to do?"

"I? Oh, I shall return to Paris."

"What? Without chastising this insolent boy?" asked the lady.

The unknown was about to reply, but the moment he opened his mouth, d'Artagnan, who had heard all, rushed forward through the open door.

"This insolent boy chastises others," cried he, "and I have good hope that he whom he means to chastise will not escape him as he did before."

"Will not escape him?" replied the unknown, knitting his brow.

"No! before a woman, you would not dare to fly, I presume?"

"Remember," said milady, seeing the unknown lay his hand on his sword, "remember that the least delay may ruin everything."

22

"True," cried the gentleman; "begone, then, on your part, and I will depart as quickly on mine." And, bowing to the lady, he sprang into his saddle, her coachman at the same time applying the whip vigorously to his horses. The two interlocutors thus started at a full gallop, taking opposite directions.

"Your reckoning! your reckoning!" vociferated the host, whose respect for the traveler was changed into profound contempt on seeing him depart without settling his bill.

"Pay him, booby!" cried the unknown to his servant, without checking the speed of his horse, and the man, after throwing two or three pieces of silver at the feet of the host, galloped after his master.

"Base coward! false nobleman!" cried d'Artagnan, springing forward, in his turn, after the servant. But his wound had rendered him too weak to support such an exertion. Scarcely had he gone ten steps when his ears began to tingle, a faintness seized him, a cloud of blood passed over his eyes and he fell in the middle of the street, crying still——

"Coward! coward! coward!"

"He is a coward indeed," grumbled the host, drawing near to d'Artagnan, and endeavoring by this little flattery to make up matters with the young man, as the heron of the fable did with the snail he had despised the evening before.

"Yes, a base coward," murmured d'Artagnan; "but she, she was very beautiful."

"What she?" demanded the host.

"Milady," faltered d'Artagnan, and fainted a second time.

"Ah! it's all one," said the host; "I have lost two customers, but this one remains, of whom I am pretty certain for some days to come; and that will be eleven crowns gained, at all events."

We must remember that eleven crowns was just the amount that was left in d'Artagnan's purse.

The host had reckoned upon eleven days of confinement at a crown a day, but he had reckoned without his guest. On the following morning, at five o'clock, d'Artagnan arose and, descending to the kitchen without help, asked, among other ingredients, the list of which has not come down to us, for some oil, wine and some rosemary. With his mother's recipe in his hand, he composed a balsam with which he anointed his numerous wounds, replacing the bandages himself and positively refusing the assistance of a doctor. Thanks, no doubt, to the efficacy of the Bohemian balsam and also, perhaps, to the absence of any doctor, d'Artagnan walked about that same evening, and was almost cured by the morrow.

But when the time came to pay for this rosemary, this oil, and this wine—the only expenses the master had incurred, as the young noble had preserved a strict abstinence, while, on the contrary, the yellow horse, according to the hostler, at least, had eaten three times as much as a horse of its size could reasonably be supposed to have done—d'Artagnan found nothing in his pocket but his little, old, velvet purse with the eleven crowns it contained. As to the letter addressed to M. de Tréville, that had disappeared.

The young man commenced his search for the letter with the greatest patience, turning out all his pockets over and over again, rummaging and re-rummaging in his valise and opening and re-opening his purse. When he had come at last to the conviction that the letter was not to be found, he flew, for the third time, into such a rage as came near costing him a fresh consumption of wine, oil and rosemary. For, upon seeing this hot-headed youth so exasperated and threatening to destroy everything in the establishment if his letter were not found, the host seized a spit, his wife a broom-handle and the servants the same sticks they had used the day before.

"My letter of recommendation!" cried d'Artagnan, "my letter of recommendation! or, I will spit you all like so many ortolans!"

Unfortunately there was one circumstance that formed a powerful obstacle to the accomplishment of this threat. As we have related, his sword had been broken in two in the first conflict, a fact which he had entirely forgotten. Hence it resulted, that when d'Artagnan proceeded to draw his sword in earnest, he found himself purely and simply armed with a stump about eight or ten inches in length, which the host had carefully placed in the scabbard. As to the rest of the blade, the cook had slyly put it aside to make himself a larding-pin.

But this deception would probably not have stopped our fiery young man, if the host had not reflected that the reclamation which his guest made was perfectly just.

"That's so," he said, lowering the point of his spit, "where is this letter?"

"Yes, where is this letter?" cried d'Artagnan. "In the first place, I warn you that it is for M. de Tréville, and must be found; if it is not quickly found, he will know how to cause it to be found, I'll answer for it!"

This threat completed the intimidation of the host. After the King and the Cardinal, M. de Tréville was the man whose name was perhaps most frequently repeated by the military, and even by citizens. There was, to be sure, Father Joseph, but his name was never pronounced but with a subdued voice, such was the terror inspired by his Grey Eminence, as the Cardinal's familiar was called.

Throwing down his spit, and ordering his wife to do the same with her broom-handle and the servants with their sticks, he set the first example of commencing an earnest search for the lost letter.

"Does the letter contain anything valuable?" asked the host, after a few minutes of useless investigation.

"Zounds! it does indeed," cried the Gascon, who reckoned upon this letter for making his way at court; "it contained my fortune!"

"Bills upon Spain?" asked the disturbed host.

"Bills upon his Majesty's private treasury," answered d'Artagnan, who, reckoning upon entering into the King's service in consequence of this recommendation, thought he could make this somewhat hazardous reply without telling a falsehood.

"The devil!" cried the host, at his wit's end.

"But it's of no importance," continued d'Artagnan, with Gascon assurance. "It's of no importance, the money is nothing—that letter is everything; I would rather lose a thousand pistoles than to have lost it." He would not have risked more if he had said twenty thousand, but a certain juvenile modesty restrained him.

A ray of light all at once broke upon the mind of the host, who was cursing himself for finding nothing.

"That letter is not lost!" he cried.

"What?" said d'Artagnan.

"No! it has been stolen from you."

"Stolen! by whom?"

"By the nobleman who was here yesterday. He came down into the kitchen, where your doublet was. He remained there some time alone. I would lay a wager he has stolen it."

"Do you think so?" answered d'Artagnan, but little convinced, as he knew better than anyone else how entirely personal the value of this letter was, and saw nothing in it likely to tempt the cupidity of anyone. The fact was that none of the servants, none of the travelers present, could have gained anything by the possession of this paper.

"Do you mean," resumed d'Artagnan, "that you suspect that impertinent gentleman?"

"I tell you I am sure of it," continued the host. "When I informed

25

him that your lordship was the protégé of M. de Tréville, and that you even had a letter for that illustrious gentleman, he appeared to be very much disturbed. He asked me where that letter was and immediately went into the kitchen, where he knew your doublet was."

"Then he's the man who has robbed me," replied d'Artagnan. "I will complain to M. de Tréville, and M. de Tréville will complain to the King." He then drew two crowns majestically from his purse, gave them to the host, who accompanied him cap in hand to the gate, and remounted his yellow steed. It bore him without any further accident to the gate of St. Antoine at Paris, where its owner sold it for three crowns, which was a very good price, considering that he had ridden it hard from Meung. And the dealer to whom d'Artagnan sold it for the said three crowns did not conceal from the young man the fact that he gave that enormous sum only on account of the originality of its color.

Thus d'Artagnan entered Paris on foot, carrying his little packet under his arm, and walked about till he found an apartment to be let on terms suited to the scantiness of his means. This chamber was a sort of garret, situated in the Rue des Fossoyeurs, near the Luxembourg.

As soon as the rent had been paid, d'Artagnan took possession of his lodging, and passed the remainder of the day in sewing on to his doublet and hose some ornamental braiding which his mother had taken from an almost new doublet of M. d'Artagnan the elder, and given to him secretly; next he went to the Quai de Ferraille, to have a new blade put to his sword, and then returned toward the Louvre, asking the first Musketeer he met to direct him to the hotel of M. de Tréville, which proved to be in the Rue du Vieux-Colombier, in the immediate vicinity of the chamber hired by d'Artagnan —a circumstance which appeared to furnish a happy augury for the success of his journey.

After which, satisfied with the way in which he had conducted himself at Meung, without remorse for the past, confident in the present and full of hope for the future, he retired to bed and slept the sleep of the brave.

This sleep, provincial as it was, brought him to nine o'clock in the morning, at which hour he rose in order to repair to the residence of M. de Tréville, in his good father's estimation the third personage in the kingdom.

The Antechamber of M. de Tréville

M. DE TROISVILLE, as his family was still called in Gascony, or M. de Tréville, as he had ended by styling himself in Paris, had really commenced life as d'Artagnan now did—that is to say, without a sou in his pocket, but with a fund of courage, shrewdness and intelligence, that makes the poorest Gascon with a pretense of gentle birth often derive more in hope from the paternal inheritance than the richest Perigordian or Berrichan nobleman actually derives from his. His insolent bravery, his still more insolent success at a time when blows poured down like hail, had borne him to the top of that ladder called court favor, which he had climbed four steps at a time.

He was the friend of the King, who honored highly, as everyone knows, the memory of his father, Henry IV. The father of M. de Tréville had served the great King so faithfully in his wars against the League, that the latter, for want of money—a thing which the Béarnais lacked all his life, constantly paying his debts with that of which he never stood in need of borrowing, namely, ready wit— authorized him, after the surrender of Paris, to assume for his arms, on a field, gules, a lion or passant, with the device, *Fidelis et fortis*. This was a great matter in the way of honor, but very little in the way of wealth; so that when the illustrious companion of the great Henry died, the only inheritance he was able to leave his son was his sword and his device. Thanks to this double gift and to the spotless name that accompanied them, M. de Tréville was admitted into the household of the young prince, where he made such good use of his sword and was so faithful to his device, that Louis XIII, one of the good blades of his kingdom, was accustomed to say that, if he ever should have a friend with a duel on his hands, he would advise him to choose as a second, himself first and Tréville next, or even, perhaps, Tréville first of all.

Therefore Louis XIII had a real liking for Tréville, a royal liking, a selfish liking, it is true, but nevertheless a liking. At that unhappy period it was an important consideration to be surrounded by such men as Tréville. Many might take for their device the epithet of *strong,* which formed the second part of his motto, but very few nobles could lay claim to the *faithful,* which constituted

27

the first. Tréville was one of the latter. His was one of those rare organizations, endowed with an obedient intelligence like that of the dog, with a blind valor, a quick eye and a prompt hand. Sight appeared only to be given to him to see if the King were dissatisfied with anyone, and his hand was ready to strike this displeasing anyone, whether a Besme, a Maurevers, a Poltiot de Méré, or a Vitry. In short, up to this period, nothing had been wanting to Tréville but opportunity; but for this he was ever on the watch and he promised himself that he would never fail to seize it by its three hairs whenever it came within reach of his hand. Louis XIII then made Tréville the captain of his Musketeers, who were to Louis XIII, in devotedness, or rather in fanaticism, what his Ordinaries had been to Henry III and his Scotch Guard to Louis XI.

The Cardinal was not behind the King. When he saw the formidable and chosen body with which Louis XIII surrounded himself, this second, or rather this first, king of France became desirous that he too should have his guard. He had his musketeers, then, as Louis XIII had his, and these two powerful rivals vied with each other in procuring the most celebrated swordsmen, not only from all the provinces of France, but even from all foreign states. It was not uncommon for Richelieu and Louis XIII to dispute, over their evening game of chess, upon the merits of their servants. Each boasted the bearing and courage of his own people and, while exclaiming loudly against duels and broils, excited them secretly to quarrel, deriving an immoderate satisfaction or a true regret from the success or defeat of his own combatants. . . .

Tréville had discovered the weak side of his master, and it was to this address that he owed the long and constant favor of a king who has not left behind him the reputation of having been very faithful in his friendships. He paraded his Musketeers before the Cardinal Armand Duplessis with an insolent air, which made the gray mustache of his Eminence curl with ire. Tréville was a master of the art of war of that period, in which he who did not live at the expense of the enemy lived at the expense of his compatriots. His soldiers formed a legion of devil-may-care fellows, perfectly undisciplined as regarded everyone but himself.

Loose, deep drinkers, truculent, the King's Musketeers, or rather M. de Tréville's, swaggered about in the cabarets, the public walks, and at the public sports, shouting, twisting their mustaches, clanking their swords, and taking great pleasure in annoying the guards of M. le Cardinal whenever they could fall in with them. They drew in the open streets, as if it were the best of all possible sports. Sometimes they were killed, but in that case they were sure to be both wept over and avenged; often they killed others, but were certain of not rotting in prison, as M. de Tréville was always there to claim them. Thus M. de Tréville was praised to the highest note by these men, who absolutely adored him and who, ruffians though they were, trembled before him like schoolboys before their master, obedient to his least word and ready to sacrifice themselves to wash out the smallest insult.

M. de Tréville employed this powerful machine for the King in the first place and the friends of the King—and then for himself and his own. For the rest, in none of the memoirs of this period, which has left so many memoirs, is this worthy gentleman accused, even by his enemies (and he had many such among men of the pen as well as among men of the sword); in no instance, we are told, was this worthy gentleman accused of deriving personal advantage from the co-operation of his minions. Endowed with a rare genius for intrigue, which rendered him the equal of the ablest intriguers, he remained an honest man. Still further, in spite of sword thrusts which weaken, and painful exercises which fatigue, he had become one of the most gallant frequenters of revels, one of the most insinuating squires of dames, one of the softest whisperers of interesting nothings of his day. . . . The captain of the Musketeers, then, was admired, feared and loved, a condition which constitutes the apogee of human fortunes. . . .

The court of his mansion, situated in the Rue du Vieux-Colombier, resembled a camp, and that by six o'clock in the morning in summer, and by eight o'clock in winter. From fifty to sixty Musketeers, who appeared to relieve each other in order always to present an imposing number, paraded constantly about, armed to the teeth and ready for anything. On one of those immense staircases upon whose space modern civilization would build a whole house, ascended and descended the solicitors of Paris, who were in search of favors of any kind: nobles from the provinces anxious to be enrolled, and servants in all sorts of liveries, bringing and carrying messages between their masters and M. de Tréville. In the antechamber, upon long, circular benches, reposed the elect, that is to say, those who were called. In this apartment a continued buzzing prevailed from morning till night, while M. de Tréville, in his office contiguous to this antechamber, received visits, listened to complaints, gave his orders and, like the King on his balcony at the Louvre, had only to place himself at the window to review both men and arms.

The day on which d'Artagnan presented himself the assemblage was imposing, particularly for a provincial just arriving from his province; it is true that this provincial was a Gascon, and that, particularly at this period, the compatriots of d'Artagnan had the reputation of not being easily intimidated. When he had once passed the massive door, covered with long, square-headed nails, he fell into the midst of a troop of men of the sword, who had met in the courtyard, calling out, quarreling and playing tricks upon each other. To make way through these turbulent and conflicting waves, one had to be an officer, a great noble or a pretty woman.

Into the midst of this tumult and disorder our young man advanced with a beating heart, ranging his long rapier against his lanky leg and keeping one hand on the edge of his cap, with that provincial half-smile which affects confidence. When he had passed one group, he began to breathe more freely, but he could not help observing that they turned round to look at him and, for the first time in his life, d'Artagnan, who had till that day entertained a very good opinion of himself, felt that he was ridiculous.

At the staircase it was still worse. There were four Musketeers on the bottom steps, who, while ten or twelve of their comrades awaited upon the landing-place their turns to take their places in the sport, amused themselves with the following exercise:

One of them, placed upon the top stair, naked sword in hand, prevented, or at least endeavored to prevent, the three others from going up.

These three others fenced against him with their agile swords which d'Artagnan at first took for foils, and believed to be buttoned. But he soon perceived, by certain scratches, that every weapon was pointed and sharpened, and that at each of these scratches, not only the spectators, but even the actors themselves, laughed like so many madmen.

The Musketeer who at the moment occupied the upper step, kept his adversaries admirably in check. A circle was formed around them. The conditions of the game required that at every attack the person hit should quit the game, losing his turn of audience in favor of the person who had touched him. In five minutes three were slightly wounded, one on the hand, another on the chin, and the third on the ear, by the defender of the stair, who himself remained intact—a piece of skill which was worth to him, according to agreement, three turns of favor.

Difficult as this might be, or rather as the man on the staircase pretended it was, this pastime really did astonish our young traveler. . . . He believed himself transported into that famous country of giants into which Gulliver since went and was so frightened; and yet he had not gained the goal, for there were still the landing-place and the antechamber.

On the landing they were no longer fighting, but amused themselves with stories about women, and in the antechamber with stories about the court. On the landing, d'Artagnan blushed; in the antechamber, he trembled. His warm and fickle imagination, which in Gascony had rendered him formidable to young chambermaids and even sometimes to their mistresses, had never dreamed, even in moments of delirium, of half the amorous wonders, or a quarter of the feats of gallantry, which were here set forth, accompanied by names the best known and with details the least delicate. But if his morals were shocked on the landing, his respect for the Cardinal was scandalized in the antechamber. There, to his great astonishment, d'Artagnan heard the policy which made all Europe tremble criticized aloud and openly, as well as the private life of the Cardinal, for daring to pry into which so many great nobles had been punished. That great man, so revered by d'Artagnan the elder, served as an object of ridicule to the Musketeers, who cracked their jokes upon his bandy legs and his stooping shoulders. . . .

Nevertheless, when the name of the King was now and then uttered unthinkingly amid all these jokes about the Cardinal, a sort of gag seemed to close for a moment all these jeering mouths. They looked hesitatingly around them and appeared to doubt the thickness of the partition between them and the closet of M. de Tréville; but a fresh allusion soon brought back the conversation to his Eminence, and then the laughter recovered its loudness and no coloring was spared for any of his actions.

"Surely these fellows will all be either put in the Bastille or hanged," thought the terrified d'Artagnan, "and I, no doubt, with them; for, from the moment I have heard them and listened to them, I shall be held to be their accomplice. What would my good father say, who so strongly pointed out to me the respect due to the

31

Cardinal, if he knew that I was in the society of such pagans?" We have no need, therefore, to say that d'Artagnan did not venture to join in the conversation. He merely looked with all his eyes and listened with all his ears, stretching his five senses so as to lose nothing; and, in spite of his confidence in the paternal monitions, he felt himself carried by his tastes and led by his instincts to praise rather than to blame the unheard-of things which were passing before him.

D'Artagnan, however, being a perfect stranger in the crowd of M. de Tréville's courtiers and this being his first appearance in that place, was at length noticed, and a person came to him and asked him his business there. At this demand he gave his name very modestly, laid stress upon the title of compatriot, and begged the servant who had put the question to him to request a moment's audience of M. de Tréville—a request which the other, with an air of protection, promised to convey in due time and season.

D'Artagnan, a little recovered from his first surprise, had now leisure to study costumes and countenances.

The center of the most animated group was a Musketeer of great height, of a haughty countenance and dressed in a costume so peculiar as to attract general attention. He did not wear the uniform cloak—which, indeed, at that time of little liberty but of great independence, was not obligatory—but a cerulean blue doublet, a little faded and worn, and over this a magnificent baldric worked in gold, which shone like water ripples in the sun. A long cloak of crimson velvet fell in graceful folds from his shoulders, disclosing in front the splendid baldric, from which was suspended a gigantic rapier.

This Musketeer, who had just come off guard, complained of having a cold and coughed from time to time affectedly. It was for this reason, he said to those around him, that he had put on his cloak and, while he spoke with a lofty air and twisted his mustache, all admired his embroidered baldric, d'Artagnan more than anyone.

"What do you wonder about?" said the Musketeer; "the fashion is coming in. It is a folly, I admit, but still it is the fashion. Besides, one must lay out one's inheritance somehow."

"Ah, Porthos!" cried one of his companions, "don't try to make us believe that you obtained that baldric by paternal generosity. It was given to you by that veiled lady I met you with the other Sunday, near the gate Saint-Honoré."

"No, 'pon honor; by the faith of a nobleman, I bought it with the contents of my own purse," answered he whom they designated by the name of Porthos.

"Yes, about in the same manner," said another Musketeer, "as I bought this new purse with the money my mistress put into the old one."

"It's true, though," said Porthos; "and the proof is that I paid twelve pistoles for it." The admiration increased, though the doubt continued to exist.

"Is it not true, Aramis?" said Porthos, turning toward another Musketeer.

This other Musketeer formed a perfect contrast with his interrogator, who had just designated him by the name of Aramis; he was a young man, about twenty-two or -three with an open, ingenuous countenance, a black, mild eye and cheeks rosy and downy as an autumn peach. His delicate mustache marked a perfectly straight line upon his upper lip; he appeared to dread to lower his hands lest their veins should swell and he pinched the tips of his ears from time to time to preserve their delicate pink transparency. Habitually he spoke little and slowly, bowed frequently, laughed without noise, showing his teeth, which were fine and of which, as of the rest of his person, he appeared to take great care. He answered the appeal of his friend by an affirmative nod of the head.

This affirmation appeared to dispel all doubts with regard to the baldric. They continued to admire it, but said no more about it and, by a rapid change of thought, the conversation passed suddenly to another subject.

"What do you think of the story Chalais' esquire relates?" asked another Musketeer, without addressing anyone in particular.

"What does he say?" asked Porthos, in a self-sufficient tone.

"He relates that he met Rochefort at Brussels, the tool of the Cardinal, disguised as a Capuchin, and that this cursed Rochefort, thanks to his disguise, had tricked M. de Laigues, like the simpleton that he is."

"A simpleton, indeed!" said Porthos; "but is it true?"

"I had it from Aramis," replied the Musketeer.

"Indeed!"

"Why, you know it is, Porthos," said Aramis; "I told you of it yesterday—let us say nothing more about it."

"Say nothing more about it—that's your opinion!" replied Porthos.

"Say nothing more about it! The devil! you come to your conclusions quickly. What! the Cardinal sets a spy upon a gentleman, has his letters stolen from him by means of a traitor, a brigand, a rascal— has, with the help of this spy and thanks to this correspondence, Chalais' throat cut, under the stupid pretext that he wanted to kill the King and marry Monsieur to the Queen. Nobody knew a word of this enigma. You unraveled it yesterday, to the great satisfaction of all and, while we are still gaping with wonder at the news, you come and tell us today—'Let us say nothing more about it.'"

"Well, then, let us speak about it, since you desire it," replied Aramis patiently.

"This Rochefort," cried Porthos, "if I were poor Chalais' esquire, should pass a minute or two very uncomfortably with me."

"And you—you would pass rather a sad half-hour with the Red Duke," replied Aramis.

"Oh! oh! the Red Duke! bravo! bravo! the Red Duke!" cried Porthos, clapping his hands and nodding his head. "The Red Duke is capital. I'll circulate that saying, be assured, my dear fellow. Who says this Aramis is not a wit? What a misfortune it is you did not follow your first vocation—what a delightful abbé you would have made!"

"Oh, it's only a temporary postponement," replied Aramis. "I shall be one, some day. You know very well, Porthos, that I continue to study theology for that purpose."

"He will be one, as he says," cried Porthos; "he will be one, sooner or later."

"Soon," said Aramis.

"He only waits for one thing to determine him to resume his cassock, which hangs behind his uniform," said another Musketeer.

"What is he waiting for?" asked another.

"Only till the Queen has given an heir to the crown of France."

"No jokes upon that subject, gentlemen," said Porthos; "thank God, the Queen is still of an age to give one."

"They say that M. de Buckingham is in France," replied Aramis, with a significant smile, which gave to this sentence, apparently so simple, a tolerably scandalous meaning.

"Aramis, my good friend, this time you are wrong," interrupted Porthos; "your wit is always leading you astray. If M. de Tréville heard you, you would repent speaking thus."

"Are you going to teach me better, Porthos?" cried Aramis, from whose usually mild eye a flash passed like lightning.

"My dear fellow, be a Musketeer or an abbé. Be one or the other, but not both," replied Porthos. "You know what Athos told you the other day: you eat at everybody's mess. Ah! don't be angry, I beg you—that would be useless; you know what is agreed upon between you, Athos, and me. You go to Madame d'Aiguillon's, and you pay your court to her; you go to Madame de Bois-Tracy's, the cousin of Madame de Chevreuse, and you pass for being far advanced in the good graces of that lady. Oh, good Lord! don't reveal your good fortunes; no one asks for your secret—all the world knows your discretion. But since you possess that virtue, why the devil don't you make use of it with respect to her Majesty? Let whoever likes talk of the King and the Cardinal, and as he likes; but the Queen is sacred, and if anyone speaks of her, let him speak well."

"Porthos, you are as vain as Narcissus, I plainly tell you so," replied Aramis. "You know I hate moralizing, except when it is done by Athos. As to you, good sir, you wear too magnificent a baldric to be strong on that head. I will be an abbé if it suits me; in the meanwhile I am a Musketeer. In that quality I say what I please and at this moment it pleases me to say that you annoy me."

"Aramis!"

"Porthos!"

"Gentlemen! gentlemen!" cried the surrounding group.

"Monsieur de Tréville awaits M. d'Artagnan," cried a servant, throwing open the door of the cabinet.

At this announcement, during which the door remained open, everyone became mute and amid the general silence the young man crossed the antechamber in a part of its length and entered the apartment of the captain of the Musketeers, congratulating himself with all his heart at having so narrowly escaped the end of this strange quarrel.

The Audience

M. DE TRÉVILLE was at the moment in rather an ill humor; nevertheless, he saluted politely the young man, who bowed to the very ground, and smiled on receiving his compliment, the Béarnese accent of which recalled to him at the same time his youth and his country, a double remembrance which makes a man smile at all ages. But stepping toward the antechamber, and making a sign to d'Artagnan with his hand, as if to ask his permission to finish with others before he began with him, he called three times, with a louder voice each time, so that he went through all the tones between the imperative accent and the angry accent:

"Athos! Porthos! Aramis!"

The two Musketeers with whom we have already made acquaintance, and who answered to the last two of these three names, immediately quitted the group of which they formed a part and advanced toward the office, the door of which closed after them as soon as they had entered. Their appearance, although it was not quite at ease, excited by its carelessness, at once full of dignity and submission, the admiration of d'Artagnan, who beheld in these two men demigods, and in their leader an Olympian Jupiter, armed with all his thunders.

When the two Musketeers had entered, when the door was closed behind them, when the buzzing murmur of the antechamber, to which the summons which had been made had doubtless furnished fresh food, had recommenced; when M. de Tréville had three or four times paced in silence, and with a frowning brow, the whole length of his cabinet, passing each time before Porthos and Aramis, who were as upright and silent as if on parade, he stopped all at once full in front of them and, covering them from head to foot with an angry look, he cried:

"Do you know what the King said to me, and that no longer ago than yesterday evening—do you know, gentlemen?"

"No," replied the two Musketeers, after a moment's silence— "no, sir, we do not."

"But I hope that you will do us the honor to tell us," added Aramis, in his politest tone and with the most graceful bow.

"He told me that he should henceforth recruit his Musketeers from among the guards of M. the Cardinal."

"The guards of M. the Cardinal! and why so?" asked Porthos warmly.

"Because he plainly perceives that his piquette * stands in need of being enlivened by a mixture of good wine."

The two Musketeers colored up to the eyes. D'Artagnan did

* A liquor made of grapes

not know where he was and wished himself a hundred feet under ground.

"Yes, yes," continued M. de Tréville, growing warmer as he spoke, "and his Majesty was right, for, upon my honor, it is true that the Musketeers cut but a miserable figure at court. M. the Cardinal related yesterday, while playing with the King, with an air of condolence not very pleasing to me, that the day before yesterday those damned Musketeers, those dare-devils—he dwelt upon those words with an ironical tone still more unpleasing to me— those braggarts, added he, glancing at me with his tiger-cat's eye, had made a riot in the Rue Ferou, in a cabaret, and that a party of his guards (I thought he was going to laugh in my face) had been forced to arrest the rioters. Blast it! you must know something about it! Arrest Musketeers! You were there—you were! Don't deny it; you were recognized, and the Cardinal named you. But it's all my fault! yes, it's all my own fault, because it is myself who select my men. You, now, Aramis, why the devil did you ask me for a uniform, when you would have been so much better in a cassock? And you, Porthos, do you only wear such a fine golden baldric to suspend a sword of straw from it? And Athos—I don't see Athos! Where is he?"

"Sir," replied Aramis, in a sorrowful tone—"he is ill, very ill!"

"Ill—very ill, say you? And what is his malady?"

"It is feared that it is the smallpox, sir," replied Porthos, desirous of getting a word in the conversation; "and, what is worse, it will certainly spoil his face."

"The smallpox! That's a pretty glorious story to tell me, Porthos! Sick of the smallpox at his age! No, no; but wounded without doubt—perhaps killed. Ah, if I knew! Messieurs Musketeers, I will not have this haunting of bad places, this quarreling in the streets, this sword play in crossways; and, above all, I will not have you furnish sport for the Cardinal's guards, who are brave, quiet, skillful men, and never put themselves in a position to be arrested. Besides, they never allow themselves to be arrested, I am sure of it— they would prefer dying on the spot to being arrested, or to retreating a single step. To save themselves, to scamper away, to fly! a pretty thing to be said of the King's Musketeers."

Porthos and Aramis trembled with rage; they could willingly have strangled M. de Tréville if, at the bottom of all this, they had not felt that it was the great love he bore them which made him speak thus. They stamped upon the carpet, bit their lips till the blood sprang and grasped the hilts of their swords with all their strength. As we have said, all outside had heard M. de Tréville calling for Athos, Porthos, and Aramis, and had guessed from the tone of his voice that he was very angry about something. Ten curious heads were glued to the door-tapestry and became pale with fury, for their ears, closely applied to the door, did not lose a syllable of what he said, while their mouths repeated, word for word, his insulting expressions to the whole crowd assembled in the antechamber. In an instant, from the door of the cabinet to the street gate, the whole mansion was in a state of commotion.

"Ah! the King's Musketeers are arrested by the guards of M. de Cardinal, are they!" continued M. de Tréville, as furious at heart as his soldiers, but emphasizing his words and plunging them one by one into the bosoms of his auditors, like so many blows of a stiletto. "What! six of his Eminence's guards have arrested six of his Majesty's Musketeers! Blast it! my part is taken! I will go straight to the Louvre to hand in my resignation as captain of the King's Musketeers. I will ask for a lieutenancy in the Cardinal's guards, and if he refuses me, blast it! I will turn abbé."

At these words the murmur without became an explosion. Nothing was to be heard but oaths and blasphemies. D'Artagnan looked around for some tapestry behind which he might hide himself, and felt an immense inclination to crawl under the table.

"Well, my captain," said Porthos, quite beside himself, "it is true that we were six against six. But we were not captured by fair means and before we had time to draw our swords, two of our party were dead and Athos, grievously wounded, was very little better. For you know Athos. Well, captain, he endeavored twice to get up and fell back twice. And we did not surrender—no! they dragged us away by force. On the way we escaped. As for Athos, they believed him dead, and left him very quietly on the field of battle, not thinking it worth the trouble to carry him away. Now, that's the whole story. What the devil, captain, one cannot win all one's battles! The great Pompey lost that of Pharsalia; and Francis the First, who was, as I have heard say, as good a fighter as they make them, nevertheless lost the battle of Pavia."

"And I have the honor of assuring you that I killed one of them with his own sword," said Aramis, "for mine was broken at the first

38

parry. Killed him, or poniarded him, sir, as is most agreeable to you."

"I did not know that," replied M. de Tréville, in a somewhat softened tone. "M. the Cardinal exaggerated, as I perceive."

"But pray, sir," continued Aramis, who, seeing his captain somewhat appeased, ventured to risk a prayer—"pray, sir, do not say that Athos is wounded; he would be in despair if that should come to the ears of the King; and as the wound is very serious, seeing that after piercing the shoulder it penetrates into the chest, it is to be feared——"

At this instant the tapestry was raised and a noble, handsome, but frightfully pale head appeared under the fringe.

"Athos!" cried the two Musketeers.

"Athos!" repeated M. de Tréville.

"You have sent for me, sir," said Athos to the latter, in a feeble but perfectly calm voice—"you have sent for me, as my comrades inform me, and I have hastened to receive your orders. I am here, sir; what do you want with me?"

And at these words the Musketeer, irreproachably dressed as usual, entered the office with a tolerably firm step. Moved to the bottom of his heart by this proof of courage, M. de Tréville sprang toward him.

"I was about to say to these gentlemen," added he, "that I forbid my Musketeers to expose their lives needlessly; for brave men are very dear to the King, and the King knows that his Musketeers are the bravest fellows on earth. Your hand, Athos!"

And without waiting for the newcomer's answer to this proof of affection, M. de Tréville seized his right hand and pressed it with all his might, without perceiving that Athos, whatever might be his self-command, allowed a slight murmur of pain to escape him and, if possible, grew paler than he was before.

The door had remained open, so strong was the excitement produced by the arrival of Athos, whose wound, though kept as secret as possible, was known to all. A burst of satisfaction hailed the last words of the captain and two or three heads, carried away by the enthusiasm of the moment, appeared through the openings of the tapestry. M. de Tréville was about to reprehend this infraction of the rules of etiquette, when he felt the hand of Athos stiffen within his own and, turning his eyes toward him, perceived that he was

39

about to faint. At the same instant Athos, who had rallied all his energies to contend against the pain, was at length overcome by it, and fell upon the floor as if he were dead.

"A surgeon!" cried M. de Tréville, "mine! the King's! the best that can be found!—a surgeon! or my brave Athos will die!"

At M. de Tréville's cries the whole assemblage rushed into the office without his thinking of shutting the door against anyone, and all crowded around the wounded man. But all this eager attention might have been useless, had not the doctor so loudly called for chanced to be in the house. He pushed through the crowd, approached Athos, who was still insensible, and, as all this noise and commotion inconvenienced him greatly, required, as the first and most urgent thing, that the Musketeer should be carried into another room. M. de Tréville immediately opened a door and pointed the way to Porthos and Aramis, who bore their comrade in their arms. Behind this group walked the surgeon and as the surgeon passed through, the door closed.

The cabinet of M. de Tréville, generally held so sacred, became in an instant filled from the antechamber. Everyone spoke, harangued and vociferated, swearing, cursing and consigning the Cardinal and his guards to all the devils.

An instant after, Porthos and Aramis re-entered, the surgeon and M. de Tréville alone remaining with the wounded man.

At length M. de Tréville himself returned. Athos had recovered his senses and the surgeon declared that the Musketeer's condition had nothing in it to render his friends uneasy, his weakness having been purely and simply caused by loss of blood.

Then M. de Tréville made a sign with his hand and all retired except d'Artagnan, who did not forget that he had an audience and, with the tenacity of a Gascon, remained in his place.

When all had gone out and the door was closed, M. de Tréville, on turning around, found himself alone with the young man. The stirring event which had just passed had in some degree broken the thread of his ideas. He inquired what was the will of his persevering visitor. D'Artagnan then repeated his name and in an instant, recovering all his remembrances of the present and the past, M. de Tréville was in possession of the current circumstances.

"Pardon me," said he, smiling, "pardon me, my dear compatriot, but I had perfectly forgotten you. But what can I do? A captain is nothing but a father of a family, charged with even a greater responsibility than the father of an ordinary family. Soldiers are great children, but as I desire that the orders of the King, and more particularly those of M. the Cardinal, shall be executed——"

D'Artagnan could not restrain a smile. By this smile, M. de Tréville judged that he had not to deal with a fool and, changing the subject, came straight to the point.

"I respected your father very much," he said. "What can I do for the son? Tell me quickly, my time is not my own."

"Monsieur," said d'Artagnan, "on quitting Tarbes and coming here, it was my intention to request from you, in remembrance of the friendship which you have not forgotten, the uniform of a Musketeer. But after all that I have seen, during the last two hours, I have become aware of the value of such a favor and tremble lest I should not merit it."

"Well, young man," replied M. de Tréville, "it is, in fact, a favor, but it may not be so far beyond your hopes as you believe, or rather as you appear to believe. Still, an edict of his Majesty provides for cases such as yours and I inform you with regret that no one becomes a Musketeer without the preliminary ordeal of several campaigns, certain brilliant actions, or a service of two years in some regiment of less reputation than ours."

D'Artagnan bowed without replying, feeling his desire to don the Musketeer's uniform vastly increased by the difficulties which he learned preceded its attainment.

"But," continued M. de Tréville, fixing upon his compatriot a look so piercing that it might be said he wished to read the thoughts of his heart; "but, for the sake of my old companion, your father, I will do something for you, young man, as I have said. Our cadets from Béarn are not generally very rich and I have no reason to think matters have much changed in this respect since I left the province. I dare say you have not brought too large a stock of money with you?"

D'Artagnan drew himself up with an air that plainly said, "I ask charity of no man."

"Oh! that's all very well, young man," continued M. de Tréville, "that's all very well. I am well acquainted with all those lofty airs: I myself came to Paris with four crowns in my purse and would have fought with anyone who would have dared to tell me I was not in a condition to purchase the Louvre."

D'Artagnan's carriage became still more imposing. Thanks to the

41

sale of his horse, he commenced his career with four crowns more than M. de Tréville had possessed at the commencement of his.

"You should, I was going to say, husband the means you have, however large the sum may be, but you should also endeavor to perfect yourself in the exercises becoming a gentleman. I will write a letter today to the director of the Royal Academy and tomorrow he will admit you without any expense to yourself. Do not refuse this little service. Our highest-born and richest gentlemen sometimes solicit it, without being able to obtain it. You will be taught riding, swordsmanship in all its branches and dancing; you will make some desirable acquaintances and from time to time, you can call upon me, just to tell me how you are getting on and to tell me whether I can be of further service to you."

D'Artagnan, strange as he was to all the manners of a court, could not but perceive a little coldness in this reception.

"Alas! sir," said he, "I cannot but perceive how sadly I miss the letter of introduction which my father gave me to present to you."

"I certainly am surprised," replied M. de Tréville, "that you should undertake so long a journey without that necessary item, the only resource of us poor Béarnese."

"I had one, sir, and, thank God, such as I could wish, but it was perfidiously stolen from me."

He then related the adventure of Meung, described the unknown gentleman with the greatest minuteness and all with a warmth and truthfulness that delighted M. de Tréville.

"This is all very strange," said M. de Tréville, after meditating a minute. "You mentioned my name, then, aloud?"

"Yes, sir, I certainly committed that imprudence, but why should I have done otherwise? A name like yours must be as a buckler to me on my way. Why should I not avail myself of it?"

Flattery was at that period very current and M. de Tréville loved incense as well as a king, or even a cardinal. He could not refrain from a smile of visible satisfaction, but it soon disappeared; and, returning to the adventure of Meung——

"Tell me," continued he, "had not this gentleman a slight scar on his cheek?"

"Yes, such a one as would be made by the grazing of a ball."

"Was he not a fine-looking man?"

"Yes."

"Of lofty stature?"

42

"Yes."

"Of pale complexion and brown hair?"

"Yes, yes, that is he; how is it, sir, that you are acquainted with this man? If ever I should meet him again, and I will find him, I swear—were it in hell. . . ."

"He was waiting for a woman?" continued Tréville.

"He departed, at least, immediately after having conversed for a minute with the one for whom he appeared to have been waiting."

"You did not gather the subject of their discourse?"

"He gave her a box, told her that that box contained her instructions and desired her not to open it before she arrived in London."

"Was this woman English?"

"He called her 'milady.' "

"It is he! it must be he!" murmured Tréville. "I thought he was still at Brussels!"

"Oh! sir, if you know who and what this man is," cried d'Artagnan, "tell me who he is, and whence he comes. I will then release you from all your promises—even that of procuring my admission into the Musketeers; for, before everything, I am desirous of avenging myself."

"Beware, young man!" cried Tréville. "If you see him coming on one side of the street, pass by on the other! Do not cast yourself against such a rock: he would smash you like glass."

"That thought will not prevent me," replied d'Artagnan, "if ever I should happen to meet him."

"In the meantime, if you will take my advice, you will not seek him," said Tréville.

All at once the captain stopped, as if struck by a sudden suspicion. This great hatred which the young traveler manifested so loudly for this man, who—a rather improbable thing—had stolen his father's letter from him!—was there not some perfidy concealed under this hatred? Might not this young man be sent by his Eminence? Might he not have come for the purpose of laying a snare for him? This pretended d'Artagnan, was he not an emissary of the Cardinal, who sought to introduce himself into his house that he might win his confidence, and afterward bring about his ruin, as had been practiced in a thousand other instances? He fixed his eyes upon d'Artagnan, even more earnestly than before. He was moderately reassured, however, by the aspect of that countenance, full of shrewd intelligence and affected humility.

"I know he is a Gascon," he reflected, "but he may be one for the Cardinal as well as for me. Let us try him."—"My friend," he said slowly, "as you are the son of an old friend of mine—for I consider this story of the lost letter perfectly true—I wish, in order to repair the coldness you may have remarked in my reception of you, to make you acquainted with the secrets of our policy. The King and the Cardinal are the best of friends; their apparent bickerings are only feints to deceive fools. I am not willing that a compatriot, a handsome cavalier, a brave youth, quite fit to make his way, should become the dupe of all these artifices and fall into the snare, after the example of so many others, who have been ruined by it. Be assured that I am devoted to both these all-powerful masters and that my earnest endeavors have no other aim than the service of the King and that of the Cardinal, one of the most illustrious geniuses that France has ever produced.

"Now, young man, regulate your conduct accordingly; and if you have, whether from your family, your relations, or even from your instincts, any of those enmities which we see constantly breaking out against the Cardinal, bid me adieu and let us separate. I will aid you in many ways, but without attaching you to my person. I hope that my frankness, at least, will make you my friend, for you are the only young man to whom I have hitherto spoken as I have done to you."

Tréville said to himself—

"If the Cardinal has set this young fox upon me, he will certainly not have failed, he, who knows how bitterly I execrate him, to tell his spy that the best means of making his court to me is to rail at him; therefore, in spite of all my protestations, if it be as I suspect, my cunning gossip here will launch out in abuse of his Eminence."

It proved, however, otherwise. D'Artagnan answered with the greatest simplicity—

"I have come to Paris with exactly such intentions, sir. My father advised me to stoop to nobody but the King, the Cardinal, and you—whom he considered the three first personages in France."

D'Artagnan added M. de Tréville to the others, as may be perceived; but he thought this adjunction would do no harm.

"I hold, therefore, the Cardinal in the greatest veneration," he continued, "and have the greatest respect for his actions. So much the better for me, sir, if you speak to me, as you say, with frankness—for then you will do me the honor to esteem the resemblance of our opinions; but if you have entertained any doubt, as naturally you may, I feel that I am ruining myself by speaking the truth. But I still trust you will not esteem me the less for it, and that is my object beyond all others."

M. de Tréville was surprised to the greatest degree. So much penetration—so much frankness—awakened his admiration, but did not entirely remove his suspicion; the more this young man was superior to others, the more he was to be dreaded, if he meant to deceive him. Nevertheless, he pressed d'Artagnan's hand, and said to him:

"You are an honest youth; but, at the present moment, I can only do for you that which I just now offered. My house will be always open to you. Being now able to ask for me at all hours, and consequently to take advantage of all opportunities, you will probably obtain later on what you desire."

"That is to say, sir," replied d'Artagnan, "that you will wait till I have proved myself worthy of it. Well! be assured," he added, with the familiarity of a Gascon, "you shall not wait long." And he bowed on retiring, as if he considered the future in his own hands.

"But wait a minute," said M. de Tréville, stopping him. "I promised you a letter for the director of the Academy; are you too proud to accept it, young gentleman?"

"No, sir," said d'Artagnan; "and I will answer for it that this one shall not fare like the other. I will guard it so carefully that I will be sworn it shall arrive at its address, and woe be to him who shall attempt to take it from me!"

M. de Tréville smiled at this little flourish and, leaving his young companion in the embrasure of the window, where they had talked together, he seated himself at a table to write the promised letter of recommendation. While he was doing this, d'Artagnan, having no better employment, amused himself with beating a march upon the window and with looking at the Musketeers, who went away, one after another, following them with his eyes till they disappeared at the turning of the street.

M. de Tréville, having written the letter, sealed it and approached the young man, in order to give it to him. But at the very moment that d'Artagnan stretched out his hand to receive it, M. de Tréville was highly astonished to see his protégé make a sudden spring, become crimson with passion and rush from the cabinet, crying—"Ah! he shall not escape me this time!"

"Who? who?" asked M. de Tréville.

"He, my thief!" replied d'Artagnan. "Ah! the traitor!" and he disappeared.

"The devil take the madman!" murmured M. de Tréville; "unless," he added, "this is a cunning mode of escaping, seeing that he has failed in his purpose!"

The Shoulder of Athos, the Baldric of Porthos and the Handkerchief of Aramis

D'ARTAGNAN, IN A STATE OF FURY, crossed the antechamber at three bounds and was darting toward the stairs, which he reckoned upon descending four at a time, when, in his heedless course, he ran head foremost against a Musketeer who was coming out of one of M. de Tréville's back rooms and, striking his shoulder violently, made him utter a cry, or rather a howl.

"Excuse me," said d'Artagnan, endeavoring to resume his course, "excuse me, but I am in a hurry."

Scarcely had he descended the first stair, when a hand of iron seized him by the belt and stopped him.

"You are in a hurry," said the Musketeer, as pale as a sheet; "under that pretense, you run against me; you say, 'Excuse me!' and you believe that that is sufficient? Not at all, my young man. Do you fancy that because you have heard M. de Tréville speak to us a little cavalierly today, that other people are to treat us as he speaks to us? Undeceive yourself, my merry companion, you are not M. de Tréville."

"My lord!" replied d'Artagnan, recognizing Athos, who, after the dressing performed by the doctor, was going to his own apartment, "I did not do it intentionally and, not doing it intentionally, I said, 'Excuse me!' It appears to me that that is quite enough. I repeat to you, however—and this time, I think, perhaps, too often —that I am in great haste—very great haste. Leave your hold, then, I beg of you, and let me go where my business calls me."

"Monsieur," said Athos, letting him go, "you are not polite; it is easy to perceive that you come from a distance."

D'Artagnan had already strode down three or four stairs, when Athos' last remark stopped him short.

"Blast it, monsieur!" said he, "from however far I may have come, it is not you who can give me a lesson in good manners, I warn you."

"Perhaps!" said Athos.

"Ah! if I were not in such haste, and if I were not running after someone—" said d'Artagnan.

"Mister gentleman in a hurry, you can find *me* without running after me, do you understand?"

"And where, I pray you?"

"Near the Carmes Deschaux."

"At what hour?"

"About noon."

"About noon; that will do, I will be there."

"Endeavor not to make me wait, for at a quarter past twelve I will cut off your ears as you run."

"Good!" cried d'Artagnan, "I will be there ten minutes before twelve."

And he set off running as if the devil possessed him, hoping that he might yet find the unknown, whose slow pace could not have carried him far.

But at the street gate Porthos was talking with the soldier on guard. Between the two talkers there was just room for a man to pass. D'Artagnan thought it would suffice for him, and he sprang forward like a dart between them. But he had reckoned without the wind. As he was about to pass, the wind blew out Porthos' long cloak and d'Artagnan rushed straight into the middle of it. Without doubt, Porthos had reasons for not abandoning this part of his vestments, for, instead of quitting his hold of the flap in his hand, he pulled it toward him, so that d'Artagnan rolled himself up in the velvet, by a rotating movement to be explained by the persistent hold of Porthos.

D'Artagnan, hearing the Musketeer swear, wished to escape from under the cloak which blinded him, and endeavored to find his way in its folds. He was particularly anxious to avoid marring the freshness of the magnificent baldric we are acquainted with, but, on timidly opening his eyes, found himself with his nose fixed between Porthos' two shoulders—that is to say, exactly upon the baldric.

Alas! how most of the things in this world have nothing in their favor but appearances! The baldric was glittering with gold in front, but was nothing but simple buff behind. Vainglorious as he was, Porthos could not afford to have an entirely gold-worked baldric, but had, at least, half of one. His care for his cold and the necessity of the cloak became intelligible.

"Bless me!" cried Porthos, making strong efforts to get rid of d'Artagnan, who was wriggling about his back, "the fellow must be mad to run against people in this manner!"

"Excuse me!" said d'Artagnan, reappearing under the shoulder of the giant, "but I am in such haste—I was running after someone and——"

"And do you always forget your eyes when you happen to be in a hurry?" asked Porthos.

"No," replied d'Artagnan, piqued, "no; thanks to my eyes, I can see what other people cannot see."

Whether Porthos understood him or not, he gave way to his anger.

"Monsieur," he said, "you stand a chance of getting chastised if you run against Musketeers in this fashion."

"Chastised, monsieur!" said d'Artagnan; "the expression is strong."

"It is one that becomes a man accustomed to look his enemies in the face."

"Ah! by Heaven! I know full well that you don't turn your back to yours!" And the young man, delighted with his joke, went away laughing loudly.

Porthos foamed with rage and made a movement to rush after d'Artagnan.

"Presently, presently," cried the latter, "when you haven't your cloak on."

"At one o'clock then, behind the Luxembourg."

"Very well, at one o'clock, then," replied d'Artagnan, turning the angle of the street.

But neither in the street he had passed through, nor in the one which his eager glance pervaded, could he see anyone; however slowly the unknown had walked, he had gone on his way, or perhaps entered some house. D'Artagnan inquired of everyone he met, went down to the ferry, came up again by the Rue de Seine and the Croix Rouge; but nothing, absolutely nothing! This chase was, however, advantageous to him in one sense, for, in proportion as the perspiration broke from his forehead, his heart began to cool.

He began to reflect upon the events that had passed. They were numerous and inauspicious; it was scarcely eleven o'clock in the morning and yet this morning had already brought him into disgrace with M. de Tréville, who could not fail to think the manner in which d'Artagnan had left him a little cavalier.

Besides this, he had drawn upon himself two good duels with two men, each capable of killing three d'Artagnans—with two Musketeers—in short, with two of those beings whom he esteemed so greatly that he placed them in his mind and heart above all other men.

Appearances were sad. Sure of being killed by Athos, it may easily be understood that the young man was not very uneasy about Porthos. As hope, however, is the last thing extinguished in the heart of man, he finished by hoping that he might survive, although terribly wounded in both these duels and, on the chance of surviving, he fell to blaming his own conduct as follows:

"What a hare-brained, stupid fellow I am! That brave and unfortunate Athos was wounded exactly on the shoulder against which I ran headforemost like a ram. The only thing that astonishes me is that he did not strike me dead at once; he had good cause to do so; the pain I gave him must have been atrocious. As to Porthos— oh! as to Porthos, faith! that's a droll affair!"

And, in spite of himself, the young man began to laugh aloud, looking around carefully, however, to see that his solitary laugh, without any apparent cause in the eyes of passers-by, offended no one.

"As to Porthos, that is certainly droll, but I am not the less a giddy fool. Are people to be run against without warning? No! and have I any right to go and peep under their cloaks to see what is not there? He would have pardoned me, he would certainly have pardoned me, if I had not said anything to him about that cursed baldric—in ambiguous words, it is true, but rather drolly ambiguous! Ah! cursed Gascon that I am, I get from one hobble into another. Friend d'Artagnan," he continued, speaking to himself with all the amenity that he thought due to himself, "if you escape, of which there is not much chance, I would advise you to practice perfect politeness in the future. You must henceforth be admired and quoted as a model of it. To be obliging and polite does not necessarily make a man a coward. Look at Aramis now: Aramis is mildness and grace personified. Well! did ever anybody dream of saying that Aramis is a coward? No, certainly not, and from this moment I will endeavor to model myself upon him. Ah! that's strange! here he is!"

D'Artagnan, walking and soliloquizing, had arrived within a few steps of the Hotel d'Arguillon, and in front of that mansion perceived Aramis chatting gaily with three gentlemen of the King's guards. On his part Aramis perceived d'Artagnan, but, as he had not forgotten that it was before this young man that M. de Tréville had been so angry in the morning and that a witness of the rebuke the Musketeers had received was not likely to be at all agreeable, he pretended not to see him. D'Artagnan, on the contrary, quite full of his plans of conciliation and courtesy, approached the young man with a profound bow, accompanied by a most gracious smile. Aramis bowed his head slightly, but did not smile. All four, besides, immediately broke off their conversation.

D'Artagnan was not so dull as not to perceive that he was not wanted; but he was not sufficiently broken into the fashions of the world to know how to extricate himself gallantly from a false position, as is generally that of a man who comes up and mingles with people he is scarcely acquainted with and in a conversation that does not concern him. He was seeking in his mind, then, for the least awkward means of retreat, when he remarked that Aramis had dropped his handkerchief and, by mistake, no doubt, had placed his foot upon it. This appeared a favorable opportunity to repair his false step: he stooped and, with the most gracious air he could assume, drew the handkerchief from under the foot of the Musketeer, in spite of the latter's efforts to keep it there and, holding it out to him, said:

"I believe, monsieur, that this is a handkerchief you would be sorry to lose?"

The handkerchief was, in fact, richly embroidered and had a coronet and arms at one of its corners. Aramis blushed excessively and snatched rather than took the handkerchief from d'Artagnan's hand.

"Ah! ah!" cried one of the guards, "will you persist in saying, most discreet Aramis, that you are not on good terms with Madame de Bois-Tracy, when that gracious lady has the kindness to lend you her handkerchief?"

Aramis darted at d'Artagnan one of those looks which inform a man that he has made a mortal enemy; then resuming his mild air—

"You are deceived, gentlemen," said he; "this handkerchief is not mine and I cannot fancy why monsieur has taken it into his head to offer it to me rather than to one of you, and as a proof of what I say, here is mine in my pocket."

So saying, he pulled out his own handkerchief, which was likewise very elegant and of fine cambric, though cambric was then dear, but a handkercheif with embroidery and without arms, only ornamented with a single cipher, that of the Musketeer.

This time d'Artagnan was not hasty: he perceived his mistake; but the friends of Aramis were not at all convinced by his assertion and one of them, addressing the young Musketeer with affected seriousness, said:

"If it were as you pretend it is, I should be forced, my dear Aramis, to reclaim it myself; for, as you very well know, Bois-Tracy is an intimate friend of mine and I cannot allow the property of his wife to be sported as a trophy."

"You make the demand awkwardly," replied Aramis, "and while acknowledging the justice of your claim, I refuse it on account of the form."

"The fact is," hazarded d'Artagnan timidly, "I did not see the handkerchief fall from the pocket of M. Aramis. He had his foot upon it, that is all, and I thought, from his having his foot upon it, the handkerchief was his."

"And you were deceived, my dear sir," replied Aramis coldly, very little sensible to the reparation; then turning toward that one of the guards who had declared himself the friend of Bois-Tracy, he continued: "Besides, I have reflected, my dear intimate friend of Bois-Tracy, that I am not less tenderly his friend than you can possibly be, so that decidedly this handkerchief is as likely to have fallen from your pocket as mine."

"No, upon my honor!" cried his Majesty's guard.

"You are about to swear upon your honor, and I upon my word and then it will be pretty evident that one of us has lied. Now, here, Montaran, we will do better than that; let us each take half."

"Of the handkerchief?"

"Yes."

"Perfectly just," cried the two other guards—"the judgment of

51

King Solomon! Aramis, you certainly are cram full of wisdom!"

The young men burst into a loud laugh and, as may be supposed, the affair had no other consequence. In a moment or two the conversation ceased and the three guards and the Musketeer, after having cordially shaken hands, separated, the guards going one way and Aramis another.

"Now is my time to make my peace with this gentleman," thought d'Artagnan, who had stood on one side during the whole of the latter part of the conversation. With this good intention, he drew near to Aramis, who was going away without paying any heed to him and said:

"Monsieur, you will excuse me, I hope."

"Ah! monsieur," interrupted Aramis, "permit me to observe to you that you have not acted in this affair as a man of good breeding should have done."

"What, monsieur!" cried d'Artagnan, "you suppose——"

"I suppose, monsieur, that you are not a fool and that you knew very well, although coming from Gascony, that people do not tread upon pocket-handkerchiefs without a reason. What the devil! Paris is not paved with cambric!"

"Monsieur, you are wrong to try to mortify me," said d'Artagnan, with whom the natural quarrelsome spirit began to speak more loudly than his pacific resolutions. "I am from Gascony, it is true; and since you know it, there is no occasion to tell you that Gascons are not very patient, so that when they have begged to be excused once, were it even for a folly, they are convinced that they have done already at least as much again as they ought to have done."

"Monsieur, what I say to you about the matter," said Aramis, "is not for the sake of seeking a quarrel. Thank God! I am not an assassin and, being a Musketeer but for a time, I only fight when I am forced to do so and always with great repugnance; but this time the affair is serious, for here is a lady compromised by you."

"By us, you mean," cried d'Artagnan.

"Why did you so injudiciously restore the handkerchief to me?"

"Why did you so awkwardly let it fall?"

"I have said, monsieur, that the handkerchief did not fall from my pocket."

"Well, and by saying so, you have lied twice, monsieur, for I saw it fall."

52

"Oh, oh! you take it up in that way, do you, Master Gascon? Well, I will teach you how to behave yourself."

"And I will send you back to your mass-book, Master Abbé. Draw, if you please, and instantly——"

"Not so, if you please, my good friend—not here, at least. Do you not perceive that we are opposite the Hotel d'Arguillon, which is full of the Cardinal's creatures? How do I know that it is not his Eminence who has honored you with the commission to bring him my head? Now I entertain a ridiculous partiality for my head, it seems to suit my shoulders so admirably. I have no objection to killing you, depend upon that, but quietly, in a snug, remote place, where you will not be able to boast of your death to anybody."

"I agree, monsieur; but do not be too confident. Take away your handkerchief; whether it belongs to you or to another, you may perhaps stand in need of it."

"Monsieur is a Gascon?" asked Aramis.

"Yes. Monsieur does not postpone an interview through prudence?"

"Prudence, monsieur, is a virtue sufficiently useless to Musketeers, I know, but indispensable to Churchmen; and as I am only a Musketeer provisionally, I hold it good to be prudent. At two o'clock I shall have the honor of expecting you at the house of M. de Tréville. There I will point out to you the best place and time."

The two young men bowed and separated, Aramis ascending the street which led to the Luxembourg, while d'Artagnan, perceiving that the appointed hour was approaching, took the road to the Carmes-Deschaux, saying to himself: "Decidedly I can't draw back; but at least, if I am killed, I shall be killed by a Musketeer!"

The King's Musketeers and the Cardinal's Guards

D'ARTAGNAN WAS ACQUAINTED with nobody in Paris. He went, therefore, to his appointment with Athos without a second, determined to be satisfied with those his adversary would choose. Besides, he had determined to offer the brave Musketeer all suitable apologies, although without meanness or weakness, fearing that that might result from this duel which generally results from an affair of this kind, when a young and vigorous man fights with an adversary who is wounded and weakened: if conquered, he doubles the triumph of his antagonist; if a conqueror, he is accused of foul play and want of courage.

Now, we must have failed in painting the character of our adventurer if our readers have not already perceived that d'Artagnan was not a common man; therefore, while repeating to himself that his death was inevitable, he did not make up his mind to die as quietly as another, less courageous and less moderate than he, might have done in his place. He reflected upon the different characters of the men he had to fight with and began to view his situation more clearly. He hoped, by means of loyal excuses, to make a friend of Athos, whose noble air and austere courage pleased him much. He flattered himself he should be able to frighten Porthos with the adventure of the baldric, which he might, if not killed upon the spot, relate to everybody—a recital which, well managed, would cover Porthos with ridicule; as to the astute Aramis, he did not entertain much dread of him and if he should succeed in getting so far, he determined to dispatch him in good style, or at least to damage forever the beauty of which he was so proud, by hitting him in the face, as Caesar recommended his soldiers to do to those of Pompey.

In addition to this, d'Artagnan possessed that invincible stock of resolution which the counsels of his father had implanted in his heart—Endure nothing from anyone but the King, the Cardinal, and M. de Tréville. He flew, rather than walked, toward the convent of the Carmes Déchaussés, or rather Dechaux, as it was called at that period, a sort of building without a window, surrounded by barren fields, an accessory to the Pré-aux-Clercs and generally used at that time as the place for the encounters of men who had no time to lose.

When d'Artagnan arrived in sight of the bare spot of ground which extended along the base of the monastery, Athos had been waiting about five minutes, and twelve o'clock was striking. . . .

Athos, who still suffered grievously from his wound, though it had been dressed by M. de Tréville's surgeon at nine, was seated on a post and waiting for his adversary with that placid countenance and that noble air which never forsook him. At the sight of d'Artagnan, he rose and came politely a few steps to meet him. The latter, on his side, saluted his adversary with hat in hand, his feather even touching the ground.

"Monsieur," said Athos, "I have engaged two of my friends as seconds; but these two friends have not yet come, at which I am astonished, as it is not at all their custom to be late."

"I have no seconds on my part, monsieur," said d'Artagnan, "for, having only arrived yesterday in Paris, I know as yet no one but M. de Tréville, to whom I was recommended by my father, who has the honor to be, in some degree, one of his friends."

Athos reflected for an instant.

"You know no one but M. de Tréville?" he asked.

"No, monsieur; I only know him."

"Well, but then," continued Athos, speaking partly to himself, "well, but then, if I kill you, I shall have the air of a boy-slayer."

"Not too much so," replied d'Artagnan, with a bow that was not deficient in dignity, "not too much so, since you do me the honor to draw a sword with me while suffering from a wound which is very painful."

"Very painful, upon my word, and you hurt me devilishly, I can tell you. But I will take the left hand—I usually do so in such circumstances. Do not fancy that I favor you—I use both hands equally well, and it will even be a disadvantage to you—a left-handed man is very troublesome to people who are not used to it. I regret I did not inform you sooner of this circumstance."

"I assure you, monsieur," said d'Artagnan, bowing again, "that no one could be more grateful than I am for your admirable courtesy."

"You embarrass me," replied Athos, with his grand air; "let us talk of something else, if you please. Ah! how you have hurt me! my shoulder quite burns."

"If you would permit me——" said d'Artagnan, with timidity.

"What, monsieur?"

"I have a miraculous balsam for wounds—a balsam given to me by my mother, and of which I have made a trial upon myself."

"Well?"

"Well, I am sure that in less than three days this balsam would cure you; and at the end of three days, when you would be cured —well, sir, it would still do me a great honor to be your man."

D'Artagnan spoke these words with a simplicity that did honor to his courtesy, without throwing the least doubt upon his courage.

"By Heaven, monsieur!" said Athos, "that's a proposition that pleases me; not that I accept it, but it savors of the gentleman a league off. It was thus that spoke the gallant knights of the time of

Charlemagne, in whom every knight ought to seek his model. Unfortunately, we do not live in the time of the great emperor; we live in the times of Monsieur the Cardinal, and three days hence, however well the secret might be guarded, it would be known, I say, that we were to fight and our combat would be prevented. I think these fellows will never come."

"If you are in haste, monsieur," said d'Artagnan, with the same simplicity with which a moment before he had proposed to him to put off the duel for three days, "if you are in haste, and if it be your will to dispatch me at once, do not inconvenience yourself—I am ready."

"Well, that is again well said," cried Athos, with a gracious nod to d'Artagnan, "that did not come from a man without brains and certainly not from a man without a heart. Monsieur, I love men of your kidney and I foresee plainly that, if we don't kill each other, I shall hereafter find much pleasure in your conversation. We will wait for these gentlemen, if you please; I have plenty of time and it will be more correct. Ah! here is one of them, I think."

In fact, at the end of the Rue Vanguard, the gigantic form of Porthos began to appear.

"What!" cried d'Artagnan, "is your first second M. Porthos?"

"Yes. Is that unpleasant to you?"

"Oh, not at all."

"And here comes the other."

D'Artagnan turned in the direction pointed to by Athos and perceived Aramis.

"What!" cried he, in an accent of greater astonishment than before, "is your second witness M. Aramis?"

"Doubtless he is. Are you not aware that we are never seen one without the others, and that we are called in the Musketeers and the guards, at court and in the city, Athos, Porthos, and Aramis, or the Three Inseparables? And yet, as you come from Dax or Pau——"

"From Tarbes," said d'Artagnan.

"It is probable that you are ignorant of this circumstance," said Athos.

"Indeed!" replied d'Artagnan, "you are well named, gentlemen, and my adventure, if it should make any noise, will prove at least that your union is not founded upon contrasts."

In the meantime Porthos had come up. He waved his hand to

Athos and then, turning toward d'Artagnan, stood quite astonished.

Permit us to say, in passing, that he had changed his baldric, and was without his cloak.

"Ah, ah!" said he, "what does this mean?"

"This is the gentleman I am going to fight with," said Athos, pointing to d'Artagnan with his hand and saluting him with the same gesture.

"Why, it is with him I also am going to fight," said Porthos.

"But not before one o'clock," replied d'Artagnan.

"Well, and I also am going to fight with that gentleman," said Aramis, coming on the ground as he spoke.

"But not till two o'clock," said d'Artagnan, with the same calmness.

"But what are you going to fight about, Athos?" asked Aramis.

"Well, I don't very well know; he hurt my shoulder. And you, Porthos?"

"Well, I am going to fight, because I am going to fight," answered Porthos, coloring deeply.

Athos, whose keen eye lost nothing, perceived a faintly sly smile pass over the lips of the young Gascon, as he replied:

"We had a short discussion upon dress."

"And you, Aramis?" asked Athos.

"Oh, ours is a theological quarrel," replied Aramis, making a sign to d'Artagnan to keep secret the cause of their dispute.

Athos saw a second smile on the lips of d'Artagnan.

"Indeed?" said Athos.

"Yes, a passage of St. Augustine, upon which we could not agree," said the Gascon.

"By Jove! this is a clever fellow," murmured Athos.

"And now you are all assembled, gentlemen," said d'Artagnan, "permit me to offer you my excuses."

At this word *excuses,* a cloud passed over the brow of Athos, a haughty smile curled the lip of Porthos and a negative sign was the reply of Aramis.

"You do not understand me, gentlemen," said d'Artagnan, throwing up his head, the sharp and bold lines of which were at the moment gilded by a bright sun ray. "I ask to be excused in case I should not be able to discharge my debt to all three; for M. Athos has the right to kill me first, which must abate your valor in your own estimation, M. Porthos, and render yours almost null, M.

57

Aramis. And now, gentlemen, I repeat, excuse me, but on that account only, and—guard!"

At these words, with the most gallant air possible, d'Artagnan drew his sword.

The blood had mounted to his head and at that moment he would have drawn his sword against all the Musketeers in the kingdom as willingly as he now did against Athos, Porthos and Aramis.

It was a quarter past midday. The sun was in its zenith and the spot chosen for the theater of the duel was exposed to its full power.

"It is very hot," said Athos, drawing his sword in his turn, "and yet I cannot take off my doublet; for I just now felt my wound begin to bleed again and I should not like to annoy monsieur with the sight of blood which he has not drawn from me himself."

"That is true, monsieur," replied d'Artagnan, "and, whether drawn by myself or another, I assure you, I shall always view with regret the blood of so brave a gentleman; I will therefore fight in my doubtlet, as you do."

"Come, come, enough of compliments," cried Porthos; "please remember we are waiting for our turns."

"Speak for yourself, when you are inclined to utter such incongruities," interrupted Aramis. "For my part, I think what they say is very well said and quite worthy of two gentlemen."

"When you please, monsieur," said Athos, putting himself on guard.

"I waited your orders," said d'Artagnan, crossing swords.

But scarcely had the two rapiers clicked in meeting, when a company of the guards of his Eminence, commanded by M. de Jussac, turned the angle of the convent.

"The Cardinal's guards! the Cardinal's guards!" cried Aramis and Porthos at the same time. "Sheathe swords! gentlemen! sheathe swords!"

But it was too late. The two combatants had been seen in a position which left no doubt of their intentions.

"Hola!" cried Jussac, advancing toward them and making a sign to his men to do likewise, "hola Musketeers! fighting here, are you? And the edicts, what of them?"

"You are very generous, gentlemen of the guards," said Athos with acrimony, for Jussac was one of the aggressors of the preceding day. "If we were to see you fighting, I can assure you that we would make no effort to prevent you. Leave us alone, then, and you will enjoy a little amusement without cost to yourself."

"Gentlemen," said Jussac, "it is with great regret that I pronounce the thing impossible. Duty before everything. Sheathe, then, if you please, and follow us."

"Monsieur," said Aramis, parodying Jussac, "it would afford us great pleasure to obey your polite invitation, if it depended upon ourselves; but, unfortunately, the thing is impossible; M. de Tréville has forbidden it. Pass on your way, therefore; it is the best thing you can do."

This raillery exasperated Jussac.

"We will charge upon you," he said, "if you disobey."

"There are five of them," said Athos, half aloud, "and we are but three; we shall be beaten again, and must die on the spot, for, on my part, I declare I will never appear before the captain again as a conquered man."

Athos, Porthos and Aramis instantly closed in, and Jussac drew up his soldiers.

This short interval was sufficient to determine d'Artagnan on the part he was to take. It was one of those events that decide the life of a man—it was a choice between the King and the Cardinal. The choice made, it must be persisted in. To fight was to disobey the law, to risk his head, to make at once an enemy of a minister more powerful than the King himself. All this the young man perceived and yet he did not hesitate a second. Turning toward Athos and his friends—

"Gentlemen," he said, "allow me to correct your words, if you please. You said you were but three, but it appears to me we are four."

"But you are not one of us," said Porthos.

"That's true," replied d'Artagnan; "I do not wear the uniform, but I am one of you in spirit. My heart is that of a Musketeer; I feel it, monsieur, and that impels me on."

"Withdraw, young man," cried Jussac, who, doubtless by his gestures and the expression of his countenance, had guessed d'Artagnan's design. "You may retire, we allow you to do so. Save your skin, begone quickly."

D'Artagnan did not move.

"Decidedly you are a pretty fellow," said Athos, pressing the young man's hand.

"Come, come, decide one way or the other," replied Jussac.

"Well," said Porthos to Aramis, "we must do something."

"Monsieur is very generous," said Athos.

But all three reflected upon the youth of d'Artagnan and dreaded his inexperience.

"We should only be three, one of whom is wounded, with the addition of a boy," resumed Athos, "and yet it would be said none the less that we were four men."

"Yes, but to yield!" said Porthos.

"That's rather difficult," replied Athos.

D'Artagnan understood whence a part of their hesitation arose.

"Try me, gentlemen," he said, "and I swear to you by my honor that I will not go hence if we are conquered."

"What is your name, my brave fellow?" said Athos.

"D'Artagnan, monsieur."

"Well, then! Athos, Porthos, Aramis and d'Artagnan, forward!" cried Athos.

"Come, gentlemen, have you made up your minds?" cried Jussac, for the third time.

"We have, gentlemen," said Athos.

"And what do you mean to do?" asked Jussac.

"We are about to have the honor of charging you," replied Aramis, lifting his hat with one hand and drawing his sword with the other.

"Oh! you resist, do you?" cried Jussac.

"We do! Does that astonish you?"

And the nine combatants rushed upon each other with a fury that did not exclude a certain degree of method.

Athos fixed upon a certain Cahusac, a favorite of the Cardinal; Porthos had Bicarat and Aramis found himself opposed to two adversaries. As to d'Artagnan, he sprang toward Jussac himself. . . .

The young Gascon fought like a furious tiger, turning ten times around his adversary, and changing his ground and his guard twenty times. Jussac was, as they expressed it in those days, a fine blade and had had much practice; nevertheless, it required all his skill to defend himself against an adversary, who, active and energetic, departed every instant from received rules, attacking him on all sides at once and yet parrying like a man who had the greatest respect for his own skin.

This contest at length exhausted Jussac's patience. Furious at being held in check by him whom he had considered a boy, he grew

60

hot and began to make mistakes. D'Artagnan, who, though wanting in practice, had a good theory, redoubled his agility. Jussac, anxious to put an end to this, springing forward aimed a terrible thrust at his adversary, but the latter parried it and, while Jussac was recovering himself, glided like a serpent beneath his blade, and passed his sword through his body. Jussac fell like a dead mass.

D'Artagnan then cast an anxious and rapid glance over the field of battle.

Aramis had killed one of his adversaries, but the other pressed him warmly. Nevertheless, Aramis was in a good position and able to defend himself.

Bicarat and Porthos had just made counter-hits; Porthos had received a thrust through his arm and Bicarat one through the thigh. But neither of the wounds was serious and they only fought the more earnestly for them.

Athos, wounded again by Cahusac, became evidently paler, but did not give way an inch: he had only changed his sword-hand and fought with his left hand.

According to the laws of dueling at that period, d'Artagnan was at liberty to help whom he pleased. While he was endeavoring to find out which of his companions stood in greatest need, he caught a glance from Athos. This glance was of sublime eloquence. Athos would have died rather than appeal for help, but he could look and with that look ask help. D'Artagnan interpreted it. With a terrible bound, he sprang to the side of Cahusac, crying:

"To me, monsieur! guard, or I will slay you!"

Cahusac turned; it was time, for Athos, whose great courage alone supported him, sank upon his knee.

"No!" he cried to d'Artagnan, "do not kill him, young man, I beg you; I have an old affair to settle with him, when I am cured and sound again. Disarm him only—make sure of his sword; that's it! that's it! well done! very well done!"

This exclamation was drawn from Athos by seeing Cahusac's sword fly twenty paces from him. D'Artagnan and Cahusac sprang forward at the same instant, the one to recover, the other to obtain the sword; but d'Artagnan, being the more active, reached it first and placed his foot upon it.

Cahusac immediately ran to that of one of the guards that Aramis had killed and returned toward d'Artagnan; but on his way he met Athos, who, during this relief which d'Artagnan had procured him, had recovered his breath and who, for fear that d'Artagnan should kill his enemy, wished to resume the fight.

D'Artagnan perceived that it would be disobliging Athos not to leave him alone and in a few minutes Cahusac fell, with a sword thrust through his throat.

At the same instant Aramis placed his sword-point on the breast of his fallen enemy and compelled him to ask for mercy.

Porthos and Bicarat were left. The former made a thousand fanfaronnades, asking Bicarat what time it could be, and offering him his compliments upon his brother's having just obtained a company in the regiment of Navarre; but, joke as he might, he gained no advantage—Bicarat was one of those iron men who only fall when dead.

Nevertheless, it was necessary to put an end to the affair. The watch might come up and take all the combatants, wounded or not, royalists or cardinalists. Athos, Aramis and d'Artagnan surrounded Bicarat and required him to surrender. Though alone against all, and with a wound in his thigh, Bicarat wished to hold out; but Jussac, who had risen upon his elbow, cried out to him to yield. Bicarat was a Gascon, like d'Artagnan. He turned a deaf ear and contented himself with laughing; and between two parries, finding time to point to a spot of earth with his sword—

"Here," cried he, parodying a verse of the Bible, "here will Bicarat die, the only one of those who are with him."

"But there are four against you; leave off, I command you."

"Ah! if you command me, that's another thing," said Bicarat; "you being my brigadier, it is my duty to obey."

And springing backward, he broke his sword across his knee, to avoid the necessity of surrendering it, threw the pieces over the convent wall and crossed his arms, whistling a cardinalist air.

Bravery is always respected, even in an enemy. The Musketeers saluted Bicarat with their swords and returned them to their sheaths. D'Artagnan did the same; then, assisted by Bicarat, the only one left standing, he bore Jussac, Cahusac, and that one of Aramis' adversaries who was only wounded under the porch of the convent. The fourth, as we have said, was dead. They then rang the bell and, carrying away four swords out of five, took their road, intoxicated with joy, toward the house of M. de Tréville.

They walked arm in arm, occupying the whole width of the street and accosting every Musketeer they met, so that in the end it became a triumphal march. D'Artagnan's heart swam in delight; he marched between Athos and Porthos, pressing them tenderly.

"If I am not yet a Musketeer," he said to his new friends, as he passed through the gateway of M. de Tréville's house, "I have at least entered upon my apprenticeship, haven't I?"

[*Though officially reprimanded for their brawl, the Musketeers were privately applauded by M. de Tréville and were granted an audience with the King. Before the audience took place, d'Artagnan severely wounded one of the Cardinal's guards in a duel, but the King pardoned the youth, rewarded him with money, and ordered him to be given a place in the guards, where he would serve his apprenticeship for the Musketeers. Athos, Porthos, Aramis and d'Artagnan formed a friendship governed by the motto, "All for one, one for all."*

One day M. Bonacieux, d'Artagnan's landlord, a rich mercer, sought his help. His young and pretty wife, a seamstress to the Queen, had been abducted. The man whom the landlord suspected turned out to be d'Artagnan's enemy at Meung. The four friends were about to undertake the search for Mme. Bonacieux when M. Bonacieux himself was suddenly arrested and a watch was placed on his apartment. The next evening d'Artagnan overheard a scuffle in the apartment; he burst in and rescued Mme. Bonacieux. He was enchanted by her beauty. He hid her in Athos' apartment while he sought out M. Laporte, her godfather and a confidential valet to the Queen. His mission completed, d'Artagnan went to Aramis' house where he witnessed a secret exchange of handkerchiefs through a window. He followed one of the participants and discovered Mme. Bonacieux. He conducted her to her destination which, despite his persistent questioning and his protestations of love, she refused to identify. Perplexed by all these proceedings, he returned home, to find that Athos, who had been awaiting him, was arrested by agents who mistook him for d'Artagnan. As d'Artagnan went off to the Louvre in search of M. de Tréville, he spied a woman and a Musketeer who, he thought, was Aramis. He accosted the couple and found Mme. Bonacieux, who was secretly conducting the disguised Duke of Buckingham to the Louvre.]

George Villiers, Duke of Buckingham

M ADAME BONACIEUX AND THE DUKE entered the Louvre without difficulty. She was known to belong to the Queen, the duke wore the uniform of the Musketeers of M. de Tréville, who were that evening on guard. Besides, Germain, the keeper of the wicket on the side of the Rue de l'Echelle, was on the Queen's side and, if anything should happen, Madame Bonacieux would only be accused of having introduced her lover into the Louvre. She took the risk upon herself; to be sure, her reputation was jeopardized, but of what value in the world was the reputation of the little wife of a mercer?

Once within the interior of the court, the duke and the young woman kept along the wall for about twenty-five steps. This space passed, Madame Bonacieux pushed a little side door, open by day, but generally closed at night. The door yielded: both entered, and found themselves in darkness. Madame Bonacieux, however, was acquainted with all the turnings and windings of this part of the Louvre, destined for the people of the household. She closed the door after her, took the duke by the hand, advanced a little, feeling her way, came to a balustrade, put her foot upon the bottom step and began to ascend a flight of stairs; the duke counted two stories. She then turned to the right, followed the course of a long corridor, redescended a story, went a few steps farther, introduced a key into a lock, opened a door and pushed the duke into an apartment lighted only by a night-lamp, saying, "Remain here, milord duke; someone will come." She then went out by the same door, which she locked, so that the duke found himself literally a prisoner.

Nevertheless, isolated as he was, we must say that the Duke of Buckingham did not experience an instant of fear: one of the salient sides of his character was the quest of adventures and a love of the romantic. Brave, even rash, and enterprising, this was not the first time he had risked his life in such attempts. He had learned that the pretended message from Anne of Austria, upon the strength of which he had come to Paris, was a snare and, instead of regaining England, he had, forcing the position in which he had been placed, declared to the Queen that he would not go back without having seen

64

her. The Queen had at first positively refused, but at length became afraid that the duke, if exasperated, would commit some rashness. She had already decided upon seeing him and urging his immediate departure, when, on the very evening of coming to this decision, Madame Bonacieux, who was charged with going to fetch the duke and conducting him to the Louvre, was carried off. During two days it was not known what had become of her and everything remained in suspense. But, once she had been set free and placed in communication with Laporte, matters resumed their course and she accomplished the perilous enterprise which, but for her abduction, would have been executed three days earlier.

Buckingham, on being left alone, walked toward a mirror. His Musketeer's uniform became him wonderfully well.

At thirty-five, which was then his age, he passed, with just title, for the handsomest gentleman and the most elegant cavalier of France or England.

The favorite of two kings, immensely rich, all-powerful in a kingdom which he threw into disorder at his fancy and calmed again at his caprice, George Villiers, Duke of Buckingham, led one of those fabulous existences which continue to be after the course of centuries an astonishment to posterity.

Thus, sure of himself, convinced of his own power, certain that the laws which rule other men could not reach him, he went straight to the object he aimed at, even were this object so elevated and so dazzling that it would have been madness in any other man but to have contemplated it. It was thus he had succeeded in gaining access several times to the beautiful and haughty Anne of Austria, and to make her love him by dazzling her.

George Villiers, as we have said, went to the mirror, re-arranged the waving curls of his beautiful hair, which the weight of his hat had disordered, twirled his mustache and, with a heart swelling with joy, happy and proud at being near the moment he had so long sighed for, smiled upon himself with pride and hope.

At this moment a door concealed in the tapestry opened and a woman appeared. Buckingham saw this apparition in the glass; he uttered a cry—it was the Queen!

Anne of Austria was then between twenty-six and twenty-seven years of age—that is to say, she was in the full splendor of her beauty.

65

Her carriage was that of a queen or a goddess; her eyes, which flashed like emeralds, were perfectly beautiful and yet, at the same time, full of sweetness and majesty.

Her mouth was small and rosy and, although her under lip, like that of the princes of the house of Austria, protruded slightly beyond the upper, it was eminently lovely in its smile, but profoundly disdainful in its expression of contempt.

Her skin was admired for its velvety softness, her hands and arms were of surpassing beauty, all the poets of the time describing them as incomparable.

Lastly, her hair, which, from being light in her first youth, had become chestnut and which she wore curled very plainly and with much powder, admirably set off her face, in which the most rigid critic could only have wished for a little less rouge and the most fastidious sculptor for a little more fineness in the nose.

Buckingham remained for a moment dazzled. Never had Anne of Austria appeared to him so beautiful, amid balls, fetes, or carousals, as she appeared to him at this moment, dressed in a simple robe of white satin and accompanied by Donna Estafania, the only one of her Spanish women that had not been driven from her by the jealousy of the King, or by the persecutions of the Cardinal.

Anne of Austria made two steps forward; Buckingham threw himself at her feet and, before the Queen could prevent him, kissed the hem of her robe.

"Duke, you already know that it is not I who have caused you to be written to."

"Yes, yes, madame! yes, your Majesty!" cried the duke; "I know that I must have been mad, senseless, to believe that snow would become animated, or marble warm; but then! they who love easily believe in love—besides, this voyage is not a loss, since I see you."

"Yes," replied Anne, "but you know why and how I see you, milord! I see you out of pity for yourself; I see you, because, insensible to all my sufferings, you persist in remaining in a city where, by doing so, you run the risk of your own life and make me run the risk of my honor. I receive you to tell you that everything separates us, the depths of the sea, the enmity of kingdoms, the sanctity of vows. It is sacrilege to struggle against so many things, milord. In short, I see you now to tell you that we must never see each other again."

"Speak on, madame, speak on, my queen," said Buckingham,

66

"the sweetness of your voice covers the harshness of your words. You talk of sacrilege! why, the sacrilege is the separation of two hearts formed by God for each other."

"Milord!" cried the Queen, "you forget that I have never told you I loved you."

"But you have never told me that you did not love me and truly, to speak such words to me would be, on the part of your Majesty, too great an ingratitude. For tell me, where can you find a love like mine, a love which neither time, nor absence, nor despair can extinguish; a love which contents itself with a lost ribbon, a stray look or a chance word? It is now three years, madame, since I saw you for the first time and during those three years I have loved you thus.

"Shall I tell you how you were dressed the first time I saw you? shall I describe to you every one of the ornaments you wore? Mark! I see you now. You were seated upon cushions, in the Spanish fashion; you wore a robe of green satin embroidered with gold and silver; hanging sleeves, fastened up upon your beautiful arms, upon those lovely arms, with large diamonds; you wore a close ruff, a small cap upon your head of the same color as your robe and in that cap a heron's feather.

"Oh, madame! madame! I shut my eyes, and I can see you such as you then were; I open them again and I see you such as you are now—a hundred times more beautiful!"

"What folly!" murmured Anne of Austria, who had not the courage to find fault with the duke for having so well preserved her portrait in his heart. "What folly to feed a vain passion with such remembrances!"

"And upon what, then, must I live? I have nothing but remembrances. They are my happiness, my treasure, my hopes. Every time that I see you is a fresh diamond which I enclose in the casket of my heart. This is the fourth which you have let fall and I have picked up; for, in three years, madame, I have only seen you four times; the first which I have just described to you, the second at the mansion of Madame de Chevreuse, the third in the gardens of Amiens."

"Duke," said the Queen, blushing, "never name that evening."

"Oh, yes! let me speak of it, on the contrary, let me speak of it; that is the most happy and brilliant evening of my life! Do you not remember what a beautiful night it was? How soft and perfumed the air, how lovely the blue, star-enameled sky?

67

"Ah! that time, madame, I was able for one instant to be alone with you; that time you were about to tell me all, the isolation of your life, the griefs of your heart. You leaned upon my arm; upon this one, madame! I felt, by leaning my head toward you, your beautiful hair touching my cheek and every time that it did touch me, I trembled from head to foot. Oh, Queen, Queen! you do not know what felicity from heaven, what joys from paradise, are comprised in a moment like that! I would give all my wealth, all my good fortune, all my glory, all the days I have to live, for such an instant, for a night like that! for that night, madame, that night you loved me, I will swear it."

"Milord, yes, it is possible that the influence of the place, the charm of the beautiful evening, the fascination of your look, the thousand circumstances, in short, which sometimes unite to destroy a woman, were grouped around me on that fatal evening. But, milord, you saw the Queen come to the aid of the woman who faltered; at the first word you dared to utter, at the first liberty to which I had to reply, I summoned my attendants."

"Yes, yes! that is true, and any other love but mine would have sunk beneath this ordeal, but mine came out from it more ardent and more eternal. You believed you should fly from me by returning to Paris, you believed that I should not dare to quit the treasure over which my master had charged me to watch. What to me were all the treasures in the world, or all the kings of the earth? Eight days later I was back again, madame. That time you had nothing to say to me; I had risked my life and my favor to see you but for a second. I did not even touch your hand, and you pardoned me on seeing me so submissive and repentant."

"Yes, but calumny seized upon all those follies in which I took no part, as you well know, milord. The King, excited by the Cardinal, made a terrible clamor; Madame de Vernet was driven from me, Putange was exiled, Madame de Chevreuse fell into disgrace and when you wished to come back as ambassador to France, the King himself, remember, milord, the King himself opposed it."

"Yes, and France is about to pay for her King's refusal with a war. I am not allowed to see you, madame, but you shall every day hear of me! What object, think you, have this expedition to Ré and this league with the Protestants of Rochelle which I am projecting? The pleasure of seeing you.

"I have no hope of penetrating sword in hand to Paris, I know that well; but this war may bring a peace, this peace will require a negotiator, that negotiator shall be I. They will not dare to refuse me then and I shall see you and be happy for an instant. Thousands of men, it is true, will have to pay for my happiness with their lives, but what will that signify to me, provided I see you again? All this is perhaps madness, folly, but tell me what woman has a lover more truly in love? what queen has a servant more faithful or more ardent?"

"Milord! milord! you invoke in your defense things which accuse you more strongly; milord, all these proofs of love that you boast are little better than crimes."

"Because you do not love me, madame. If you loved me, you would view all this otherwise. If you loved me—— Oh! if you loved me, that would be happiness too great, and I should go mad. Ah! Madame de Chevreuse, of whom you spoke but now, Madame de Chevreuse was less cruel than you. Holland loved her and she responded to his love."

"Madame de Chevreuse was not a queen," murmured Anne of Austria, overcome in spite of herself by the expression of so profound a passion.

"You would love me, then, if you were not one; you, madame, say that you would love me then? I am then to believe that it is the dignity of your rank alone that makes you cruel to me? I may believe that if you had been Madame de Chevreuse, poor Buckingham might have hoped? Thanks for those sweet words! oh, my lovely Queen! a hundred times, thanks!"

"Oh! milord! you have ill understood, wrongly interpreted; I did not mean to say——"

"Silence! silence!" cried the duke; "if I am happy in an error do not have the cruelty to deprive me of it. You have told me yourself, madame, that I have been drawn into a snare and perhaps I shall leave my life in it; for, although it be strange, I have for some time had a presentiment that I shall shortly die." And the duke smiled, with a smile at once sad and charming.

"Oh! my God!" cried Anne of Austria, with an accent of terror which proved how much greater an interest she took in the duke than she ventured to tell.

"I do not tell you this, madame, to terrify you; no, it is even ridiculous in me to say it to you and, believe me, I take no heed of such dreams. But the words you have just spoken, the hope you have almost given me, will have richly paid for all—were it my life."

"Oh! but I," said Anne, "I, duke, have had presentiments likewise, I have had dreams. I dreamed that I saw you lying bleeding, wounded."

"In the left side, was it not, and with a knife?" interrupted Buckingham.

"Yes, it was so, milord, it was so, in the left side, and with a knife. Who can possibly have told you I had had that dream; I have imparted it to no one but my God, and that in my prayers."

"I ask for no more; you love me, madame! it is enough."

"I love you! I!"

"Yes, yes. Would God send the same dreams to you as to me, if you did not love me? Should we have the same presentiments if our existences were not associated by our hearts? You love me, my beautiful Queen, and you will weep for me?"

"Oh! my God! my God!" cried Anne of Austria, "this is more than I can bear! In the name of Heaven, duke, leave me, go! I do not know whether I love you or do not love you, but what I know is that I will not be a perjured woman. Take pity on me, then, and go. Oh! if you are struck in France, if you die in France, if I could imagine that your love for me was the cause of your death, nothing could console me, I should go mad. Depart, go then, I implore you!"

"Oh! how beautiful you are thus! Oh! how I love you!" said Buckingham.

"Oh! but go! go! I implore you, and come back hereafter; come back as ambassador, come back as minister, come back surrounded with guards who will defend you, with servants who will watch over you, and then—then I shall be no longer in fear for your days and I shall be happy in seeing you."

"Oh! is this true, is it true what you say?"

"Yes."

"Oh! then, some pledge of your indulgence, some object which, coming from you, may assure me that I have not dreamed; something you have worn, and that I may wear in my turn—a ring, a necklace, a chain."

"Will you go then, will you go, if I give you what you ask for?"

"Yes."

"This very instant?"

"Yes."

"You will leave France, you will return to England?"

"I will, I swear to you I will."

"Wait, then, wait."

And Anne of Austria re-entered her apartment and came out again almost immediately, holding in her hand a casket made of rosewood, with her cipher upon it in gold letters.

"Here, milord, here," said she, "keep this in memory of me."

Buckingham took the casket and fell a second time on his knees.

"You promised me you would go," said the Queen.

"And I keep my word. Your hand, madame, your hand, and I depart."

Anne of Austria stretched forth her hand, closing her eyes, and leaned with the other upon Estafania, for she felt her strength ready to fail her.

Buckingham applied his lips passionately to that beautiful hand and then rising, said:

"Within six months, if I am not dead, I shall have seen you again, madame; even if I have brought disaster upon the whole world for that object, I shall have seen you again."

Faithful to the promise he had made, with a desperate effort he rushed out of the apartment.

In the corridor he met Madame Bonacieux, who waited for him and who, with the same precautions and the same good fortune, conducted him out of the Louvre.

[By a judicious mixture of threats, gifts and promises, Cardinal Richelieu attached the timorous Bonacieux to his interest and made him an unwitting spy on his own wife. He also discovered from Count de Rochefort, d'Artagnan's enemy at Meung, that the rosewood casket which the Queen had given Buckingham contained twelve diamond studs of great value and beauty, a recent present to her from the King. Richelieu sent orders to "milady" at London to steal two of the studs from Buckingham at the first ball that he attended. Milady did as she was told; and as soon as Richelieu knew he would have the studs on a certain date, he proposed that the King give a great ball at which, he suggested, the Queen should wear her new diamond studs.]

71

Bonacieux at Home

IT WAS THE SECOND TIME the Cardinal had mentioned these diamond studs to the King. Louis XIII was struck with the repetition, and began to fancy that his recommendation concealed some
mystery.

More than once the King had been humiliated by the Cardinal,
whose police, without having yet attained the perfection of the modern police, were excellent, being better informed than himself even
upon what was going on in his own household. He hoped, then, in
a conversation with Anne of Austria, to obtain some information,
and afterward to come upon his Eminence with some secret, which
the Cardinal either knew or did not know, but which, in either case,
would raise him infinitely in the eyes of his minister.

He went to the Queen, and, according to custom, accosted her with
fresh menaces against those who surrounded her. Anne of Austria
hung down her head, allowed the torrent to flow on without replying,
and hoped that it would end by stopping of itself; but this was not
what Louis XIII meant. He wanted a discussion, from which some
light or other might break, convinced as he was that the Cardinal
had some afterthought and was preparing for him one of those terrible surprises which his Eminence was so skillful in getting up. He
gained his end by his persistence in accusing.

"But," cried Anne of Austria, tired of these vague attacks, "but,
sire, you do not tell me all that you have in your heart. What have
I done? Let me know what crime I have committed? It is impossible
that your Majesty can make all this to-do about a letter written to
my brother!"

The King, attacked in so direct a manner, did not know what to
answer, and thought that this was the moment for expressing the
desire which he was not to have made until the evening before the
fete.

"Madame," he said, with dignity, "there will shortly be a ball at
the Hotel de Ville; * I wish that, to do honor to our worthy
aldermen, you should appear at it in ceremonial costume and particularly ornamented with the diamond studs which I gave you on
your birthday. That is my answer."

* City Hall

72

The answer was terrible. Anne of Austria believed that Louis XIII knew all and that the Cardinal had persuaded him to employ this long dissimulation of seven or eight days, which, likewise, was characteristic. She became excessively pale, leaned her beautiful hand upon a console, which hand appeared then like one of wax, and looking at the King, with terror in her eyes, was unable to reply by a single syllable.

"You hear, madame," said the King, who enjoyed this embarrassment to its full extent, but without guessing its cause—"you hear, madame?"

"Yes, sire, I hear," stammered the Queen.

"You will appear at this ball?"

"Yes."

"And with those studs?"

"Yes."

The Queen's paleness, if possible, increased. The King perceived it and enjoyed it with that cold cruelty which was one of the worst sides of his character.

"Then that is agreed," said the King, "and that is all I had to say to you."

"But on what day will this ball take place?" asked Anne of Austria.

Louis XIII felt instinctively that he ought not to reply to this question, the Queen having put it in an almost inaudible voice.

"Oh! very shortly, madame," said he, "but I do not precisely recollect the date. I will ask the Cardinal."

"It was the Cardinal, then, who informed you of this fete?"

"Yes, madame," replied the astonished King; "but why do you ask that?"

"It was he who told you to desire me to appear there with these studs?"

"That is to say, madame——"

"It was he, sire, it was he!"

"Well; and what does it signify whether it was he or I? Is there any crime in this request?"

"No, sire."

"Then you will appear?"

"Yes, sire."

"That's well," said the King, retiring, "that's well, I depend upon you."

The Queen made a courtesy, less from etiquette than because her knees were sinking under her.

"I am lost," murmured the Queen, "lost! for the Cardinal knows all, and it is he who urges on the King, who as yet knows nothing, but will soon know everything. I am lost! my God! my God! my God!"

She knelt upon a cushion and prayed, with her head buried between her palpitating arms.

In fact, her position was terrible. Buckingham had returned to London, Madame de Chevreuse was at Tours. More closely watched than ever, the Queen felt certain that one of her women betrayed her, without knowing how to tell which. Her footman, Laporte, could not leave the Louvre; she had not a soul in the world in whom she could confide.

Thus, while contemplating the misfortune which threatened her and the abandonment in which she was left, she broke out into sobs and tears.

"Can I be of no service to your Majesty?" said all at once a voice full of sweetness and pity.

The Queen turned sharply around, for there could be no deception in the expression of that voice: it was a friend who spoke thus.

In fact, at one of the doors which opened into the Queen's apartment appeared the pretty Madame Bonacieux. She had been engaged in arranging the dresses and linen in a closet, when the King entered; she could not get out and had heard all.

The Queen uttered a piercing cry at finding herself surprised, for in her trouble she did not at first recognize the young woman who had been given to her by Laporte.

"Oh! fear nothing, madame!" said the young woman, clasping her hands and weeping herself at the Queen's sorrows; "I am your Majesty's, body and soul, and however far I may be from you, however inferior may be my position, I believe I have discovered a means of extricating your Majesty from your trouble."

"You! oh, heavens! you!" cried the Queen; "but look me in the face. I am betrayed on all sides, can I trust in you?"

"Oh, madame!" cried the young woman, falling on her knees, "upon my soul, I am ready to die for your Majesty!"

This expression sprang from the very bottom of the heart and, like the first, there was no mistaking it.

"Yes," continued Madame Bonacieux, "yes, there are traitors here, but by the holy name of the Virgin, I swear that none is more devoted to your Majesty than I am. Those studs which the King speaks of, you gave them to the Duke of Buckingham, did you not? Those studs were in a little rosewood box, which he held under his arm? Am I deceived? Is it not so, madame?"

"Oh! my God! my God!" murmured the Queen, whose teeth chattered with fright.

"Well, those studs," continued Madame Bonacieux, "we must have them back again."

"Yes, without doubt, it must be so," cried the Queen, "but how am I to act? How can it be effected?"

"Someone must be sent to the duke."

"But who? who? in whom can I trust?"

"Place confidence in me, madame; do me that honor, my Queen, and I will find a messenger."

"But I must write."

"Oh yes; that is indispensable. Two words from the hand of your Majesty and your own private seal."

"But these two words would bring about my condemnation, divorce, exile!"

"Yes, if they fell into infamous hands. But I will answer for it that these two words will be delivered to their address."

"Oh! my God! I must then place my life, my honor, my reputation, all in your hands?"

"Yes, yes, madame, you must, and I will save them all."

"But how—at least, tell me how?"

"My husband has been set at liberty these two or three days; I have not yet had time to see him again. He is a worthy, honest man, who entertains neither love nor hatred for anybody. He will do anything I wish, and will set out upon receiving an order from me, without knowing what he carries. He will remit your Majesty's letter, without even knowing it is from your Majesty, to the address which shall be upon it."

With a burst of emotion, the Queen took the two hands of the young woman, gazed at her as if to read her very heart and, seeing nothing but sincerity in her beautiful eyes, embraced her tenderly.

"Do that," she cried, "and you will have saved my life, you will have saved my honor!"

"Oh! do not exaggerate the service I have the happiness to render your Majesty. I have nothing to save; your Majesty is only the victim of perfidious plots."

"That is true, that is true, my child," said the Queen; "you are right."

"Give me that letter, madame; time presses."

The Queen ran to a little table, upon which were pens, ink and paper, wrote two lines, sealed the letter with her private seal and gave it to Madame Bonacieux.

"And now," said the Queen, "we are forgetting one very necessary thing."

"What is that, madame?"

"Money."

Madame Bonacieux blushed.

"Yes, that is true," she said, "and I will confess to your Majesty that my husband——"

"Your husband has none; is that what you would say?"

"Oh, yes! he has some, but he is very avaricious; that is his fault. Nevertheless, let not your Majesty be uneasy, we will find means."

"And I have none, either," said the Queen. Those who have read the *Memoirs of Madame de Motteville* will not be astonished at this reply. "But wait a minute."

Anne of Austria ran to her jewel case.

"Here," she said, "here is a ring of great value, as I have been assured; it came from my brother, the King of Spain. It is mine and I am at liberty to dispose of it. Take this ring, make money of it and let your husband set out."

"In an hour you shall be obeyed, madame."

"You see the address," said the Queen, speaking so low that Madame Bonacieux could hardly hear what she said—"To Milord Duke of Buckingham, London."

"The letter shall be given to him himself."

"Generous girl!" cried Anne of Austria.

Madame Bonacieux kissed the Queen's hands, concealed the paper in the bosom of her dress and disappeared with the lightness of a bird.

Ten minutes afterward she was at home. As she told the Queen, she had not seen her husband since his liberation, and consequently was ignorant of the change of feeling that had taken place in him with respect to the Cardinal, a change which had since been strengthened by two or three visits from the Count de Rochefort, who had become his best friend and had persuaded him that nothing culpable had been intended by the carrying off of his wife, but that it was only a piece of political precaution.

She found Bonacieux alone. With much trouble, the poor man was restoring order in his house, the furniture of which he had found mostly broken and his chests and drawers mostly empty, justice not being one of the three things which King Solomon named as leaving no traces of their passage. As to the servant, she had run away at the moment of her master's arrest. Terror had had such an effect upon the poor girl that she had never ceased walking after leaving Paris till she got to Burgundy, her native province.

Immediately upon entering his house, the worthy mercer had communicated to his wife the news of his happy return and the latter had replied by congratulating him and telling him that the first moment she could steal from her duties should be devoted to him.

This first moment had been delayed five days, which, under any other circumstances, might have appeared rather long to Monsieur Bonacieux, but he had, in the visit he had made to the Cardinal, and in the visits Rochefort had made to him, ample subjects for reflection and, as everybody knows, nothing makes time pass more quickly than reflection.

This was all the more so because Bonacieux's reflections were all rose-colored. Rochefort called him his friend, his dear Bonacieux, and never ceased telling him that the Cardinal had a great respect for him. The mercer fancied himself already on the high road to honors and fortune.

On her side, Madame Bonacieux also had reflected, but, it must be admitted, upon something widely different from ambition. In spite of herself, her thoughts constantly reverted to that handsome young man, who was so brave, and who appeared to be so much in love. Married at eighteen to Monsieur Bonacieux, having always lived among her husband's friends, people very little capable of inspiring any sentiment whatever in a young woman whose heart was above her position, Madame Bonacieux had remained insensible to vulgar seductions. But at this period the title of nobleman had a particularly great influence with the bourgeoisie, or citizen class, and d'Artagnan was a nobleman; besides, he wore the uniform of the guards, which, next to that of the Musketeers, was most admired by the ladies. He was, we repeat, handsome, young and bold, he spoke

77

of love like a man who did love and was anxious to be loved in return: there was certainly enough in all this to turn a head only twenty-three years old, and Madame Bonacieux had just attained that happy period of life.

The married couple, then, although they had not seen each other for eight days, and although during that time serious events had taken place in which both were concerned, accosted each other with a degree of preoccupation. Nevertheless, M. Bonacieux manifested real joy and advanced toward his wife with open arms.

Madame Bonacieux presented her cheek to him.

"Let us talk a little," she said.

"What!" said Bonacieux, astonished.

"Yes; I have something of great importance to tell you."

"True," he said, "and I have some questions sufficiently serious to put to you. Describe to me how you were carried off."

"Oh! that's of no consequence just now," said Madame Bonacieux.

"And what do you allude to, then? To my captivity?"

"I heard of it the day it happened, but, as you were not guilty of any crime, as you were not guilty of any intrigue, as, in short, you knew nothing that could compromise yourself or anybody else, I attached no more importance to that event than it merited."

"You speak pretty much at your ease, madame," said Bonacieux, hurt at the little interest his wife seemed to take in him. "Do you know that I was plunged during a whole day and a whole night in a dungeon of the Bastille?"

"Oh! a day and a night soon pass away; let us return to the object that brings me here."

"What! to that which brings you home to me! Is it not the desire of seeing a husband again from whom you have been separated for a week?" asked the mercer, piqued to the quick.

"Yes, that first, and other things afterward."

"Speak then."

"It is a thing of the highest importance, and upon which perhaps our future fortune depends."

"The complexion of our fortune has changed very much since I saw you, Madame Bonacieux, and I should not be astonished if, in the course of a few months, it were to excite the envy of many folks."

"Particularly if you obey the instructions I am about to give you."

"To me?"

78

"Yes, to you. There is a good and holy action to be performed, monsieur, and much money to be gained at the same time."

Madame Bonacieux knew that by naming money to her husband she attacked him on his weak side. But a man, were he even a mercer, when he has talked for ten minutes with the Cardinal de Richelieu, is no longer the same man.

"Much money to be gained?" said Bonacieux, protruding his lip.

"Yes, much."

"About how much, pray?"

"A thousand pistoles, perhaps."

"Humph! What you have to ask of me, then, is serious?"

"It is, indeed."

"What is to be done?"

"You must set out immediately. I will give you a paper with which you must not part on any account and which you will deliver into the proper hands."

"And where am I to go to?"

"London."

"I go to London! You are joking. I have nothing to do in London."

"But others require that you should go there."

"But who are those others? I warn you that I will never again work in the dark and that I will know not only to what I expose myself, but for whom I expose myself."

"An illustrious person sends you, an illustrious person awaits you; the recompense will exceed your expectations, that is all I promise you."

"More intrigues! nothing but intrigues! Thank you, madame, I am aware of them now; the Cardinal has enlightened me on that head."

"The Cardinal!" cried Madame Bonacieux. "Have you seen the Cardinal?"

"He sent for me," answered the mercer proudly.

"And you went! you imprudent man!"

"Well, I can't say I had much choice about going or not going, for I was taken to him between two guards. I must also confess that as I did not then know his Eminence, if I had been able to have declined the visit, I should have been delighted to do so."

"He ill-treated you, then? he threatened you?"

"He gave me his hand, and he called me his friend—his friend! do you hear that, madame? I am the friend of the great Cardinal."

"Of the great Cardinal!"

"Perhaps you would dispute his right to that title, madame?"

"Oh! I would dispute his right to nothing, but I tell you that the favor of a minister is ephemeral and that a man must be mad to attach himself to a minister. There are powers above his which do not depend upon a man or the issue of an event and it is around these powers that we should endeavor to range ourselves."

"I am sorry for it, madame, but I acknowledge no other power but that of the great man whom I have the honor to serve."

"You serve the Cardinal?"

"Yes, madame, and as his servant, I will not allow you to be concerned in plots against the safety of the state, or to assist in the intrigues of a woman who is not a Frenchwoman, and who has a Spanish heart. Fortunately, we have the great Cardinal; his vigilant eye watches over and penetrates to the bottom of hearts."

Bonacieux was repeating, word for word, a sentence which he had heard the Count de Rochefort make use of; but the poor wife, who had reckoned on her husband, and who, in that hope, had answered for him to the Queen, did not tremble the less, both at the danger into which she had nearly cast herself and at the helpless state to which she was reduced. Nevertheless, knowing her husband's weakness and more particularly his cupidity, she did not despair of bringing him around to her purpose.

"Ah! you are a Cardinalist, monsieur, are you?" cried she, "and you serve the party who ill-treat your wife and insult your Queen?"

"Private interests are as nothing before the interests of all. I am for those who save the state," said Bonacieux emphatically.

This was another of the Count de Rochefort's sentences which he had retained. He had waited for the occasion to use it.

"And what do you know about the state you talk of?" said Madame Bonacieux, shrugging her shoulders. "Be satisfied with being a plain, straightforward bourgeois, and turn your attention to that side which holds out the greatest advantages."

"Eh! eh!" said Bonacieux, slapping a plump round bag, which returned a sound of money, "what do you think of this, madame preacher?"

"Where does that money come from?"

"Can't you guess?"

"From the Cardinal?"

"From him, and from my friend the Count de Rochefort."

80

"The Count de Rochefort! Why, it was he who carried me off!"

"Perhaps it was, madame."

"And you receive money from that man?"

"Did you not yourself tell me that that carrying off was entirely political?"

"Yes, but that event had for its object to make me betray my mistress, to draw from me by tortures confessions that might have compromised the honor and perhaps the life of my august mistress."

"Madame," replied Bonacieux, "your august mistress is a perfidious Spaniard and what the Cardinal does is well done."

"Monsieur," said the young woman, "I know you to be cowardly, avaricious and weak, but I never till now believed you to be infamous!"

"Madame!" said Bonacieux, who had never seen his wife in a passion and who retreated before this conjugal anger, "madame, what is that you say?"

"I say you are a miserable, mean creature!" continued Madame Bonacieux, who saw she was regaining some little influence over her husband. "You meddle with politics, do you? And still more, with Cardinalist politics! Why, you are selling yourself, body and soul, to the devil, for money!"

"No, only to the Cardinal."

"It's the same thing!" cried the young woman. "Who says Richelieu says Satan!"

"Hold your tongue! hold your tongue, madame! we may be overheard."

"Yes, you are right, I should be ashamed for anyone to know your baseness."

"But what do you require of me, after all? Come let us see!"

"I have told you. You must set out instantly, monsieur, you must accomplish loyally the commission with which I deign to charge you, and on that condition I pardon everything, I forget everything and still further"—and she held out her hand to him—"I give you my love again."

Bonacieux was a coward and he was avaricious, but he loved his wife—he was softened. A man of fifty cannot long bear malice with a pretty wife of twenty-three. Madame Bonacieux saw that he hesitated.

"Come! have you made up your mind?" said she.

"But, my dear love, reflect a little upon what you require of me. London is far from Paris, very far, and perhaps the commission with which you charge me is not without dangers."

"Of what consequence is that, if you avoid them?"

"Well, Madame Bonacieux," said the mercer, "well, then, I positively refuse: intrigues terrify me. I have seen the Bastille; I—whew! —that's a frightful place, that Bastille! Only to think of it makes my flesh crawl. They threatened me with torture! Do you know what the torture is? Wooden points that they stick in between your legs till your bones burst out! No, positively I will not go. Blast it! why do you not go yourself? for, in truth, I think I have before been deceived in you. I really believe you are a man, and a violent one too."

"And you—you are a woman, a miserable woman, stupid and brutified. You are afraid, are you? Well, if you do not go this very instant, I will have you arrested by the Queen's orders and I will have you placed in that Bastille which you dread so much."

Bonacieux fell into a profound reflection. He turned the two angers in his brain, that of the Cardinal and that of the Queen; that of the Cardinal predominated enormously.

"Have me arrested on the part of the Queen," he said, "and I—I will appeal to his Eminence."

Madame Bonacieux saw at once that she had gone too far, and was terrified at having communicated so much. For a moment she contemplated with terror that stupid countenance, showing the invincible resolution of a fool overcome by fear.

"Well, be it so!" she said. "Perhaps, when all is considered, you are right: in the long run, a man knows more about politics than a woman does, particularly such as have, like you, Monsieur Bonacieux, conversed with the Cardinal. And yet it is very hard," she added, "that a man upon whose affection I thought I might depend, treats me thus unkindly and will not comply with any of my fancies."

"That is because your fancies might lead you too far," replied the triumphant Bonacieux, "and I mistrust them."

"Well, I will give it up, then," said the young woman, sighing. "It is as well as it is, say no more about it."

"You might tell me, at least, what I should have had to do in London," replied Bonacieux, who remembered, a little too late, that Rochefort had desired him to endeavor to obtain his wife's secrets.

"It is of no use for you to know anything about it," said the young woman, whom an instinctive mistrust now impelled to draw back. "It was about one of those purchases that interest women, a purchase by which much might have been gained."

But the more the young woman excused herself, the more important Bonacieux conceived the secret to be, which she declined to communicate to him. He resolved, therefore, that instant to hasten to the residence of the Count de Rochefort and to tell him that the Queen was seeking a messenger to send to London.

"Pardon me for leaving you, my dear Madame Bonacieux," he said, "but not knowing you would come to see me, I had made an engagement with a friend. I shall soon return and if you will wait only a few minutes for me, as soon as I have concluded my business with that friend, I will conduct you back to the Louvre, as it is growing late."

"Thank you, monsieur, you are not obliging enough to be of any use to me whatever," replied Madame Bonacieux. "I shall return very safely to the Louvre by myself."

"As you please, Madame Bonacieux," said the ex-mercer; "shall I have the pleasure of seeing you soon again?"

"Yes, next week, I hope my duties will afford me a little liberty, and I will take advantage of it to come and put things in order here, as they must necessarily be much deranged."

"Very well, I shall expect you. You are not angry with me?"

"Who, I?—Oh! not the least in the world."

"Till next week then?"

"Till then, adieu!"

Bonacieux kissed his wife's hand and set off at a quick pace.

"Well!" said Madame Bonacieux when her husband had shut the street door and she found herself alone, "there was nothing wanting to complete that poor creature but being a Cardinalist! And I, who have answered for him to the Queen! I, who have promised my poor mistress! Ah! my God! my God! she will take me for one of those wretches with whom the palace swarms, who are placed about her as spies! Ah! Monsieur Bonacieux! I never did love you much, but now it is worse than ever. I hate you! and by my word, you shall pay for this!"

At the moment she spoke these words, a rap on the ceiling made her raise her head and a voice, which reached her through the plaster, cried:

"Dear Madame Bonacieux, open the little passage door for me, and I will come down to you."

[*The voice was d'Artagnan's, who had overheard the whole conversation. He volunteered to accomplish the Queen's mission. M. de Tréville gave Athos, Porthos, and Aramis a fortnight's leave of absence, ostensibly to go to the waters of Forges to heal Athos' wound, and obtained a similar leave for d'Artagnan. The four young men and their servants set out immediately.*]

The Journey

AT TWO O'CLOCK in the morning our four adventurers left Paris by the barrier St. Denis. As long as it was dark they remained silent; in spite of themselves, they felt the influence of the obscurity and apprehended ambushes everywhere.

With the first rays of the sun their tongues became loosened; with day their gaiety revived. It was like the eve of a battle; the heart beat, the eyes laughed and they felt that the life they were perhaps going to lose was, after all, worth something.

Besides, the appearance of the caravan was formidable; the black horses of the Musketeers, their martial carriage, with the squadron-like step of these noble companions of the soldier, would have betrayed the most strict incognito. The lackeys followed, armed to the teeth.

All went well till they arrived at Chantilly, which they reached about eight o'clock in the morning. They stood in need of breakfast and alighted at the door of an inn, recommended by a sign representing St. Martin giving half his cloak to a poor man. They ordered the lackeys not to unsaddle the horses and to hold themselves in readiness to set off again immediately.

They entered the common room and placed themselves at a table. A gentleman, who had just arrived by the route of Dammartin, was seated at the same table and was taking his breakfast. He opened the conversation by talking of rain and fine weather; the travelers replied; he drank to their good health and the travelers returned his politeness.

But at the moment Mousqueton came to announce that the horses were ready, and as they were rising from table, the stranger proposed to Porthos to drink to the health of the Cardinal. Porthos replied that he asked no better, if the stranger in his turn would drink to the health of the King. The stranger cried that he acknowledged no other king but his Eminence. Porthos told him he was drunk and the stranger drew his sword.

"You have committed a piece of folly," said Athos, "but it can't be helped; there is no drawing back now. Kill the fellow and rejoin us as soon as you can."

And all three mounted their horses and set out at a good pace, while Porthos was promising his adversary to perforate him with all the thrusts known in fencing schools.

"There goes one!" cried Athos, at the end of five hundred paces.

"But why did that man attack Porthos, rather than any other of us?" asked Aramis.

"Because, as Porthos was talking louder than the rest, he took him for the leader of the party," said d'Artagnan.

"I always said that this cadet from Gascony was a well of wisdom," murmured Athos.

And the travelers continued their route.

At Beauvais they stopped two hours, as well to breathe their horses a little as to wait for Porthos. At the end of the two hours, as Porthos did not come and as they heard no news of him, they resumed their journey.

At a league from Beauvais, where the road was confined between two high banks, they fell in with eight or ten men, who, taking advantage of the road being unpaved in this spot, appeared to be employed in digging holes and filling up the ruts with mud.

Aramis, not liking to soil his boots with this artificial mortar, apostrophized them rather sharply. Athos wished to restrain him, but it was too late. The laborers began to jeer the travelers and by their insolence disturbed the equanimity even of the cool Athos, who urged on his horse against one of them.

The men all immediately drew back to the ditch, from which each took a concealed musket; the result was that our seven travelers were outnumbered in weapons. Aramis received a ball, which passed through his shoulder, and Mousqueton another ball, which lodged in the fleshy part of the loins. Mousqueton alone fell from his horse, not because he was severely wounded, but, not being able to see the wound, he judged it to be more serious than it really was.

"It is an ambush!" shouted d'Artagnan; "don't waste a charge! forward!"

Aramis, wounded as he was, seized the mane of his horse, which carried him on with the others. Mousqueton's horse rejoined them and galloped by the side of his companions.

"That will serve us for a relay," said Athos.

"I would rather have had a hat," said d'Artagnan, "mine was carried away by a ball. By my faith, it is very fortunate that the letter was not in it."

"Well, but they will kill poor Porthos, when he comes up," said Aramis.

"If Porthos were on his legs, he would have rejoined us by this time," said Athos. "My opinion is that when they came to the point, the drunken man proved to be sober enough."

They continued at their best speed for two hours, although the horses were so fatigued that it was feared that they would soon be unable to continue.

The travelers had chosen crossroads, in the hope that they might meet with less interruption; but at Crèvecoeur, Aramis declared he could proceed no farther. In fact, it required all the courage which he concealed beneath his elegant form and polished manners to bear him so far. He grew more pale every minute and they were obliged to support him on his horse. They lifted him off at the door of a cabaret, left Bazin with him, who was more embarrassing than useful in a skirmish, and set forward again in the hope of sleeping at Amiens.

"Blast!" said Athos, as soon as they were again in motion, "reduced to two masters and Grimaud and Planchet! Blast! I won't be their dupe, I will answer for it; I will neither open my mouth nor draw my sword between this and Calais. I swear by——"

"Don't waste time in swearing," said d'Artagnan, "let us gallop, if our horses will consent to it."

And the travelers buried their rowels in their horses' flanks, who, thus vigorously stimulated, recovered their energies. They arrived at Amiens at midnight and alighted at the inn of the Lis d'Or.

The host had the appearance of as honest a man as any on earth. He received the travelers with his candlestick in one hand and his cotton nightcap in the other, and wished to lodge the two travelers each in a charming chamber, but, unfortunately, these charming chambers were at the opposite extremities of the inn and d'Artagnan and Athos declined them. The host replied that he had no other worthy of their excellencies, but his guests declared that they would sleep in the common chamber, each upon a mattress, which might be thrown upon the ground. The host insisted, but the travelers were firm and he was obliged to comply with their wishes.

They had just prepared their beds and barricaded their door within, when someone knocked at the shutter; they demanded who was there, and upon recognizing the voices of their lackeys, opened the shutter.

In fact, it was Planchet and Grimaud.

"Grimaud can take care of the horses," said Planchet; "if you are willing, gentlemen, I will sleep across your doorway, and you will then be certain that nobody can come to you."

"And what will you sleep upon?" said d'Artagnan.

"Here is my bed," replied Planchet, producing a bundle of straw.

"Come, then," said d'Artagnan, "you are right, the host's face does not please me at all, it is too civil by half."

"Nor me either," said Athos.

Planchet got in through the window and installed himself across the doorway, while Grimaud went and shut himself up in the stable, promising that, by five o'clock in the morning, he and the four horses would be ready.

The night passed off quietly enough, it is true, till about two o'clock in the morning, when somebody endeavored to open the door. But as Planchet woke in an instant and cried, "Who is there?" this same somebody replied that he had made a mistake and went away.

At four o'clock in the morning there was a terrible riot in the stables. Grimaud had tried to waken the stableboys and the stableboys had set upon him and beaten him. When they opened the window they saw the poor lad lying senseless, with his head split by a blow with a forkhandle.

Planchet went down into the yard and proceeded to saddle the horses. But the horses were all exhausted. Mousqueton's horse alone, which had traveled for five or six hours without a rider the day before, might have been able to pursue the journey; but, by an inconceivable error, a veterinary surgeon, who had been sent for, as it appeared, to bleed one of the host's horses, had bled Mousqueton's.

This began to be annoying. All these successive accidents were, perhaps, the result of chance; but they might, quite as probably, be the fruits of a plot. Athos and d'Artagnan went out, while Planchet was sent to inquire if there were not three horses to be sold in the neighborhood. At the door stood two horses, fresh, strong and fully

87

equipped. These would just have suited them. He asked where the masters of them were, and was informed that they had passed the night in the inn and were then settling with the master.

Athos went down to pay the reckoning, while d'Artagnan and Planchet stood at the street door. The host was in a lower and back chamber, to which Athos was requested to go.

Athos entered without the least mistrust and took out two pistoles to pay the bill. The host was alone and seated before his desk, one of the drawers of which was partly open. He took the money which Athos offered to him and, after turning and turning it over and over in his hands, suddenly cried out that it was bad and that he would have him and his companions arrested as counterfeiters.

"You scoundrel!" cried Athos, stepping toward him. "I'll cut your ears off!"

But the host stooped, took two pistols from the half-open drawer, pointed them at Athos and called out for help.

At the same instant, four men, armed to the teeth, entered by lateral doors and rushed upon Athos.

"I am taken!" shouted Athos, with all the power of his lungs. "Go on, d'Artagnan! spur, spur!" and he fired two pistols.

D'Artagnan and Planchet did not need bidding twice; they unfastened the two horses that were waiting at the door, leaped upon them, buried their spurs in their sides and set off at full gallop.

"Do you know what has become of Athos?" asked d'Artagnan of Planchet, as they galloped on.

"Ah, monsieur," said Planchet, "I saw one fall at each of his shots and he appeared to me, through the glass door, to be fighting with his sword with the others."

"Brave Athos!" murmured d'Artagnan; "and to think that we are compelled to leave him, while the same fate awaits us, perhaps, two paces hence! Forward, Planchet, forward! you are a brave fellow!"

"Didn't I tell you, monsieur," replied Planchet, "that we Picards are found out by being used? Besides, I am in my own country here and that puts me on my mettle!"

And both, with free use of the spur, arrived at St. Omer without drawing bit. At St. Omer they breathed their horses with their bridles passed under their arms, for fear of accident, and ate a morsel in their hands, standing in the road, after which they started again.

At a hundred paces from the gates of Calais, d'Artagnan's horse sank under him and could not by any means be got up again, the blood flowing from both its eyes and its nose. There still remained Planchet's horse, but, after it had stopped, it remained quite still and could not be urged to move a step.

Fortunately, as we have said, they were within a hundred paces of the city. They left their two nags upon the high road and ran toward the port. Planchet called his master's attention to a gentleman who had just arrived with his lackey and preceded them by about fifty paces.

They made all speed to come up with this gentleman, who appeared to be in great haste. His boots were covered with dust and he inquired if he could not instantly cross over to England.

"Nothing would be more easy," said the captain of a vessel ready to set sail, "but this morning an order arrived that no one should be allowed to cross without express permission from the Cardinal."

"I have that permission," said the gentleman, drawing a paper from his pocket; "here it is."

"Have it examined by the governor of the port," said the captain, "and give me the fare."

"Where shall I find the governor?"

"At his country house."

"Where is that?"

"At a quarter of a league from the city. Look, you may see it from here—at the foot of that little hill, that slated roof."

"Very well," said the gentleman.

And, with his lackey, he took the road to the governor's country house.

D'Artagnan and Planchet followed the gentleman at a distance, not to be noticed; but when he was out of the city, d'Artagnan quickly came up with him, just as he was entering a little wood.

"Monsieur," said d'Artagnan, "you appear to be in great haste?"

"No one can be more so, monsieur."

"I am sorry for that," said d'Artagnan; "for, as I am in great haste likewise, I wished to beg you to render me a service."

"What service?"

"To let me go first."

"That's impossible," said the gentleman. "I have traveled sixty leagues in forty-four hours, and by tomorrow, at mid-day, I must be in London."

"I have performed the same distance in forty hours, and by tomorrow, at ten o'clock in the morning, I must be in London."

"Very sorry, monsieur; but I was here first, and will not go second."

"I am sorry too, monsieur; but I arrived second, and will go first."

"The King's service!" said the gentleman.

"My own service!" said d'Artagnan.

"But this is a needless quarrel you are fastening upon me, I think."

"By Heaven! what do you wish it to be?"

"What do you want?"

"Would you like to know?"

"Certainly."

"Well, then, I want that order of which you are the bearer, seeing that I have not one of my own and must have one."

"You are joking, I presume."

"I seldom joke."

"Let me pass."

"You shall not pass."

"My brave young man, I will blow out your brains. Hola, Lubin! my pistols!"

"Planchet," called out d'Artagnan, "take care of the lackey; I will manage the master."

Planchet, emboldened by the first exploit, sprang upon Lubin and, being strong and vigorous, he soon got him on the broad of his back and placed his knee upon his breast.

"Go on with your affair, monsieur," cried Planchet; "I have finished mine."

Seeing this, the gentleman drew his sword and sprang upon d'Artagnan; but he had more than he expected to deal with.

In three seconds d'Artagnan had wounded him three times, exclaiming at each thrust:

"One for Athos! one for Porthos! and one for Aramis!"

At the third hit the gentleman fell heavily to the ground.

D'Artagnan believed him to be dead, or at least insensible, and went toward him for the purpose of taking the order; but at the moment he stretched out his hand to search for it, the wounded man, who had not dropped his sword, plunged the point into his breast, crying:

"And one for you!"

"And one for me! the best for the last!" cried d'Artagnan in a rage, nailing him to the earth with a fourth thrust through his body.

90

This time the gentleman closed his eyes and fainted. D'Artagnan searched his pockets and took from one of them the order for the passage. It was in the name of the Count de Wardes.

Then, casting a glance on the handsome young man, who was scarcely twenty-five years of age, and whom he was leaving in his gore, senseless and perhaps dead, he gave a sigh at that unaccountable destiny which leads men to destroy each other for the interests of people who are strangers to them and who often do not even know that their defenders exist. But he was soon roused from these reflections by Lubin, who uttered loud cries and screamed for help with all his might.

Planchet grasped him by the throat and pressed as hard as he could.

"Monsieur," he said, "as long as I hold him in this manner he can't cry, I'll bet; but as soon as I let go, he will howl again as loud as ever. I have found out that he's a Norman, and Normans are all obstinate."

In fact, tightly held as he was, Lubin still endeavored to get out a cry.

"Stay!" said d'Artagnan and, taking out his handkerchief, he gagged him.

"Now," said Planchet, "let us bind him to a tree."

This being properly done, they drew the Count de Wardes close to his servant; and as night was approaching and as the wounded man and the bound man were at some little distance within the wood, it was evident they were likely to remain there till the next day.

"And now," said d'Artagnan, "to the governor's house."

"But you appear to me to be wounded," said Planchet.

"Oh! that's nothing! Let us dispatch that which is most pressing first and we will attend to my wound afterward; besides, I don't think it seems a very dangerous one."

And they both set forward as fast as they could toward the country house of the worthy functionary.

The Count de Wardes was announced and d'Artagnan was introduced.

"You have an order signed by the Cardinal?"

"Yes, monsieur," replied d'Artagnan; "here it is."

"Ah, ah! it is quite regular and explicit," said the governor.

"Most likely," said d'Artagnan; "I am one of his most faithful servants."

"It appears that his Eminence is anxious to prevent someone from crossing to England?"

"Yes; a certain d'Artagnan, a Béarnese gentleman, who left Paris in company of three of his friends, with the intention of going to London."

"Do you know him personally?" asked the governor.

"Whom?"

"This d'Artagnan."

"Oh, yes! perfectly well."

"Describe him to me, then."

"Nothing more easy."

And d'Artagnan gave, feature for feature, and in every way, the most minute description of the Count de Wardes.

"Is he accompanied by anyone?"

"Yes, by a lackey, named Lubin."

"We will keep a sharp lookout for them; and if we lay hands upon them, his Eminence may be assured they shall be reconducted to Paris under a good escort."

"And by doing so, monsieur governor," said d'Artagnan, "you will have merited well of the Cardinal."

"Will you see him on your return?"

"Doubtless I shall."

"Tell him, I beg you, that I am his humble servant."

"I will not fail."

And, delighted with this assurance, the governor signed the passport and delivered it to d'Artagnan, who lost no time in useless compliments, but thanked the governor, bowed and departed.

When once out, he and Planchet set off as fast as they could, avoided the wood by making a detour and re-entered the city by another gate.

The vessel was quite ready to sail and the captain waiting in the port.

"Well?" said he, on perceiving d'Artagnan.

"Here is my pass, examined," said the latter.

"And that other gentleman?"

"He will not go today," said d'Artagnan; "but here, I'll pay you for us two."

"In that case, we will start at once," said the captain.

"Yes, as soon as you please," replied d'Artagnan.

He leaped, with Planchet, into the boat and five minutes after they were on board. And it was time; for they had scarcely sailed half a league, when d'Artagnan saw a flash and heard a detonation— it was the cannon which announced the closing of the port.

He had now leisure to look to his wound. Fortunately, as he had thought, it was not dangerous: the point of the sword had struck a rib, and glanced along the bone; still further, his shirt had stuck to the wound, and he had lost but very little blood.

D'Artagnan was worn out with fatigue. A mattress was laid upon the deck for him; he threw himself upon it and fell fast asleep.

At break of day they were still three or four leagues from the coast of England: the breeze had been so light during the night that they had made little way.

At ten o'clock the vessel cast anchor in the port of Dover, and at half past ten d'Artagnan placed his foot on English land, crying: "Here I am at last!"

But that was not all: they had to get to London. In England the post was well served; d'Artagnan and Planchet took post-horses, with a postillion, who rode before them, and in a few hours were in the capital.

D'Artagnan did not know London; he was not acquainted with one word of English: but he wrote the name of Buckingham on a piece of paper and everyone to whom he showed it pointed out to him the way to the duke's palace.

The duke was at Windsor, hunting with the King.

D'Artagnan inquired for the confidential valet of the duke, who, having accompanied him in all his voyages, spoke French perfectly well; he told him that he came from Paris, on an affair of life and death and that he must speak with his master instantly.

The confidence with which d'Artagnan spoke convinced Patrick, which was the name of this person. He ordered two horses to be saddled and himself went as guide to the young guardsman. As for Planchet, he had been lifted from his horse as stiff as a rush; the poor lad's strength was almost exhausted. D'Artagnan seemed to be made of iron.

On their arrival at the castle they inquired for the duke, and learned that he was hawking with the King in the marshes, at some distance.

They were quickly on the spot named, and Patrick almost at the moment caught the sound of his master's voice, recalling his falcon.

"Whom must I announce to my lord duke?" asked Patrick.

"The young man who one evening sought a quarrel with him on the Pont Neuf, opposite the Samaritaine."

"Rather a singular introduction?"

"You will find that it is as good as another."

Patrick galloped off, reached the duke and announced to him, in the terms directed, that a messenger awaited him.

Buckingham at once remembered the circumstance and suspected that something was going on in France of which it was necessary he should be informed. He only took the time to inquire where the messenger was and, recognizing the uniform of the guards, he put his horse into a gallop and rode straight up to d'Artagnan, Patrick discreetly keeping in the background.

"No misfortune has happened to the Queen?" cried Buckingham, the instant he came up, throwing all his fear and love into the question.

"I believe not; nevertheless, I believe she is in some great peril from which your grace alone can extricate her."

"I!" cried Buckingham. "What is it? I should be but too happy to render her any service! Speak! speak!"

"Take this letter," said d'Artagnan.

"This letter! from whom does this letter come?"

"From her Majesty, I think."

"From her Majesty!" said Buckingham, becoming so pale that d'Artagnan feared he would faint—and he broke the seal.

"What is this tear?" said he, showing d'Artagnan a place where it had been pierced through.

"Ah! ah!" said d'Artagnan, "I did not see that; it was the sword of the Count de Wardes that made that hole when he ran into my breast."

"Are you wounded?" asked Buckingham, as he opened the letter.

"Oh! nothing, milord, only a scratch," said d'Artagnan.

"Just Heavens! what have I read!" cried the duke. "Patrick, remain here, or rather join the King, wherever he may be, and tell his Majesty that I beg him to excuse me, but an affair of the greatest importance calls me to London. Come, monsieur, come!" and both set off toward the capital at full gallop.

The Countess de Winter

A^{s} THEY RODE ALONG, the duke endeavored to draw from d'Artagnan, not what had passed, but what d'Artagnan himself knew. By adding all that he heard from the mouth of the young man to his own remembrances, he was enabled to form a pretty exact idea of a position of the seriousness of which, in addition, the Queen's letter, however short and explicit, rendered him quite aware. But that which astonished him most was that the Cardinal, so deeply interested in preventing this young man from setting his foot on the soil of England, had not succeeded in arresting him on the road. It was then, and upon the manifestation of this astonishment, that d'Artagnan related to him the precaution taken and how, thanks to his three friends, whom he had left scattered on the road, he had succeeded in coming off with a single sword-thrust, which had pierced the Queen's letter and for which he had repaid M. de Wardes in such terrible coin. While he was listening to this account, which was delivered with the greatest simplicity, the duke looked from time to time at the young man with astonishment, as if he could not comprehend how so much prudence, courage and devotedness could be allied with a countenance evidently not more than twenty years of age.

The horses went like the wind and in an incredibly short time they were in London. D'Artagnan imagined that on arriving in the city the duke would slacken his pace; but it was not so: he kept on his way, heedless of whom he might ride against. In fact, in crossing the city, two or three accidents of this kind happened, but Buckingham did not even turn his head to see what became of those he had knocked down. D'Artagnan followed him amid cries which very much resembled curses.

On entering the court of his palace, Buckingham sprang from his horse and, without taking heed of the noble animal, threw the bridle on his neck and ran toward the vestibule. D'Artagnan did the same, with a little more concern, however, for the fine creatures, whose merits he fully appreciated; but he had the satisfaction to see three or four grooms run from the stables and take charge of them.

The duke walked so fast that d'Artagnan had some trouble in keeping up with him. He passed through several apartments of an elegance of which even the greatest nobles of France had not even an idea and arrived at length in a bedchamber which was at once a miracle of taste and of splendor. In the alcove of this chamber was a door among the tapestry. The duke opened it with a small gold key, which he wore suspended from his neck by a chain of the same metal. From discretion, d'Artagnan remained behind; but at the moment of Buckingham's passing through the door he turned around and, seeing the hesitation of the young man, invited him to enter.

"Come in! come in!" he cried, "and if you have the good fortune to be admitted to her Majesty's presence, tell her what you have seen."

Encouraged by this invitation, d'Artagnan followed the duke, who closed the door after them.

He found himself with the duke in a small chapel covered with a tapestry of Persian silk worked with gold and brilliantly lit by a vast number of wax lights. Over a species of altar, and beneath a canopy of blue velvet, surmounted by white and red plumes, was a full-length portrait of Anne of Austria, so perfect in its resemblance that d'Artagnan uttered a cry of surprise on beholding it: it might be believed that the Queen was about to speak.

Upon the altar and beneath the portrait, was the casket containing the diamond studs.

The duke approached the altar, fell on his knees as a priest might have done before a crucifix and opened the casket.

"Here," he said, drawing from the casket a large bow of blue ribbon all sparkling with diamonds; "here are the precious studs which I have taken an oath should be buried with me. The Queen gave them to me, the Queen requires them back again; her will be done, like that of God, in all things."

Then he began to kiss, one after the other, those dear studs with which he was about to part. All at once he uttered a terrible cry.

"What is the matter?" exclaimed d'Artagnan anxiously, "what has happened to you, milord?"

"All is lost! all is lost!" cried Buckingham, turning as pale as death; "two of the studs are missing! there are but ten of them!"

"Can you have lost them, milord, or do you think they have been stolen?"

"They have been stolen!" replied the duke, "and it is the Cardinal who has dealt me this blow. See, the ribbons which held them have been cut with scissors."

"If milord suspects they have been stolen—perhaps the person who stole them still has them."

96

"Let me reflect," said the duke. "The only time I wore these studs was at a ball given by the King a week ago at Windsor. The Countess de Winter, with whom I had had a quarrel, became reconciled to me at that ball. That reconciliation was nothing but the vengeance of a jealous woman. I have never seen her from that day. The woman is an agent of the Cardinal's."

"Why, then, he has agents throughout the whole world!" cried d'Artagnan.

"Yes, yes," said Buckingham, gnashing his teeth with rage, "he is a terrible antagonist! But when is this ball to take place?"

"Next Monday."

"Next Monday! Still five days before us; that's more time than we need. Patrick!" cried the duke, opening the door of the chapel, "Patrick!"

His confidential valet, who had that moment returned, appeared at his call.

"My jeweler and my secretary."

The valet went out with a mute promptitude which showed that he was accustomed to obey implicitly and without reply.

But, although the jeweler had been mentioned first, it was the secretary who first made his appearance, simply because he lived in the palace. He found Buckingham seated at a table in his bed-chamber, writing orders with his own hand.

"Master Jackson," said he, "go instantly to the Lord Chancellor and tell him that I desire him to execute these orders. I wish them to be promulgated immediately."

"But, my lord, if the Lord Chancellor asks me what motives have led your grace to adopt such an extraordinary measure, what reply shall I make?"

"That such is my pleasure, and that I answer for my will to no man."

"Will that be the answer," replied the secretary, smiling, "which he must transmit to his Majesty, if, by chance, his Majesty should have the curiosity to know why no vessel is to leave any of the ports of Great Britain?"

"You are right, Master Jackson," replied Buckingham. "He will say, in that case, to the King, that I am determined on war, and that this measure is my first act of hostility against France."

The secretary bowed and retired.

"We are safe on that side," said Buckingham, turning toward

97

d'Artagnan. "If the studs have not yet gone to Paris, they will not arrive till after you."

"How so, milord?"

"I have just placed an embargo on all vessels at present in his Majesty's ports and, without particular permission, not one can lift an anchor."

D'Artagnan looked with stupefaction at the man who thus employed the unlimited power with which he was clothed by the confidence of a king, who was busied in nothing but his amours. Buckingham saw by the expression of the young man's face what was passing in his mind and smiled.

"Yes," said he, "yes, Anne of Austria is my true Queen; upon a word from her, I would betray my country, I would betray my King—I would betray my God. She asked me not to send the Protestants of La Rochelle the help I promised them; I have not done so. I broke my word, it is true; but what signifies that? I obeyed my love and have I not been richly paid for that obedience? It was to that obedience I owe her portrait!"

D'Artagnan reflected on what fragile and unknown threads the destinies of nations and the lives of men are sometimes hung.

He was lost in these thoughts when the goldsmith entered. He was an Irishman, one of the most skillful of his craft. He himself confessed that he gained a hundred thousand livres a year by the Duke of Buckingham.

"Master O'Reilly," said the duke to him, leading him into the chapel, "look at these diamond studs, and tell me what they are worth apiece."

The goldsmith cast a glance at the elegant manner in which they were set, calculated one with another what the diamonds were worth, and without hesitation—

"Fifteen hundred pistoles each, my lord," replied he.

"How many days would it require to make two studs exactly like them? You see there are two missing."

"A week, my lord."

"I will give you three thousand pistoles each for two, if I can have them by the day after tomorrow."

"My lord, you shall have them."

"You are a jewel of a man, Master O'Reilly, but that is not all. These studs cannot be trusted to anybody; the work must be done in the palace."

98

"Impossible, my lord; there is no one but myself who can execute them so that the new may not be distinguished from the old."

"Therefore, my dear Master O'Reilly, you are my prisoner and though you wish ever so much to leave my palace, you cannot; so make the best of it. Name me such of your workmen as you stand in need of and point out the tools they must bring."

The goldsmith knew the duke: he knew that all objection would be useless and instantly determined how to act.

"May I be permitted to inform my wife?" he said.

"Oh! you may even see her if you like, my dear Master O'Reilly. Your captivity shall be mild, be assured; and as every inconvenience deserves its indemnification, here is, in addition to the price of the studs, an order for a thousand pistoles, to make you forget the annoyance I cause you."

D'Artagnan could not get over the surprise created in him by this minister, who thus, open-handedly, sported with men and millions.

As to the goldsmith, he wrote to his wife, sending her the order for the thousand pistoles and charging her to send him, in exchange, his most skillful apprentice, an assortment of diamonds, of which he gave the names and the weight and the necessary tools.

Buckingham led the goldsmith to the chamber destined for him and which, at the end of half an hour, was transformed into a workshop. Then he placed a sentinel at each door, with an order to admit nobody, upon any pretense, but his valet, Patrick. We need not add that the goldsmith, O'Reilly, and his assistant, were prohibited from going out on any account.

All this being arranged, the duke turned to d'Artagnan.

"Now, my young friend," said he, "England is all our own. What do you wish for? What do you desire?"

"A bed, milord," replied d'Artagnan. "At present, I confess, that is the thing I stand most in need of."

Buckingham assigned to d'Artagnan a chamber adjoining his own. He wished to have the young man at hand, not that he mistrusted him, but for the sake of having someone to whom he could constantly talk about the Queen.

One hour after, the ordinance was published in London that no vessel bound for France should leave the ports—not even the packet boat with letters. In the eyes of everybody this was a declaration of war between the two kingdoms.

On the day after the morrow, by eleven o'clock, the two diamond studs were finished. They were so completely imitated, so perfectly alike, that Buckingham could not tell the new ones from the old, and the most practiced in such matters would have been deceived as he was.

He immediately called d'Artagnan.

"Here," he said, "are the diamond studs that you came to fetch, and be my witness that I have done all that human power could do."

"Be satisfied, milord; I will tell all that I have seen. But does your grace mean to give me the studs without the casket?"

"The casket would only encumber you. Besides, the casket is the more precious from being all that is left to me. You will say that I keep it."

"I will perform your commission word for word, milord."

"And now," resumed Buckingham, looking earnestly at the young man, "how shall I ever acquit myself of the debt I owe you?"

D'Artagnan colored up to the eyes. He saw that the duke was searching for a means of making him accept something and the idea that the blood of himself and his friends was about to be paid for with English gold was strangely repugnant to him.

"Let us understand each other, milord," replied d'Artagnan, "and let us make things clear, in order that there may be no mistake. I am in the service of the King and Queen of France and form part of the company of M. des Essarts, who, as well as his brother-in-law, M. de Tréville, is particularly attached to their Majesties. What I have done, then, has been for the Queen and not at all for your grace. And, still further, it is very probable that I should not have done anything of this, if it had not been to make myself agreeable to someone who is my lady, as the Queen is yours."

"I understand," said the duke, smiling, "and I even believe that I know that other person; it is——"

"Milord! I have not named her!" interrupted the young man warmly.

"That is true," said the duke, "and it is to this person I am bound to discharge my debt of gratitude."

"You have said it, milord; for truly, at this moment, when there is question of war, I confess to you that I see nothing in your grace but an Englishman and consequently an enemy, whom I should have much greater pleasure in meeting on the field of battle than in the park at Windsor or the halls of the Louvre; all which, how-

100

ever, will not prevent me from executing, to the very point, my commission, or from laying down my life, if there be need of it, in accomplishing it. But I repeat it to your grace, I will do this without your having personally on that account more to thank me for in this second interview than for what I did for you in the first."

"We say, 'proud as a Scotchman,'" murmured the Duke of Buckingham.

"And we say, 'proud as a Gascon,'" replied d'Artagnan; "the Gascons are the Scots of France."

D'Artagnan bowed to the duke and was about to retire.

"Well! you are going away in that manner? But where? and how?"

"That's true!"

" 'Fore Gad, these Frenchmen have no consideration!"

"I had forgotten that England was an island, and that you were king of it."

"Go to the port, ask for the brig *Sund* and give this letter to the captain; he will convey you to a little port, where you are certainly not expected, a port which is ordinarily frequented by fishermen only."

"What is the name of that port?"

"St. Valery; but listen. When you have arrived there, you will go to a mean inn, without a name and without a sign—a mere fisherman's hut. You cannot be mistaken, there is but one."

"And then?"

"You will ask for the host, and will repeat to him the word, *Forward!*"

"Which means?"

"In French, *en avant;* that is the password. He will give you a ready-saddled horse and will point out to you the road you are to take. You will find, in this manner, four relays on your route. If you will give at each of these relays your address in Paris, the four horses will follow you thither. You already know two of them and you appeared to appreciate them like an expert. They were those we rode on, and you may rely upon me that the others are not inferior to them. These horses are equipped for the field. However proud you may be, you will not refuse to accept one of them and to request your three companions to accept the others: that is in order to make war against us, besides. The end excuses the means, as you Frenchmen say, does it not?"

101

"Yes, milord, I accept them," said d'Artagnan; "and, if it pleases God, we will make a good use of your presents."

"Well, now, your hand, young man; perhaps we shall soon meet on the field of battle; but in the meantime we shall part good friends, I hope?"

"Yes, milord, but with the hope of soon becoming enemies?"

"Be satisfied on that score; I promise you."

"I depend upon your word, milord."

D'Artagnan bowed to the duke and made his way as quickly as possible to the port. Opposite the Tower he found the vessel that had been named to him, delivered his letter to the captain, who, after having it examined by the governor of the port, made immediate preparations to sail.

Fifty vessels were waiting to set out, in momentary expectation of the removal of the prohibition. When passing alongside one of them, d'Artagnan fancied that he perceived on board it the lady of Meung, the same whom the unknown gentleman had styled 'milady,' and whom d'Artagnan had thought so handsome; but thanks to the tide of the river and fair wind, his vessel passed so quickly that he had little more than a glimpse of her.

The next day, about nine o'clock in the morning, he landed at St. Valery. D'Artagnan went instantly in search of the inn and easily discovered it by the riotous noise which resounded from it: war between England and France was then confidently talked of and the sailors were carousing in the hopes of it.

D'Artagnan made his way through the crowd, advanced toward the host and pronounced the word, *"Forward!"* The host instantly made him a sign to follow him, went out with him by a door which opened into a yard, led him to the stable, where a ready-saddled horse awaited him and asked him if he stood in need of anything else.

"I want to know the route I am to follow," said d'Artagnan.

"Go from here to Blangy and from Blangy to Neufchâtel. At Neufchâtel go to the inn of the Herse d'Or, give the password to the host and you will find, as you have done here, a horse already saddled."

"Have I anything to pay?" demanded d'Artagnan.

"Everything is paid," replied the host, "and liberally. Begone then, and may God conduct you safely."

"Amen!" cried the young man, and set off at full gallop.

102

In four hours from starting he was in Neufchâtel. He strictly followed the instructions he had received; at Neufchâtel, as at St. Valery, he found a horse quite ready awaiting him; he was about to remove the pistols from the saddle he had vacated to the one he was about to occupy, but he found the holsters furnished with similar pistols.

"Your address at Paris?"

"Hotel of the Guards, company of des Essarts."

"Enough," replied the interrogator.

"Which route must I take?" demanded d'Artagnan in his turn.

"That of Rouen; but you will leave the city on your right. You must stop at the little village of Ecouis, in which there is but one inn, L'Ecu de France. Don't condemn it from appearances; you will find a horse in the stables quite as good as this."

"The same password?"

"Exactly."

"Adieu, master!"

"A good journey, sir! Do you want anything?"

D'Artagnan shook his head in reply and set off at full speed. At Ecouis the same scene was repeated; he found as provident a host and as fresh a horse. He left his address as he had done before and set off again at the same pace for Pontoise. At Pontoise he changed his horse for the last time and at nine o'clock galloped into the yard of M. de Tréville's mansion. He had performed nearly sixty leagues in little more than twelve hours.

M. de Tréville received him as if he had seen him that same morning; only, when pressing his hand a little more warmly than usual, he informed him that the company of M. des Essarts was on duty at the Louvre, and that he might repair at once to his post.

The Ballet of the Merlaison

ON THE MORROW, nothing was talked of in Paris but the ball which the aldermen of the city were to give to the King and Queen and in which the King and Queen were to dance the famous Merlaison, the King's favorite ballet.

The whole of the last week had been occupied in preparations at the Hotel de Ville for this important evening. The city carpenters had erected scaffolds upon which the ladies invited were to be placed; the city grocer had ornamented the chambers with two hundred flambeaux of white wax, which was a piece of luxury unheard of at that period; twenty violins were ordered and the price paid for them fixed at double the usual rate, upon condition, said the report, that they should be played all night.

At ten o'clock in the morning, the Sieur de la Coste, ensign in the King's guards, followed by two exempts and several archers of that body, came to the city registrar, named Clement, and demanded of him all the keys of the chambers and offices of the building. These keys were given up to him instantly. Each of them had a ticket attached to it, by which it might be known, and from that moment the Sieur de la Coste was charged with the guarding of all the doors and all the avenues.

At eleven o'clock came in his turn Duhallier, captain of the guard, bringing with him fifty archers, who were distributed immediately through the building, at the doors which had been assigned to them.

At three o'clock arrived two companies of the guards, one French, the other Swiss. The company of French guards was composed half of M. Duhallier's men, and half of M. des Essarts' men.

At nine o'clock Madame la Première Présidente arrived. As, next to the Queen, this was the most considerable personage of the fete, she was received by the notables of the city and placed in a box opposite to that which the Queen was to occupy.

At ten o'clock the King's collation, consisting of confitures and other delicacies, was prepared in the little chamber on the side of the church of St. Jean, in front of the silver buffet of the city, which was guarded by four archers.

At midnight great cries and loud acclamations were heard; it was the King, who was passing through the streets which led from the Louvre to the Hotel de Ville, and which were illuminated with colored lamps.

Immediately the aldermen, clothed in their cloth robes, and preceded by six sergeants, holding each a flambeau in his hand, went to attend upon the King, whom they met on the steps, where the provost of the merchants offered him the compliment of welcome, a compliment to which his Majesty replied by an apology for coming so late, but laying the blame upon the Cardinal, who had detained him till eleven o'clock, talking of affairs of state.

His Majesty, in full dress, was accompanied by his royal high-

ness the Count de Soissons, the Grand Prior, the Duke de Longue-
ville, the Duke d'Elboeuf, the Count d'Harcourt, the Count de la
Roche-Guyon, M. de Liancourt, M. de Baradas, the Count de
Cramail and the Chevalier de Souveray.

Everybody observed that the King looked dull and preoccupied.

A closet had been prepared for the King, and another for the
Cardinal. In each of these closets were placed masquerade habits.
The same had been done with respect to the Queen and Madame
la Présidente. The nobles and ladies of their Majesties' suites were
to dress, two by two, in chambers prepared for the purpose.

Before entering his closet the King desired to be informed the
moment the Cardinal arrived.

Half an hour after the entrance of the King, fresh acclamations
were heard: these announced the arrival of the Queen. The aldermen did as they had done before and, preceded by the sergeants,
went to receive their illustrious guest.

The Queen entered the great hall; and it was remarked, that,
like the King, she looked dull and, moreover, fatigued.

At the moment she entered, the curtain of a small gallery which
to that time had been closed, was drawn and the pale face of the
Cardinal appeared, he being dressed as a Spanish cavalier. His
eyes were fixed upon those of the Queen and a smile of terrible
joy passed over his lips. The Queen did not wear her diamond
studs.

The Queen remained for a short time to receive the compliments
of the city gentlemen and to reply to the salutations of the ladies.

All at once the King appeared at one of the doors of the hall.
The Cardinal was speaking to him in a low voice and the King was
very pale.

The King made his way through the crowd without a mask, and
the ribbons of his doublet scarcely tied; he went straight to the
Queen and in an altered voice said:

"Why, madame, have you not thought proper to wear your
diamond studs, when you know it would have given me so much
gratification?"

The Queen cast a glance around her and saw the Cardinal standing behind her, with a diabolical smile on his countenance.

"Sire," replied the Queen, with a faltering voice, "because in the
midst of such a crowd as this I feared some accident might happen
to them."

105

"And you were wrong, madame! if I made you that present, it was that you might adorn yourself with it. I tell you, again, you were wrong."

And the voice of the King was tremulous with anger. The company looked and listened with astonishment, comprehending nothing of what passed.

"Sire," said the Queen, "I can send for them to the Louvre, where they are, and thus your Majesty's wishes will be complied with."

"Do so, madame! do so and that at the quickest; for within an hour the ball will commence."

The Queen bent in token of submission and followed the ladies who were to conduct her to her closet. On his part the King returned to his.

A moment of trouble and confusion ensued in the assembly. Everybody had remarked that something had passed between the King and Queen; but both of them had spoken so low that all out of respect had kept a distance of several steps, so that nobody had heard anything. The violins began to sound with all their might, but nobody listened to them.

The King came out first from his closet. He was in a hunting costume of the most elegant description and the other nobles were dressed as he was. This was the costume that became the King best and when thus dressed he really appeared the first gentleman of his kingdom.

The Cardinal drew near to the King and placed in his hand a small casket. The King opened it and found in it two diamonds.

"What does this mean?" demanded he of the Cardinal.

"Nothing," replied the latter; "only, if the Queen has the studs, which I very much doubt, count them, sire, and if you only find ten, ask her Majesty who can have stolen from her the two studs that are here."

The King looked at the Cardinal as if to interrogate him; but he had not time to address any question to him—a cry of admiration burst from every mouth. If the King appeared to be the first gentleman of his kingdom, the Queen was, without doubt, the most beautiful woman in France.

It is true that the habit of a huntress became her admirably. She wore a beaver hat with blue feathers, a surtout of pearl-gray velvet, fastened with diamond clasps, and a petticoat of blue satin, embroidered with silver. On her left shoulder sparkled the diamond studs upon a bow of the same color as the plumes and the petticoat.

The King trembled with joy, and the Cardinal with vexation; nevertheless, distant as they were from the Queen, they could not count the studs. The Queen had them; the only question was, had she ten or twelve?

At that moment the violins sounded the signal for the ball. The King advanced toward Madame la Présidente, with whom he was to dance, and his highness the Count de Soissons with the Queen. They took their places and the ball began.

The King figured opposite the Queen and every time he passed by her he devoured with his eyes those studs of which he could not ascertain the number. A cold sweat covered the brow of the Cardinal.

The ball lasted an hour.

It ended amid the applause of the whole assemblage and everyone reconducted his lady to her place; but the King took advantage of the privilege he had of leaving his lady, to advance eagerly toward the Queen.

"I thank you, madame," said he, "for the deference you have shown to my wishes; but I think you lack two of the studs and I bring them back to you."

At these words he held out to the Queen the two studs the Cardinal had given him.

"How, sire!" cried the young Queen, affecting surprise, "you are giving me, then, two more; I shall have fourteen!"

In fact, the King counted them, and the twelve studs were all on her Majesty's shoulder.

He called the Cardinal to him.

"What does this mean, Monsieur Cardinal?" asked the King in a severe tone.

"This means, sire," replied the Cardinal, "that I was desirous of presenting her Majesty with these two studs and that, not daring to offer them myself, I adopted these means of inducing her to accept them."

"And I am the more grateful to your Eminence," replied Anne of Austria, with a smile which proved that she was not the dupe of this ingenious piece of gallantry, "from being certain that these two studs have cost you as dearly as all the others cost his Majesty."

107

Then, after bowing to the King and the Cardinal, the Queen resumed her way to the chamber in which she had dressed and where she was to take off her ball costume.

The attention which we have been obliged to give at the commencement of this chapter to the illustrious personages we have introduced in it, has diverted us for an instant from him to whom Anne of Austria owed the extraordinary triumph she had obtained over the Cardinal and who, confounded, unknown, lost in the crowd gathered at one of the doors, looked on at this scene, comprehensible only to four persons—the King, the Queen, his Eminence and himself.

The Queen had just regained her chamber and d'Artagnan was about to retire, when he felt his shoulder lightly touched. He turned around and saw a young woman who made him a sign to follow her. The face of this young woman was covered with a black velvet mask, but, notwithstanding this precaution, which was, in fact, taken rather against others than against him, he at once recognized his usual guide, the light and intelligent Madame Bonacieux.

On the evening before, they had scarcely seen each other for a moment at the apartment of the porter Germain, where d'Artagnan had sent for her. The haste in which the young woman was to convey to her mistress the excellent news of the happy return of her messenger, prevented the two lovers from exchanging more than a few words. Now d'Artagnan followed Madame Bonacieux, moved by a double sentiment, love and curiosity. During the whole of the way and in proportion as the corridors became more deserted, he wished to stop the young woman, seize her and gaze upon her, were it only for a minute; but, quick as a bird, she glided between his hands and, when he wished to speak to her, her finger placed upon her mouth, she reminded him, with a little imperative gesture full of grace, that he was under the command of a power which he must blindly obey and which forbade him even to make the slightest complaint. At length, after winding about for a minute or two, Madame Bonacieux opened the door of a closet, which was entirely dark, and led d'Artagnan into it. There she made a fresh sign of silence, opened a second door concealed by a tapestry, which, on opening, spread at once a brilliant light and disappeared.

D'Artagnan remained for a moment motionless, asking himself where he could be; but soon a ray of light which penetrated into the chamber, together with the warm and perfumed air which reached him from the same aperture, the conversation of two or three ladies, in a language at once respectful and elegant and the word "Majesty" two or three times repeated, indicated clearly that he was in a closet attached to the Queen's chamber.

The young man awaited the great event quietly in comparative darkness.

The Queen appeared to be cheerful and happy, which seemed to astonish the persons who surrounded her, as they were accustomed to see her almost always sad and full of care. The Queen attributed this joyous feeling to the beauty of the fete, and to the pleasure she had experienced in the ball. As it is not permissible to contradict a Queen, whether she smiles or whether she weeps, all rivaled each other in expatiating upon the gallantry of the aldermen of the good city of Paris.

Although d'Artagnan did not know the Queen at all, he soon distinguished her voice from the others, at first by a slightly foreign accent and next by that tone of domination naturally impressed upon all sovereign expressions. He heard her approach and withdraw from the partially open door and twice or three times he even saw the shadow of a person intercept the light.

At length a hand and an arm, surpassingly beautiful in their form and whiteness, glided through the tapestry. D'Artagnan at once comprehended that this was his recompense: he cast himself on his knees, seized the hand and touched it respectfully with his lips; then the hand was withdrawn, leaving in his an object which he perceived to be a ring. The door immediately closed and d'Artagnan found himself again in complete darkness.

He placed the ring on his finger and again waited: it was evident that all was not yet over. After the reward of his devotion, that of his love was to come. Besides, although the ball was danced, the evening's pleasures had scarcely begun; supper was to be served at three and the clock of St. Jean had struck three quarters past two.

The sound of voices diminished by degrees in the adjoining chamber: the company was heard departing. Then the door of the closet in which d'Artagnan was concealed was opened and Madame Bonacieux entered quickly.

"You at last?" cried d'Artagnan.

"Silence!" said the young woman, placing her hand upon his lips —"Silence! and begone the same way you came!"

"But where and when shall I see you again?" cried d'Artagnan. "A note, which you will find at home, will tell you. Begone! begone!"

And at these words she opened the door of the corridor and pushed d'Artagnan out of the closet. He obeyed like a child, without the least resistance or objection, which proved that he was really in love.

[*On arriving home, d'Artagnan found a note arranging a rendezvous for the next evening; but the lady did not keep the appointment. Investigating, d'Artagnan learned that she had been abducted. Some time later d'Artagnan glimpsed Madame Bonacieux being hurried along the road to Chaillot in a closed carriage, apparently a prisoner. M. de Tréville advised him to leave Paris for his own safety, and d'Artagnan set out in search of his friends. He found Porthos living luxuriously in the inn where he was wounded. He found Aramis about to enter holy orders, but managed to dissuade him by delivering to him a note from his beloved. He came upon Athos in the cellar of the inn where he had left him, he and his servant outrageously drunk on the innkeeper's stores.*

While in this state Athos told d'Artagnan a story which, he made clear, was not about himself but about one of his friends. A count of twenty-five fell in love with a beautiful girl of sixteen who lived in a small town with her brother, who was a curé. Nobody knew where they had come from, but they were said to be of good extraction. The count married the girl, only to discover one day, during a hunting accident, that on her shoulder she had the brand of a fleur-de-lis, the mark of infamy. The count, having the right of sovereign justice, tied her hands behind her and hanged her on a tree. The next day Athos explained away the story by his drunkenness.

The four impoverished friends returned to Paris and found that they had a fortnight in which to equip themselves for the campaign at La Rochelle. D'Artagnan became involved with 'milady,' who turned out to be Lady Clarik, the sister-in-law of Lord de Winter. She gave d'Artagnan (masquerading as the Count de Wardes) a magnificent sapphire ring which Athos identified as one which he had given away in a love affair. During a struggle with milady, d'Artagnan discovered that she was branded on the shoulder with a fleur-de-lis. He reported his discovery to Athos, who wanted to see the lady, but d'Artagnan dissuaded him. They sold the sapphire and thus equipped themselves handsomely for the campaign.

The Cardinal, however, summoned d'Artagnan to his palace and offered him a place in his guards; the young Gascon refused, thereby turning the Cardinal into an open enemy. As the company set off for the war, milady, intent upon revenge, pointed out d'Artagnan to two evil-looking men who rode behind them.]

The Siege of La Rochelle

THE SIEGE OF LA ROCHELLE was one of the great political events of the reign of Louis XIII and one of the great military enterprises of the Cardinal. It is, then, interesting and even necessary, that we should say a few words about it, particularly as many details of this siege are too important to allow us to pass over it in silence.

The political views of the Cardinal, when he undertook this siege, were large. Let us expose them first and then pass on to the private ones, which, perhaps, had no less influence upon his Eminence than the former.

Of the important cities given up by Henry IV to the Huguenots as places of safety, there remained only La Rochelle. It became necessary, therefore, to destroy this last bulwark of Calvinism, a dangerous leaven, with which the ferments of civil revolt and foreign war were constantly mingling.

Spaniards, Englishmen and Italian malcontents, adventurers of all nations and soldiers of fortune of every or of no sect, flocked at the first summons to the standards of the Protestants and organized themselves like a vast association whose branches diverged at leisure over all parts of Europe.

La Rochelle, which had derived a new importance from the ruin of the other Calvinist cities, was then the focus of dissentious and ambitious views. Moreover, its port was the last port in the kingdom of France open to the English, and by closing it against England the Cardinal completed the work of Joan of Arc and the Duke de Guise.

Thus Bassompierre, who was at once a Protestant and a Cath-

111

olic—a Protestant by conviction and a Catholic as commander of the Order of the Holy Ghost—Bassompierre, who was a German by birth and a Frenchman at heart, and had a distinguished command at the siege of La Rochelle, said, on charging at the head of several other Protestant nobles like himself:

"You will see, gentlemen, that we shall be fools enough to take La Rochelle."

And Bassompierre was right: the cannonade of the Isle of Ré presaged to him the dragonnades of the Cévennes; the taking of La Rochelle was the preface to the revocation of the Edict of Nantes.

But we have hinted that by the side of these views of the leveling and simplifying minister, and which belong to history, the chronicler is forced to recognize the little aims of the lover and the jealous rival.

Richelieu, as everyone knows, had been in love with the Queen: was this love a simple political affair, or was it naturally one of those profound passions which Anne of Austria inspired in those who approached her? That we are not able to say; but, at all events, we have seen, by the former developments of this history, that Buckingham had had the advantage over him and in two or three circumstances, particularly that of the diamond studs, had, thanks to the devotedness of the three Musketeers and the courage and conduct of d'Artagnan, cruelly mystified him.

It was, then, Richelieu's object, not only to get rid of an enemy of France, but to avenge himself of a rival. But this vengeance ought to be great and striking and worthy in every way of a man who held in his hand, as his weapon for combat, the forces of a whole kingdom.

Richelieu knew that while combating England he was combating Buckingham—that in triumphing over England, he triumphed over Buckingham; in short, that in humiliating England in the eyes of Europe, he humiliated Buckingham in the eyes of the Queen.

On his side, Buckingham, while pretending to maintain the honor of England, was moved by interests exactly similar to those of the Cardinal. Buckingham also was pursuing a private vengeance. Buckingham could not, under any pretense, be admitted into France as an ambassador: he wished to enter it as a conqueror.

It resulted from this that the veritable stake of this game, which two of the most powerful kingdoms played for the good pleasure of two men in love, was simply—a kind look from Anne of Austria.

The first advantage had been gained by Buckingham. Arriving

unexpectedly in sight of the Isle of Ré with ninety vessels and nearly twenty thousand men, he had surprised the Count de Toirac, who commanded for the King on the isle and, after a sanguinary conflict, effected his landing. . . .

The Count de Toirac entered the citadel of St. Martin with his garrison and threw a hundred men into a little fort, called the fort of La Prée.

This event had hastened the resolutions of the Cardinal and, till the King and he could take command of the siege of La Rochelle, which had been determined on, he had sent the Count de Soissons to direct the first operations, and had ordered all the troops he could dispose of to march toward the theater of war. It was of this detachment, sent as a vanguard, that our friend d'Artagnan formed a part.

The King, as we have said, was to follow as soon as his bed of justice had been held; but, on rising from it on the twenty-eighth of June, he felt himself attacked by fever. He was, notwithstanding, anxious to set out; but his illness becoming more serious, he was forced to stop at Villeroi.

Now whenever the King stopped, the Musketeers stopped. It resulted that d'Artagnan, who was as yet purely and simply in the guards, found himself, for the time at least, separated from his good friends, Athos, Aramis and Porthos. This separation, which was no more than an unpleasant circumstance, would have certainly become a cause of serious uneasiness, if he had been able to guess by what unknown dangers he was surrounded.

He arrived, however, without accident in the camp established before La Rochelle, on the tenth of the month of September of the year 1627.

Everything was in the same state. The Duke of Buckingham and his English, masters of the Isle of Ré, continued to besiege, but without success, the citadel of St. Martin and the fort of La Prée, and hostilities with La Rochelle had commenced, two or three days before, about a fort which the Duke d'Angoulême had caused to be constructed near the city.

The guards, under the command of M. des Essarts, took up their quarters at the Minimes; but d'Artagnan, preoccupied by the ambition of passing into the Musketeers, had formed but few friendships among his comrades and felt himself isolated and left to his own reflections.

Those reflections were not very cheerful. From the time of his arrival in Paris, he had been mixed up with public affairs, but his own private affairs had not made any great progress, as regarded either love or fortune. As to love, the only woman he could have loved was Madame Bonacieux and Madame Bonacieux had disappeared, without his being able to discover what had become of her. With respect to fortune, he had made himself—he, humble as he was—an enemy of the Cardinal, that is to say, of a man before whom trembled the greatest men of the kingdom, beginning with the King.

That man had the power to crush him and yet he had not done it. For a mind so perspicuous as that of d'Artagnan, this indulgence was a light by which he caught a glimpse of a better future.

And then, he had made himself another enemy, not so much to be feared, he thought, but, nevertheless, he instinctively felt, not to be despised. That enemy was milady.

In exchange for all this, he had acquired the protection and good will of the Queen; but the favor of the Queen was, at the present time, an additional cause of persecution, while her protection, it was pretty well known, protected the objects of it very badly, as instanced in Madame Bonacieux.

What he had clearly gained in all this was the diamond, worth five or six thousand livres, which he wore on his finger. Yet even this diamond, supposing that d'Artagnan, in his projects of ambition, wished to keep it, to make it some day a pledge for the gratitude of the Queen, had not, in the meantime, more value than the stones he trod under his feet, since he could not part with it.

We say than the stones he trod under his feet, for d'Artagnan made these reflections while walking solitarily along a pretty little road which led from the camp to the village of Angoutin. Now, these reflections had led him further than he intended, and the day was beginning to decline, when, by the last ray of the setting sun, he thought he saw the barrel of a musket glitter from behind a hedge.

D'Artagnan had a quick eye and a prompt understanding. He naturally supposed that that musket had not come there by itself and that he who bore it had not concealed himself behind a hedge with any friendly intentions. He determined, therefore, to direct his course as clear from it as he could, when, on the opposite side of the road, from behind a rock, he perceived the extremity of another musket barrel.

This was evidently an ambush.

The young man cast a glance at the first musket and saw, with a certain degree of inquietude, that it was leveled in his direction; but as soon as he perceived that the orifice of the barrel was motionless, he threw himself upon the ground. At the same instant the gun was fired, and he heard the whistling of a ball pass over his head.

No time was to be lost. D'Artagnan sprang up with a bound and at the same instant the ball from the other musket tore up the stones in the very part of the road where he had thrown himself with his face to the ground.

D'Artagnan was not one of those uselessly brave men who seek a ridiculous death, in order that it may be said of them that they did not give way a single step; besides, courage was out of the question here—d'Artagnan had fallen into a premeditated ambush.

"If there should be a third shot," said he, "I am a lost man." He immediately, therefore, took to his heels, and ran toward the camp, with the swiftness of the young men of his country, so renowned for their agility; but whatever might be his speed, the first that fired, having had time to reload, fired a second shot and this time so well aimed that it struck his hat and carried it ten paces from him.

As he, however, had no other hat, he picked it up as he ran, and arrived at his quarters, very pale and quite out of breath. He sat down without saying a word to anybody and began to reflect.

This event might have three causes.

The first and most natural was that it might be an ambush of the Rochellais, who might not have been sorry to kill one of his Majesty's guards, in the first place, because it would be one enemy the less and also because this enemy might have a well-furnished purse in his pocket.

D'Artagnan took his hat, examined the hole made by the ball and shook his head. The ball was not a musket ball—it was an harquebus ball. The justness of the aim had first given him the idea that a particular kind of weapon had been employed. This could not, then, be a military ambuscade, as the ball was not of the regular caliber.

This might be a kind remembrance of the Cardinal. It may be observed that at the very moment when, thanks to the ray of the sun, he perceived the gun barrel, he was thinking with astonishment on the forbearance of his Eminence with respect to him.

But d'Artagnan again shook his head. For people toward whom he had but to put forth his hand, his Eminence had rarely recourse to such means.

It might be a vengeance of milady's—that was the most probable!

He endeavored in vain to remember the faces or dress of the assassins. He had escaped so rapidly that he had not had leisure to remark anything.

"Ah! my poor friends!" murmured d'Artagnan, "where are you? How sadly I want you!"

D'Artagnan passed a very restless night. Three or four times he started up, imagining that a man was approaching his bed for the purpose of poniarding him. Nevertheless, day dawned without darkness having brought any accident.

But d'Artagnan justly suspected that that which was deferred was not ended. He remained all day in his quarters, assigning as a reason to himself that the weather was bad.

At nine o'clock next morning, the drums beat to arms. The Duke of Orleans visited the posts. The guards were under arms and d'Artagnan took his place in the midst of his comrades.

The Count of Soissons passed along the front of the line; then all the superior officers approached him to pay their compliments, M. des Essarts, captain of the guards, as well as the others.

At the expiration of a minute or two, it appeared to d'Artagnan that M. des Essarts made him a sign to come to him. He waited for a fresh gesture on the part of his superior, for fear he might be mistaken; but this gesture being repeated, he left the ranks and advanced to receive his orders.

"The Count of Soissons is about to ask for some men of good courage for a dangerous mission, but which will do honor to those who shall accomplish it and I made you a sign in order that you might hold yourself in readiness."

"Thanks, captain!" replied d'Artagnan, who wished for nothing better than an opportunity for distinguishing himself under the eye of the lieutenant general.

In fact, the Rochellais had made a sortie during the night and had retaken a bastion of which the royal army had gained possession

116

two days before. The matter was to ascertain, by reconnoitering, how the enemy guarded this bastion.

At the end of a few minutes, Monsieur raised his voice and said:

"I want, for this mission, three or four volunteers, led by a man who can be depended upon."

"As to the man to be depended upon, I have him under my hand, monseigneur," said M. des Essarts, pointing to d'Artagnan; "and as to the four or five volunteers, monseigneur has but to make his intentions known and the men will not be wanting."

"Four men of good will who will risk being killed with me!" said d'Artagnan, raising his sword.

Two of his comrades of the guards immediately sprang forward and, two other soldiers having joined them, the number was deemed sufficient. D'Artagnan declined all others, being unwilling to injure the chance of honor of those who came forward first.

It was not known whether, after the taking of the bastion, the Rochellais had evacuated it or left a garrison in it; the object, then, was to examine the place near enough to ascertain the thing.

D'Artagnan set out with his four companions and followed the trench: the two guards marched abreast with him and the two soldiers followed behind.

They advanced thus, screened by the lining of the trench, till they came within a hundred paces of the bastion! There, on turning around, d'Artagnan perceived that the two soldiers had disappeared.

He thought that, beginning to be afraid, they had stayed behind.

At the turning of the counterscarp they found themselves within about sixty paces of the bastion. They saw no one and the bastion seemed abandoned.

The three composing our forlorn hope were deliberating whether they should proceed any further, when all at once a circle of smoke enveloped the mass of stone and a dozen balls came whistling around d'Artagnan and his companions.

They knew all they wished to know; the bastion was guarded. A longer stay in this dangerous spot would have been useless imprudence: d'Artagnan and his two companions turned their backs and commenced a retreat which looked very much like flight.

On arriving at the angle of the trench which was to serve them as a rampart, one of the guards fell; a ball passed through his breast.

The other, who was safe and sound, continued his way toward the camp.

D'Artagnan was not willing to abandon his companion thus and stooped down to raise him and assist him in regaining the lines; but at this moment two shots were fired; one ball hit the head of the already wounded guard, and the other was flattened against a rock, after having passed within two inches of d'Artagnan.

The young man turned quickly around, for this attack could not come from the bastion, which was masked by the angle of the trench; the idea of the two soldiers who had abandoned him occurred to his mind and with it that of the assassins of two evenings before. He resolved then, this time, to know what he had to trust to and fell upon the body of his comrade as if he had been dead.

He quickly saw two heads appear above an abandoned work, within thirty paces of him; they were the heads of the two soldiers. D'Artagnan had not been deceived, these two men had only followed him for the purpose of assassinating him, hoping that the young man's death would be placed to the account of the enemy.

Only, as he might be wounded and might denounce their crime, they came up to him with the purpose of making sure of him; fortunately, deceived by d'Artagnan's trick, they neglected to reload their guns.

When they were within ten paces of him, d'Artagnan, who in falling had taken care not to leave hold of his sword, sprang up close to them.

The assassins comprehended that if they fled toward the camp without having killed their man, they should be accused by him; therefore, their first idea was to pass over to the enemy. One of them took his gun by the barrel and used it as he would a club. He aimed a terrible blow at d'Artagnan, who avoided it by springing on one side; but by this movement he left a passage free to the bandit, who darted off toward the bastion. As the Rochellais who guarded the bastion were ignorant of the intentions of the man they saw coming toward them, they fired upon him, and he fell, struck by a ball, which broke his shoulder.

In the meantime, d'Artagnan had thrown himself upon the other soldier, attacking him with his sword. The conflict was not long, the wretch having nothing to defend himself with but his discharged harquebus. The sword of the guard slipped down the barrel of the now useless weapon, and passed through the thigh of the assassin,

118

who fell. D'Artagnan immediately placed the point of his sword at his throat.

"Oh, do not kill me!" cried the bandit. "Pardon, pardon! my officer! and I will tell you all."

"Is your secret of enough importance for me to spare your life for it?" asked the young man, staying his hand.

"Yes! if you think existence worth anything to a man of twenty as you are, and who may hope for everything, being handsome and brave, as you are."

"Wretch!" cried d'Artagnan, "speak, and speak quickly! Who employed you to assassinate me?"

"A woman whom I don't know, but who is called 'milady.' "

"But if you don't know this woman, how do you know her name?"

"My comrade knows her and called her so; it was with him she agreed and not with me; he even has in his pocket a letter from that person, who attaches great importance to you, as I have heard him say."

"But how did you become concerned in this villainous affair?"

"He proposed to me to undertake it with him and I agreed."

"And how much did she give you for this fine enterprise?"

"A hundred louis."

"Well, come!" said the young man, laughing, "she thinks I am worth something! A hundred louis! Well, that was a temptation for two miserable creatures like you; so I understand you accepted it and I grant you my pardon, but upon one condition!"

"What is that?" said the soldier, uneasy at perceiving that all was not over.

"That you will go and fetch me the letter your comrade has in his pocket."

"Why," cried the bandit, "that is only another way of killing me. How can I go and fetch that letter under the fire of the bastion?"

"You must, however, make up your mind to go and fetch it, or you shall die by my hand."

"Pardon! Monsieur, have pity on me! In the name of that young lady you love and whom you perhaps think is dead, but is not!" cried the bandit, throwing himself upon his knees, and leaning upon his hand, for he began to lose his strength with his blood.

"And how do you know there is a young woman whom I love, or that I thought that woman dead?" asked d'Artagnan.

"By that letter which my comrade had in his pocket."

119

"You see, then," said d'Artagnan, "that I must have that letter; so no more delay, no more hesitation, or else, whatever may be my repugnance to soiling my sword a second time with the blood of a wretch like you, I swear by the word of a nobleman——"

And at these words d'Artagnan made so menacing a gesture that the wounded man sprang up.

"Stop, stop!" he cried, regaining strength from terror, "I will go— I will go!"

D'Artagnan took the soldier's harquebus, made him go on before him and urged him toward his companion by pricking him behind with his sword.

It was a frightful thing to see this unfortunate being, leaving a long track of blood upon the ground he passed over, pale with approaching death, endeavoring to drag himself along without being seen, to the body of his accomplice, which lay at twenty paces from him.

Terror was so strongly painted on his face, covered with a cold sweat, that d'Artagnan took pity on him and, casting upon him a look of contempt—

"Stop!" said he, "I will show you the difference between a man of true courage and such a base creature as you; stay where you are, I will go myself."

And, with a light step, an eye on the watch, observing the movements of the enemy, and taking advantage of the accidents of the ground, d'Artagnan succeeded in reaching the second soldier.

There were two means of gaining his object: to search him on the spot, or to carry him away, making a buckler of his body, and searching him in the trench.

D'Artagnan preferred the second means and lifted the assassin on to his shoulders at the moment the enemy fired.

A slight shock, the dull noise of three balls which penetrated the flesh, a last cry, a convulsion of agony, proved to d'Artagnan that he who had endeavored to assassinate him had saved his life.

D'Artagnan regained the trench and threw the body down by the wounded man, who was as pale as death.

The search was instantly commenced; a leather pocketbook, a purse, in which was evidently a part of the sum which the bandit had received, with a dice box and dice, formed the heritage of the dead man.

He left the box and dice where he found them, threw the purse to the wounded man and eagerly opened the pocketbook.

Among some unimportant papers he found the following letter, which he had sought at the risk of his life:

"Since you have lost sight of that woman, and she is now in safety in the convent, at which you should never have allowed her to arrive, try, at least, not to miss the man; if you do, you know that my hand reaches far and that you shall repay me very dearly the hundred louis you have had from me."

No signature. Nevertheless it was plain that the letter came from milady. He consequently kept it as a piece of evidence and, being in safety behind the angle of the trench, he began to interrogate the wounded man. He confessed that he had undertaken with his comrade, the one who was killed, to carry off a young woman, who was to leave Paris by the barrier of La Villette, but, having stopped to drink at a cabaret, they had missed the carriage by ten minutes.

"But what were you to have done with that woman?" asked d'Artagnan, with great agitation.

"We were to have conveyed her to a house in the Place Royale," said the wounded man.

"Yes! yes!" murmured d'Artagnan; "that's the place; milady's own residence!"

The young man tremblingly felt what a terrible thirst of vengeance urged this woman on to destroy him, as well as all who loved him and how well she must be acquainted with the affairs of the court, since she had discovered everything. There could be no doubt she owed this information to the Cardinal.

But amid all this he perceived, with a feeling of real joy, that the Queen must have discovered the prison in which poor Madame Bonacieux expiated her devotedness, and that she had freed her from that prison.

From that time, also, it became possible to find Madame Bonacieux, and a convent was not impregnable.

This idea completely restored clemency to his heart. He turned toward the wounded man, who had watched with intense anxiety all the various expressions of his countenance, and holding out his arm to him—

"Come," said he, "I will not abandon you thus. Lean upon me, and let us return to the camp."

"Yes," said the man, who could scarcely believe in such magnanimity, "but are you going to have me hanged?"

"You have my word," said he: "for the second time I give you your life."

The wounded man sank upon his knees to kiss again the feet of his preserver; but d'Artagnan, who had no longer a motive for staying so near the enemy, cut short the evidences of his gratitude.

The guard who had returned at the first discharge had announced the death of his four companions. They were therefore much astonished and delighted, in the regiment, when they saw the young man come back safe and sound.

D'Artagnan explained the sword-wound of his companion by a sortie which he improvised. He described the death of the other soldier and the perils they had encountered. This recital was for him the occasion of a veritable triumph. The whole army talked of this expedition for a day and the Count of Soissons paid him his compliments upon it. Besides this, as every great action brings its own recompense with it, the great action of d'Artagnan had for result the restoration of the tranquility he had lost. In fact, he believed that he might indulge in a little tranquility, as of his two enemies, one was killed, and the other devoted to his interests.

This tranquility proved one thing, which was, that d'Artagnan was not yet perfectly acquainted with milady.

[*Soon afterward d'Artagnan received a present of a dozen bottles of fine wine, ostensibly from Athos, Porthos and Aramis. Before he had a chance to drink the wine, his three friends arrived; they disclaimed the gift, which proved to be poisoned, and assumed that the real donor was milady, who was, d'Artagnan declared, Athos' perfidious and hanged wife. The friends agreed that they must somehow come to an understanding with this dangerous woman, and further, that they must rescue Mme. Bonacieux from the convent in which she had been secreted.*

One evening, while d'Artagnan was detained with his company, the three Musketeers were stopped on the road by the Cardinal. He commanded them to accompany him to an inn. The Musketeers were put into a room where, fortunately, they could overhear the conversation taking place in the room above. The Cardinal commissioned Milady Clarik to seek an interview with Buckingham, at which she would point out that if he did not change his plans, his intrigue with the Queen would be disclosed. If this threat proved ineffective, milady was to arrange to have him

122

assassinated. In return for these services, milady asked the name of the convent in which Mme. Bonacieux was hidden, and co-operation in her scheme to have d'Artagnan destroyed. The agreement was sealed by the Cardinal's writing a note which ratified all that she did as proper for the greatest good of France.

At that point Athos, agitated, left the inn, asking his friends to tell the Cardinal that he had gone to reconnoiter the road; carefully priming his pistols and drawing sword, he took the road to the camp.]

A Conjugal Scene

As ATHOS HAD FORESEEN, it was not long before the Cardinal came down. He opened the door of the room in which the Musketeers were, and found Porthos playing an earnest game at dice with Aramis. He cast a rapid glance around the room and perceived that one of the men was missing.

"What has become of M. Athos?" asked he.

"Monseigneur," replied Porthos, "he has gone as a scout; some words of our host made him believe the road was not safe."

"And how have you amused yourself, M. Porthos?"

"I have won five pistoles from Aramis, monseigneur."

"Well, now will you return with me?"

"We are at your Eminence's orders."

"To horse, then, gentlemen, for it is getting late."

The attendant was at the door, holding the Cardinal's horse by the bridle. At a short distance, a group of two men and three horses appeared in the shade; these were the two men who were to conduct milady to the fort of La Pointe and superintend her embarkation.

The attendant confirmed to the Cardinal what the two Musketeers had already said with respect to Athos. The Cardinal made an approving gesture and retook his route with the same precautions he had used in coming.

Let us leave him to follow the road to the camp, protected by his attendant and the two Musketeers, and return to Athos.

For some distance he maintained the pace at which he started, but when out of sight, he turned his horse to the right, made a circuit and came back within twenty paces of a high hedge, to watch the passage of the little troop. Having recognized the laced hats of

123

his companions and the golden fringe of the Cardinal's cloak, he waited till the horsemen had turned the angle of the road and, having lost sight of them, returned at a gallop to the inn, which was opened to him without hesitation.

The host recognized him.

"My officer," said Athos, "has forgotten to give a piece of very important information to the lady and has sent me back to repair his forgetfulness."

"Go up," said the host, "she is still in her chamber."

Athos availed himself of the permission, ascended the stairs with his lightest step, gained the landing and through the open door perceived milady putting on her hat.

He went straight into the chamber and closed the door after him.

At the noise he made in bolting it, milady turned around.

Athos was standing before the door, enveloped in his cloak, with his hat pulled down over his eyes.

"Who are you and what do you want?" cried she.

"Humph!" murmured Athos, "it is certainly she!"

And letting fall his cloak and raising his hat, he advanced toward milady.

"Do you know me, madame?" said he.

Milady made one step forward and then drew back, as if she had seen a serpent.

"So far, good," said Athos; "I perceive you know me."

"The Count de la Fère!" murmured milady, becoming exceedingly pale and drawing back till the wall prevented her from going any further.

"Yes, milady," replied Athos, "the Count de la Fère in person, who comes expressly from the other world to have the pleasure of paying you a visit. Sit down, madame, and let us talk, as the Cardinal said."

Milady, under the influence of inexpressible terror, sat down without uttering a word.

"You certainly are a demon sent upon the earth!" said Athos. "Your power is great, I know, but you also know that with the help of God men have often conquered the most terrible demons. You have once before thrown yourself in my path! I thought I had crushed you, madame; but either I was deceived, or hell has resuscitated you!"

124

At these words, which recalled frightful remembrances, milady hung down her head with a suppressed groan.

"Yes, hell has resuscitated you," continued Athos, "hell has made you rich, hell has given you another name, hell has almost made you another countenance; but it has neither effaced the stains from your soul nor the brand mark from your body!"

Milady arose as if moved by a powerful spring and her eyes flashed lightning. Athos remained sitting.

"You believed me to be dead, did you not, as I believed you to be? and the name of Athos as well concealed the Count de la Fère as the name of Milady Clarik concealed Anne de Beuil! Was it not so you were called when your honored brother married us? Our position is truly a strange one," continued Athos, laughing. "We have only lived up to the present time because we believed each other to be dead and because a remembrance is less oppressive than a living creature, though a remembrance is sometimes a devouring thing!"

"But," said milady, in a hollow, faint voice, "what brings you back to me and what do you want with me?"

"I wish to tell you that, while remaining invisible to your eyes, I have not lost sight of you."

"You know what I have done and been?"

"I can relate to you, day by day, your actions, from your entrance into the service of the Cardinal to this evening."

A smile of incredulity passed over the pale lips of milady.

"Listen! It was you who cut off the two diamond studs from the shoulder of the Duke of Buckingham; it was you who had Madame Bonacieux carried off; it was you who, in love with de Wardes, and thinking to pass the night with him, opened the door to M. d'Artagnan; it was you who, believing that de Wardes had deceived you, wished to have him killed by his rival; it was you who, when this rival had discovered your infamous secret, wished to have him killed in his turn by two assassins, whom you sent in pursuit of him; it was you who, finding the balls had missed their mark, sent poisoned wine with a forged letter, to make your victim believe that that wine came from his friends; in short, it was you who have but now, in this chamber, seated in this chair, which I now fill, made an engagement with the Cardinal de Richelieu to cause the Duke of Buckingham to be assassinated, in exchange for the promise he has made you to allow you to assassinate d'Artagnan!"

Milady was livid.

125

"You must be Satan!" cried she.

"Perhaps," said Athos; "but, at all events, listen well to this. Assassinate the Duke of Buckingham, or cause him to be assassinated, I care very little about that! I don't know him: besides, he is an Englishman. But do not touch with the tip of your finger a single hair of d'Artagnan, who is a faithful friend, whom I love and defend, or, I swear to you by the head of my father, the crime which you shall have endeavored to commit, or shall have committed, shall be the last."

"M. d'Artagnan has cruelly insulted me," said milady, in a hollow tone; "M. d'Artagnan shall die."

"Indeed! is it possible to insult you, madame?" said Athos, laughing; "he has insulted you, and he shall die!"

"He shall die!" replied milady; "she first, he afterward."

Athos was seized with a kind of vertigo. The sight of this creature, who had nothing of the woman about her, recalled devouring remembrances. He reflected that one day, in a less dangerous situation than the one in which he was now placed, he had already endeavored to sacrifice her to his honor; his desire for blood returned, burning his brain and pervading his frame like a raging fever; he arose in his turn, reached his hand to his belt, drew forth a pistol and cocked it.

Milady, pale as a corpse, endeavored to cry out, but her swollen tongue could utter no more than a hoarse sound, which had nothing human in it, and seemed the rattle of a wild beast: fixed against the dark tapestry, with her hair in disorder, she appeared like a horrid image of terror.

Athos slowly raised his pistol, stretched out his arm, so that the weapon almost touched milady's forehead and then, in a voice the more terrible from having the supreme calmness of a fixed resolution—

"Madame," said he, "you will this instant deliver to me the paper the Cardinal signed; or, upon my soul, I will blow your brains out."

With another man, milady might have preserved some doubt, but she knew Athos. Nevertheless, she remained motionless.

"You have one second to decide," he said.

Milady saw by the contraction of his countenance that the trigger was about to be pulled; she reached her hand quickly to her bosom, drew out a paper and held it toward Athos.

126

"Take it," said she, "and be damned!"

Athos took the paper, returned the pistol to his belt, approached the lamp, to be assured that it was the paper, unfolded it and read:

"It is by my order, and for the good of the state, that the bearer of this has done what he has done.

RICHELIEU.

August 5, 1628."

"And now," said Athos, resuming his cloak and putting on his hat, "now that I have drawn your teeth, viper, bite if you can."

And he left the chamber without once looking behind him.

At the door he found the two men and the spare horse which they held.

"Gentlemen," said he, "monseigneur's order is, you know, to conduct that woman, without losing time, to the fort of La Pointe and never to leave her till she is on board."

As these orders agreed effectively with the order they had received, they bowed their heads in sign of assent.

As to Athos, he leaped lightly into the saddle and set out at full gallop; only, instead of following the road, he took across the fields, urging his horse to the utmost and stopping occasionally to listen.

In one of those halts, he heard the steps of several horses on the road. He had no doubt it was the Cardinal and his escort. He immediately made a new point in advance, rubbed his horse down with some heath and leaves of trees and came and placed himself across the road, at about two hundred paces from the camp.

"Who goes there?" he cried, as soon as he perceived the horsemen.

"That is our brave Musketeer, I think," said the Cardinal.

"Yes, monseigneur," said Porthos, "it is he."

"Monsieur Athos," said Richelieu, "receive my thanks for the good guard you have kept. Gentlemen, we have arrived. Take the gate on the left; the watchword is 'Roi et Ré.' " *

On saying these words, the Cardinal saluted the three friends with an inclination of his head and took the right hand, followed by his attendant; for, that night, he himself slept in the camp.

"Well!" said Porthos and Aramis together, as soon as the Cardinal was out of hearing; "well! he signed the paper she required!"

"I know he did," said Athos, "since here it is."

* King and (the Isle of) Ré

And the three friends did not exchange a single word till they got to their quarters, except to give the watchword to the sentinels.

They sent Mousqueton to tell Planchet that his master was requested, the instant he left the trenches, to come to the quarters of the Musketeers.

Milady, as Athos had foreseen, on finding the two men who awaited her, made no difficulty in following them. She had had for an instant an inclination to be reconducted to the Cardinal and relate everything to him, but a revelation on her part would bring about a revelation on the part of Athos. She might say that Athos had hanged her, but then Athos would tell that she was branded: she thought it best to preserve silence, to set off discreetly, to accomplish her difficult mission with her usual skill, and then, all things being performed to the satisfaction of the Cardinal, to come back and claim her vengeance.

In consequence, after having traveled all night, at seven o'clock she was at Fort La Pointe; at eight o'clock she had embarked and at nine the vessel, which, with letters of marque from the Cardinal, was supposed to be sailing for Bayonne, raised anchor and steered its course toward England.

The Bastion Saint-Gervais

O N ARRIVING AT THE LODGING of his three friends, d'Artagnan found them assembled in the same chamber. Athos was meditating, Porthos was twisting his mustaches, Aramis was reading prayers in a charming little book bound in blue velvet.

"By Heaven!" said he, "gentlemen! I hope what you have to tell me is worth the trouble; or else, I warn you, I will not pardon you for making me come here instead of getting a little rest, after a night spent in taking and dismantling a bastion. Ah! why were you not there, gentlemen? It was warm work!"

"We were in a place where it was not very cold!" replied Porthos, giving his mustache a twist which was peculiar to him.

"Hush!" said Athos.

"Oh! oh!" said d'Artagnan, comprehending the slight frown of the Musketeer, "it appears there is something fresh abroad."

"Aramis," said Athos, "you went to breakfast the day before yesterday, at the inn of the Parpaillot, I believe?"

"Yes."

"How did you fare?"

"For my part, I ate but little; the day before yesterday was a fish day and they had nothing but meat."

"What!" said Athos, "no fish at a seaport?"

"They say," said Aramis, resuming his pious studies, "that the dike which the Cardinal is making drives them all out into the open sea."

"But that is not quite what I mean to ask you," replied Athos: "I want to know if you were left alone and nobody interrupted you."

"Why, I think there were not many intruders. Yes, Athos, I know what you mean, we shall do very comfortably at the Parpaillot."

"Let us go to the Parpaillot, then; for here the walls are like sheets of paper."

D'Artagnan, who was accustomed to his friend's manner of acting and who perceived immediately by a word, a gesture, or a sign from him, that the circumstances were serious, took Athos' arm and went out without saying anything; Porthos followed, chatting with Aramis.

On their way they met Grimaud. Athos made him a sign to come with them: Grimaud, according to custom, obeyed in silence. The poor lad had nearly come to the pass of forgetting how to speak.

They arrived at the Parpaillot: it was seven o'clock in the morning and daylight began to appear. The three friends ordered breakfast and went into a room in which, the host said, they would not be disturbed.

Unfortunately, the hour was badly chosen for a private conference; the morning drum had just been beaten, everyone shook off the drowsiness of night and, to dispel the humid morning air, came to take a drop at the tavern: dragoons, Swiss, guards, Musketeers, light-horsemen, succeeded each other with a rapidity which might answer the purpose of the host very well, but agreed badly with the views of the four friends. Thus they replied very curtly to the salutations, healths and jokes of their companions.

"I see how it will be," said Athos; "we shall get into some petty quarrel or other and we don't stand in need of one just now. D'Artagnan, tell us what sort of a night you have had and we will describe ours afterward."

"Ah! yes," said a light-horseman, with a glass of brandy in his hand, which he slowly sipped, "ah! yes! I hear you gentlemen of the guards were in the trenches last night and that you did not get much the best of the Rochellais."

D'Artagnan looked at Athos to know if he ought to reply to this intruder, who mixed unasked in their conversation.

"Well!" said Athos, "don't you hear M. de Busigny, who does you the honor to ask you a question? Relate what has passed during the night, since these gentlemen desire it."

"Have you not taken a bastion?" said a Swiss, who was drinking rum out of a beer glass.

"Yes, monsieur," said d'Artagnan, bowing, "we have had that honor: we even have, as you may have heard, introduced a barrel of powder under one of the angles, which, in blowing up, made a very pretty breach, without reckoning that, as the bastion was not a new one, all the rest of the building was much shaken."

"And what bastion is it?" asked a dragoon, with his saber run through a goose, which he was taking to be cooked.

"The bastion Saint-Gervais," replied d'Artagnan, "from behind which the Rochellais annoyed our workmen."

"Was the affair hot?"

"Yes, moderately so; we lost five men, and the Rochellais eight or ten."

"*Balzempleu!*" * said the Swiss, who, notwithstanding the admirable collection of oaths possessed by the German language, had acquired a habit of swearing in French.

"But it is probable," said the light-horseman, "that they will send pioneers this morning to reinstate the bastion."

"Yes, that's probable," said d'Artagnan.

"Gentlemen," said Athos, "I have a wager to propose."

"Ah! ah! a wager!" cried the Swiss.

"What is it?" said the light-horseman.

"Stop a bit," said the dragoon, placing his saber like a spit upon the two large iron dogs which held the fire in the chimney—"stop a bit, I am in it. You, master host! a dripping pan immediately, that I may not lose a drop of the fat of this estimable bird."

"You are quite right," said the Swiss; "goose grease is good with pastry."

* *Palsambleu,* equivalent to "zounds."

130

"There!" said the dragoon. "Now for the wager. We are all attention, M. Athos."

"Ah! now for the wager!" said the light-horseman.

"Well, Monsieur de Busigny, I will bet you," said Athos, "that my three companions, Porthos, Aramis and d'Artagnan, and myself, will go and breakfast in the bastion Saint-Gervais and that we will remain there an hour, by the watch, whatever the enemy may do to dislodge us."

Porthos and Aramis looked at each other; they began to comprehend.

"Well, but," said d'Artagnan, in Athos' ear, "you are going to get us all killed without mercy."

"We are much more likely to be killed," said Athos, "if we do not go."

"In faith, gentlemen," said Porthos, turning around upon his chair, and twisting his mustache, "that's a fair bet, I hope."

"I take it," said M. de Busigny; "now let us fix the stake."

"Why, you are four, gentlemen," said Athos, "and we are four; a dinner for eight—will that do?"

"Capitally," replied M. de Busigny.

"Perfectly well," said the dragoon.

"That's just the thing," said the Swiss. The fourth auditor, who during all this conversation had played a mute part, made a sign of the head to show that he acquiesced in the proposition.

"The breakfast for these gentlemen is ready," said the host.

"Well, bring it in," said Athos.

The host obeyed. Athos called Grimaud, pointed to a large basket which lay in a corner and made a sign to him to wrap the viands up in the napkins.

Grimaud perceived that it was to be a breakfast on the grass, packed up the viands, added the bottles and then took the basket on his arm.

"But where are you going to eat my breakfast?" said the host.

"Of what consequence is that to you, if you are paid for it?" said Athos, and he threw two pistoles majestically on the table.

"Shall I give you the change, sir?" said the host.

"No; only add two bottles of champagne, and the difference will be for the napkins."

The host had not quite so good a bargain as he at first hoped for,

131

but he made amends by slipping in two bottles of Anjou wine instead of two bottles of champagne.

"Monsieur de Busigny," said Athos, "will you be so kind as to set your watch with mine, or permit me to regulate mine by yours?"

"Which you please, monsieur!" said the light-horseman, drawing from his fob a very handsome watch, surrounded with diamonds; "half-past seven," said he.

"Thirty-five minutes after seven," said Athos, "by which you perceive I am five minutes faster than you."

And, bowing to all the astonished persons present, the young men took the road to the bastion Saint-Gervais, followed by Grimaud, who carried the viands ignorant of where he was going, but, in the passive obedience which Athos had taught him, not even thinking of asking.

As long as they were within the camp, the four friends did not exchange one word; besides, they were followed by the curious, who, hearing of the wager, were anxious to know how they would come out of it. But when once they had passed the line of circumvallation, and found themselves in the open plain, d'Artagnan, who was completely ignorant of what was going forward, thought it was time to demand an explanation.

"And now, my dear Athos," said he, "do me the kindness to tell me where we are going?"

"Why, you see, plainly enough, we are going to the bastion."

"But what are we going to do there?"

"Why, you know equally well, we are going to breakfast there."

"But why did we not breakfast at the Parpaillot?"

"Because we have some very important matters to communicate to each other and it was impossible to talk five minutes in that inn without being annoyed by all those importunate fellows, who keep coming in, saluting you and addressing you; yonder," said Athos, pointing to the bastion, "they will, at least, not come and disturb us."

"It appears to me," said d'Artagnan, with that prudence which allied itself in him so naturally with excessive bravery, "it appears that we could have found some retired place on the downs or the seashore."

"Where we should have been seen all four conferring together, so that at the end of a quarter of an hour the Cardinal would have been informed by his spies that we were holding a council."

"Yes," said Aramis, "Athos is right; they keep watch on deserts."

"A desert would not have been amiss," said Porthos, "but the question was where to find it."

"There is no desert where a bird cannot pass over one's head, where a fish cannot leap out of the water, where a rabbit cannot come out of its burrow, and I believe that bird, fish and rabbit are all spies of the Cardinal. Better, then, follow up our enterprise, from which, besides, we cannot retreat without shame. We have made a wager which could not be foreseen and of which I defy anyone to guess the true cause; we are going, in order to win it, to remain an hour in the bastion. We either shall be or shall not be attacked. If we are not, we shall have all the time to talk and nobody will hear us, for, I will answer for it, the walls of the bastion have no ears; if we are attacked, we will talk of our affairs just the same and, while defending ourselves, shall cover ourselves with glory. You see that everything is to our advantage."

"Yes," said d'Artagnan, "but I think there is very little doubt that one of us will catch a ball."

"Well!" replied Athos, "I am sure you ought to know that the balls most to be dreaded are not from open enemies."

"But, for such an expedition, we surely ought to have brought our muskets."

"You are stupid, friend Porthos; why should we load ourselves with a useless burden?"

"For my part, I don't think a good musket, twelve cartridges and a powder-flask very useless things in face of an enemy."

"Well," replied Athos, "have you not heard what d'Artagnan said?"

"What did he say to the purpose?"

"D'Artagnan said that in the attack of last night, eight or ten Frenchmen were killed and as many Rochellais."

"What then?"

"The bodies were not plundered, were they? It appears the conquerors had something else to do."

"Well?"

"Well! we shall find their muskets, their cartridges and their flasks and instead of four muskets and twelve balls, we shall have fifteen guns and a hundred charges to fire."

"Oh! Athos!" said Aramis, "truly, you're a great man."

Porthos bowed, in sign of agreement. D'Artagnan alone did not appear to be quite satisfied.

Grimaud, no doubt, shared the misgivings of the young man, for, seeing that they continued to advance toward the bastion, a circumstance which he had not at first suspected, he pulled his master by the skirt of his coat.

"Where are we going?" he asked by a gesture.

Athos pointed to the bastion.

"But," said the still silent Grimaud, in the usual dialect current between him and his master, "we shall leave our skins behind us."

Athos raised his eyes and pointed with his finger toward heaven.

Grimaud put his bundle on the ground and sat down with a shake of the head.

Athos took a pistol from his belt, looked to see if it was properly primed, cocked it and placed the muzzle close to Grimaud's ear.

Grimaud was on his legs again, as if by magic. Athos then made him a sign to take up his bundle, and to walk on first. Grimaud obeyed. All that Grimaud gained by this pantomime of a minute was to pass from the rearguard to the vanguard.

When arrived at the bastion, the four friends turned around.

More than three hundred soldiers of all kinds were assembled at the gate of the camp; and in a separate group might be distinguished M. de Busigny, the dragoon, the Swiss and the fourth wagerer.

Athos took off his hat, placed it on the end of his sword and waved it in the air. All the spectators returned him his salute, accompanying this politeness with a loud hurrah which was audible at the bastion. After which, they all four disappeared into the bastion, Grimaud having preceded them.

The Council of the Musketeers

As ATHOS HAD FORESEEN, the bastion was only occupied by a dozen dead bodies, French and Rochellais.

"Gentlemen," said Athos, who had assumed the command of the expedition, "while Grimaud is laying out the breakfast, let us begin by collecting the guns and cartridges together; we can talk while performing that necessary task. These gentlemen," added he, pointing to the bodies, "cannot hear us."

"But we could throw them into the ditch," said Porthos, "after having assured ourselves they have nothing in their pockets."

134

"Yes," said Athos, "that's Grimaud's business."

"Well, then," cried d'Artagnan, "pray, let Grimaud search them and throw them over the walls at once."

"I desire he will do no such thing," said Athos, "they may be useful to us."

"These bodies useful to us? Why, Athos, you are mad!" said Porthos.

"Judge not rashly, say the Gospel and the Cardinal," replied Athos; "how many guns, gentlemen?"

"Twelve," replied Aramis.

"How many cartridges?"

"A hundred."

"That's quite as many as we shall want: let us load the guns."

The four Musketeers went to work and, as they were loading the last musket, Grimaud announced that the breakfast was ready.

Athos replied, still by gestures, that that was well and indicated to Grimaud, by pointing to a kind of pepper-castor, that he was to stand as sentinel. Only, to alleviate the tediousness of the duty, Athos allowed him to take a loaf, two cutlets and a bottle of wine.

"And now, to table," said Athos.

The four friends sat down upon the ground with their legs crossed, like Turks or tailors.

"And now," said d'Artagnan, "as there is no longer a fear of being overheard, I hope you are going to let me into this momentous secret."

"I hope, at the same time, to procure you amusement and glory, gentlemen," said Athos. "I have induced you to take a very pleasant walk; here is a delicious breakfast and five hundred persons yonder, as you may see through the loopholes, taking us for heroes or mad·men, two classes of imbeciles sufficiently resembling each other."

"But the secret! the secret!" said d'Artagnan.

"The secret is," said Athos, "that I saw milady last night."

D'Artagnan was lifting a glass to his lips, but at the name of milady, his hand shook so, that he was obliged to put the glass on the ground again, for fear of spilling the contents.

"You saw your wi——"

"Hush!" interrupted Athos, "you forget, d'Artagnan, you forget that these gentlemen are not so initiated as you are in my family affairs. I have seen milady."

"Where?" demanded d'Artagnan.

"Within two leagues of this place, at the inn of the Colombier Rouge."

"In that case, I am a lost man," said d'Artagnan.

"Not quite so yet," replied Athos, "for by this time she must have left the shores of France."

D'Artagnan breathed again.

"But, after all," asked Porthos, "who is milady?"

"A very charming woman!" said Athos, sipping a glass of sparkling wine. "Scoundrel of a host!" cried he; "he has given us Anjou wine instead of champagne and fancies we know no better! Yes," continued he, "a very charming woman, who entertained kind views toward our friend d'Artagnan, who, on his part, has given her some offense for which she endeavored to revenge herself, a month ago, by having him killed by two musket shots; a week ago by trying to poison him; and yesterday, by demanding his head from the Cardinal."

"What! by demanding my head from the Cardinal?" cried d'Artagnan, pale with terror.

"Yes, that is as true as the Gospel," said Porthos; "I heard her with my own ears."

"So did I," said Aramis.

"Then," said d'Artagnan, letting his arm fall, as if overcome by discouragement, "it is useless to struggle any longer; I may as well blow my brains out and put an end to the matter at once."

"That's the last folly to be committed," said Athos, "seeing that it is the only one for which there is no remedy."

"But I can never escape," said d'Artagnan, "with such enemies. First, there is my unknown man of Meung; then de Wardes, to whom I have given three wounds; next milady, whose secret I have discovered; and, last and worst, the Cardinal, whose vengeance I have balked."

"Well," said Athos, "that only makes four; and we are four—one for one."

"By Heaven! if we may believe the signs Grimaud is making, we are about to have to deal with a very different number of folks."

"What's the matter, Grimaud?" said Athos. "Considering the seriousness of the circumstances, I permit you to speak, my friend; but be laconic, I beg. What do you see?"

"A troop."

136

"Of how many persons?"

"Twenty men."

"What sort of men?"

"Sixteen pioneers, four soldiers."

"How far distant?"

"Five hundred paces."

"Good! We have just time to finish this fowl and to drink one glass of wine to your health, d'Artagnan!"

"To your health," repeated Porthos and Aramis.

"Well, then, to my health! although I am very much afraid that your good wishes will not be of great service to me."

"Bah!" said Athos; "God is great, as the followers of Mohammed say, and the future is in His hands."

Then, swallowing the contents of his glass, which he put down close to him, Athos arose carelessly, took the musket next to him and drew near to one of the loopholes.

Porthos, Aramis and d'Artagnan followed his example. As to Grimaud, he received orders to place himself behind the four friends, in order to reload their weapons.

At the expiration of a minute the troop appeared. It advanced along a sort of narrow channel of the trench, which kept up a means of communication between the bastion and the city.

"Good Lord!" said Athos, "it was hardly worthwhile to disturb ourselves for twenty fellows, armed with pickaxes, mattocks and shovels! Grimaud would have only needed to make them a sign to go away and I am convinced they would have left us alone."

"I doubt that," replied d'Artagnan, "for they are advancing very resolutely. Besides, in addition to the pioneers, there are four soldiers and a brigadier armed with muskets."

"That's because they don't see us," said Athos.

"Indeed!" said Aramis, "I must confess I feel a great repugnance to fire on these poor devils of bourgeois."

"He is a bad priest," said Porthos, "who feels pity for heretics!"

"In truth," said Athos, "Aramis is right—I will warn them."

"What the devil are you going to do?" cried d'Artagnan; "you will be shot!"

But Athos took no heed of his advice; and, mounting on the breach, with his musket in one hand and his hat in the other—

"Gentlemen," said he, bowing courteously and addressing the soldiers and the pioneers, who, astonished at his appearance, stopped

137

fifty paces from the bastion, "gentlemen, a few friends and myself are about to breakfast in this bastion. Now, you know nothing is more disagreeable than being disturbed when one is at breakfast. We request you, then, if you really have business here, to wait till we have finished our repast, or to come again a short time hence; unless, which would be far better, you form the salutary resolution to quit the side of the rebels and come and drink with us to the health of the King of France."

"Take care, Athos!" cried d'Artagnan; "don't you see they are preparing to fire?"

"Yes, yes," said Athos; "but they are only bourgeois—very bad marksmen and who will be sure not to hit me."

In fact, at the same instant, four shots were fired, and the balls were flattened against the wall around Athos, but not one hit him.

Four shots replied to them, almost instantaneously, but much better aimed than those of the aggressors; three soldiers fell dead and one of the pioneers was wounded.

"Grimaud," said Athos, still on the breach, "another musket!"

Grimaud immediately obeyed. On their part, the three friends had reloaded their arms; another discharge followed the second. The brigadier and two pioneers fell dead, the rest of the troop took to flight.

"Now, gentlemen, a sortie!" cried Athos.

And the four friends rushed out of the fort, gained the field of battle, picked up the four soldiers' muskets and the half-pike of the brigadier and, convinced that the fugitives would not stop till they got to the city, turned again toward the bastion, bearing with them the trophies of their victory.

"Reload the muskets, Grimaud," said Athos, "and we, gentlemen, will go on with our breakfast and resume our conversation. Where were we?"

"You were saying," said d'Artagnan, "that after having demanded my head of the Cardinal, milady had left the shores of France. Where is she going?" added he, considerably interested in the itinerary milady followed.

"She is going to England," said Athos.

"With what view?"

"With the view of assassinating, or causing to be assassinated, the Duke of Buckingham."

D'Artagnan uttered an exclamation of surprise and astonishment.

138

"But this is infamous!" cried he.

"As to that," said Athos, "I beg you to believe that I care very little about it. Now, Grimaud, take our brigadier's half-pike, tie a napkin to it, and plant it at the top of our bastion, that these rebels of Rochellais may see that they have to deal with brave and loyal soldiers of the King."

Grimaud obeyed without replying. An instant afterward, the white flag was floating over the heads of the four friends: a thunder of applause saluted its appearance: half the camp was at the barrier.

"But why do you care so little whether Buckingham is killed or not? The duke is our friend."

"The duke is an Englishman, the duke is fighting against us: let her do what she likes with the duke. I care no more about him than an empty bottle."

And Athos threw fifteen paces from him an empty bottle, from which he had poured the last drop into his glass.

"Aye, but stop a minute, I will not give up Buckingham thus," said d'Artagnan, "he gave us some very fine horses."

"And, moreover, very handsome saddles," said Porthos, who at that moment wore the lace of his on his cloak.

"Besides," said Aramis, "God desires the conversion and not the death of a sinner."

"Amen!" said Athos, "and we will return to that subject presently, if such be your pleasure. But that which, for the moment, engaged my attention most earnestly, and I am sure you will understand me, d'Artagnan, was the getting from this woman a signed letter, which she had extorted from the Cardinal, and by means of which she could with impunity get rid of you and perhaps of us."

"But this creature must be a demon!" said Porthos, holding out his plate to Aramis, who was cutting up a fowl.

"And this letter," said d'Artagnan, "this letter, does it remain in her hands?"

"No, it passed into mine, I will not say without trouble, for if I did I should tell a lie."

"My dear Athos, I shall give up counting the number of times I am indebted to you for my life."

"Then it was to go to her that you left us?" said Aramis.

"Exactly so."

"And you have that letter of the Cardinal's?"

139

"Here it is," said Athos.

And he took the invaluable paper from the pocket of his uniform.

D'Artagnan unfolded it with a hand, the trembling of which he did not even attempt to conceal, and read it.

"In fact," said Aramis, "it is an absolution in all its forms."

"That paper must be torn to pieces," said d'Artagnan, who fancied he read in it his sentence of death.

"On the contrary," said Athos, "it must be preserved carefully. I would not give this paper for as many gold pieces as would cover it."

"And what is she going to do now?" asked the young man.

"Why," replied Athos carelessly, "she is probably going to write to the Cardinal that a damned Musketeer, named Athos, has taken her *protection* from her by force. She will advise him, in the same letter, to get rid of his two friends, Aramis and Porthos, at the time he disposes of him. The Cardinal will remember that these are the same men who have so often crossed his path and then, some fine morning, he will arrest d'Artagnan, and for fear he should feel lonely, he will send us to keep him company in the Bastille."

"It appears to me you are making very dull jokes, friend Athos," said Porthos.

"I am not joking."

"Do you know," said Porthos, "that to twist that damned milady's neck would be less a sin than to twist those of these poor devils of Huguenots, who have committed no other crimes than singing in French the Psalms that we sing in Latin?"

"What says the abbé?" asked Athos quietly.

"I say I am entirely of Porthos' opinion," replied Aramis.

"And I am sure I am too," said d'Artagnan.

"Fortunately, she is a good way off," said Porthos, "for I confess she would make me very uncomfortable if she were here."

"She makes me uncomfortable in England as well as in France," said Athos.

"She makes me uncomfortable wherever she is," said d'Artagnan.

"But, when you had her in your power, why didn't you drown her, or strangle her, or hang her?" said Porthos; "it is only the dead who don't come back again."

"You think so, do you, Porthos?" replied the Musketeer, with a sad smile, which d'Artagnan alone understood.

"I have an idea," said d'Artagnan.

140

"What is it?" said the Musketeers.

"To arms!" cried Grimaud.

The young men sprang up, and seized their muskets.

This time, a small troop advanced, consisting of from twenty to twenty-five men; but they were no longer pioneers; they were soldiers of the garrison.

"Shall we return to the camp?" said Porthos; "I don't think the sides are equal."

"Impossible, for three reasons," replied Athos; "the first is that we have not finished breakfast; the second is that we have still some very important things to talk about; and the third is that it still lacks ten minutes before the hour will be elapsed."

"Well, then," said Aramis, "we must form a plan of battle."

"That's very simple," replied Athos; "as soon as the enemy are within musket-shot we must fire upon them; if they continue to advance, we must fire again—we fire as long as we have loaded guns: if such as then remain of the troop persist in coming to the assault, we will allow the besiegers to go into the ditch and then we will push down upon their heads that strip of wall, which seems only to keep its balance by a miracle."

"Bravo!" cried Porthos; "decidedly, Athos, you were born to be a general, and the Cardinal, who fancies himself a great captain, is nothing to you."

"Gentlemen," said Athos, "no divided attention, I beg you; let each one pick out his man."

"I cover mine," said d'Artagnan.

"And I mine," said Porthos.

"And I likewise," said Aramis.

"Fire, then!" said Athos.

The four muskets made only one report, but four men fell.

The drum immediately beat and the little troop advanced in charging step.

Then the shots were repeated, without regularity, but always aimed with the same correctness. Nevertheless, as if they had been aware of the numerical weakness of the friends, the Rochellais continued to advance in quick time.

Upon every three shots at least two men fell, but the march of those left untouched was not slackened.

When arrived at the foot of the bastion, there were still more than a dozen of the enemy; a last discharge welcomed them, but did not stop them. They jumped into the ditch, and prepared to scale the breach.

"Now, my friends," said Athos, "finish them at a blow: to the wall! to the wall!"

And the four friends, aided by Grimaud, pushed with the barrels of their muskets an enormous sheet of the wall, which bent over as if acted upon by the wind and, becoming detached from its base, fell with a horrible crash into the ditch. Then a fearful cry was heard, a cloud of dust mounted toward heaven—and all was over!

"Can we have destroyed them all, from the first to the last?" said Athos.

"It appears so," said d'Artagnan.

"No," cried Porthos, "there go three or four, limping away."

In fact, three or four of these unfortunate men, covered with dirt and blood, were flying along the hollow way and at length regained the city: these were all that were left of the little troop.

Athos looked at his watch.

"Gentlemen," he said, "we have been here an hour and our wager is won; but we will be fair players: besides, d'Artagnan has not told us his idea yet." And the Musketeer, with his usual coolness, went and reseated himself before the remains of the breakfast.

"My idea?" said d'Artagnan.

"Yes; you said you had an idea," said Athos.

"Oh! I remember now," said d'Artagnan. "Well, I will go into England a second time; I will go and find M. de Buckingham."

"You shall not do that, d'Artagnan," said Athos coolly.

"And why not? Have I not been there once?"

"Yes; but at that period we were not at war: at that period M. de Buckingham was an ally, and not an enemy. What you now contemplate doing would amount to treason."

D'Artagnan perceived the force of this reasoning, and was silent.

"But," said Porthos, "I think I have an idea, in my turn."

"Silence for M. Porthos' idea!" said Aramis.

"I will ask leave of absence of M. de Tréville on some pretext or other, which you must find out, as I am not very clever at pretexts. Milady does not know me; I will get access to her without her suspecting me and when I catch my beauty alone, I will strangle her."

"Well," replied Athos, "I am not far from approving the idea of M. Porthos."

142

"For shame! for shame!" said Aramis—"kill a woman? No, listen to me; I have the best idea."

"Let us hear your idea, Aramis," said Athos, who entertained much deference for the young Musketeer.

"We must acquaint the Queen."

"Ah, indeed! yes," said Porthos and d'Artagnan at the same time, "we are coming nearer to it now."

"Acquaint the Queen!" said Athos; "and how will you do that? Have we any relations with the court? Could we send anyone to Paris without its being known in the camp? From here to Paris it is a hundred and forty leagues; before our letter was at Angers, we should be in a dungeon."

"As to remitting a letter with safety to her Majesty," said Aramis, coloring, "I will take that upon myself. I know a clever person at Tours——"

Aramis stopped on seeing Athos smile.

"Well, will you adopt this means, Athos?" said d'Artagnan.

"I do not reject it altogether," said Athos; "but I wish to remind Aramis that he cannot quit the camp and that nobody but one of ourselves could be trusted. Two hours after the messenger had set out, all the Capuchins, all the black caps of the Cardinal would know your letter by heart and you and your clever person would be arrested."

"Without reckoning that the Queen would save M. de Buckingham, but would take no heed of us."

"Gentlemen," said d'Artagnan, "what Porthos says is full of sense."

"Ah, ah! but what's going on in the city yonder?" said Athos.

"They are beating the alarm."

The four friends listened, and plainly heard the sound of the drum.

"You will see, they are going to send a whole regiment against us," said Athos.

"You don't think of holding out against a whole regiment, do you?" said Porthos.

"Why not?" said the Musketeer. "I feel myself quite in the humor for it and I would hold out before a whole army if we had had the precaution to bring a dozen more bottles of wine."

"Upon my word, the drum draws near," said d'Artagnan.

"Let it come," said Athos. "It is a quarter of an hour's journey

143

hence to the city, consequently a quarter of an hour's journey from the city hither; that is more than time enough for us to devise a plan. If we go from this place, we shall never find another so suitable. Ah! stop! I have it, gentlemen—the right idea has just occurred to me."

"Tell us what it is, then."

"Allow me to give Grimaud some indispensable orders."

Athos made a sign for his lackey to draw near.

"Grimaud," said Athos, pointing to the bodies which lay under the wall of the bastion, "take those gentlemen, set them up against the wall, put their hats upon their heads, and their guns in their hands."

"Oh, the great man!" cried d'Artagnan; "I comprehend now."

"You comprehend?" said Porthos.

"And do you comprehend, Grimaud?" said Aramis.

Grimaud made a sign in the affirmative.

"That's all that's necessary," said Athos; "now for my idea."

"I should like, however, to comprehend," said Porthos.

"Not at all necessary."

"Athos' idea! Athos' idea!" cried Aramis and d'Artagnan at the same time.

"This milady—this woman—this creature—this demon has a brother-in-law, as I think you have told me, d'Artagnan?"

"Yes, I know him very well, and I also believe that he has not a very warm affection for his sister-in-law."

"There is no harm in that; if he detested her, it would be all the better," replied Athos.

"In that case, we have found it."

"And yet," said Porthos, "I should like to comprehend what Grimaud is about."

"Silence, Porthos!" said Aramis.

"What is her brother's name?"

"Lord de Winter."

"Where is he now?"

"He returned to London at the first rumor of war."

"Well, that's just the man we want," said Athos; "it is he we must warn. We will have him informed that his sister-in-law is on the point of having someone assassinated, and beg him not to lose sight of her. There is in London, I hope, some establishment like that of the Madelonnettes, or of the Filles Repenties.* He must place his sister in one of these, and we shall be in peace."

"Yes," said d'Artagnan, "until she gets out again."

"Ah, indeed!" said Athos, "you require too much, d'Artagnan. I have given you all I had and I beg leave to tell you that that is the bottom of my sack."

"But I think it would be still better," said Aramis, "to inform the Queen and M. de Winter at the same time."

"Yes; but who is to carry the letter to Tours and who to London?"

"I answer for Bazin," said Aramis.

"And I for Planchet," said d'Artagnan.

"Aye," said Porthos, "if we cannot leave the camp, our lackeys may."

"To be sure they may, and this very day we will write the letters," said Aramis; "give them money and set them forward."

"We will give them money?" replied Athos. "Have you any money, then?"

The four friends looked at each other and a cloud came over the brows which lately had been so cheerful.

"Quick! quick!" cried d'Artagnan, "I see black points and red points moving yonder. What! did you talk of a regiment, Athos? It is an army!"

"Yes, yes," said Athos, "there they are. Think of the sneaks coming without beat of drum or sound of trumpet. Ah, ah! have you finished, Grimaud?"

Grimaud made a sign in the affirmative and pointed to a dozen bodies which he had set up in the most picturesque attitudes: some ported arms, others seemed to be taking aim and the remainder appeared merely to be ready, sword in hand.

"Bravo!" said Athos, "that does honor to your imagination."

"Aye, I dare say it's all very well," said Porthos, "but I should like to comprehend."

"Let us decamp first and you can comprehend afterward."

"Stop one minute, gentlemen; give Grimaud time to collect the breakfast things."

"Ah, ah!" said Aramis, "the black points and the red points are visibly enlarging. I am of d'Artagnan's opinion—we have no time to lose to regain our camp."

* Sanctuaries for fallen women

"In truth," said Athos, "I have nothing more to say against a retreat; we bet upon one hour and we have stayed an hour and a half. Nothing can be said; let us be off, gentlemen, let us be off!"

Grimaud went on before with the basket; the four friends followed, about ten paces behind him.

"What the devil shall we do now, gentlemen?" cried Athos.

"Have you forgotten anything?" said Aramis.

"The white flag! we must not leave a flag in the hands of the enemy, even if that flag is only a napkin."

And Athos ran back to the bastion, mounted the platform and bore off the flag; but as the Rochellais had arrived within musket range, they opened a terrible fire upon this man, who appeared to expose himself for pleasure's sake.

But Athos might be said to bear a charmed life: the balls passed and whistled all around him; not one hit him. Athos waved his flag, turning his back to the city guards and saluting those of the camp. On both sides loud cries arose—on the one side cries of anger, on the other cries of enthusiasm.

A second discharge followed the first and three balls, by passing through it, made the napkin really a flag. Cries were heard from the camp, "Come down! come down!"

Athos came down; his friends, who anxiously awaited him, saw him return with joy.

"Come along, Athos, come along!" cried d'Artagnan; "now we have found everything except money, it would be stupid to be killed."

But Athos continued to march majestically, whatever observations his companions made and they, finding their observations useless, regulated their pace by his.

Grimaud and his basket were far in advance, out of the reach of the balls.

At the end of an instant, a furious firing was heard.

"What's that?" asked Porthos, "what are they firing at now? I hear no balls, and I see nobody!"

"They are firing upon Grimaud's dead company," replied Athos.

"But the dead cannot return their fire."

"Certainly not; they will then fancy it is an ambush, they will deliberate and by the time they have found out the joke, we shall be out of the reach of their balls. That renders it useless to get a pleurisy by too much haste."

146

"Oh, I comprehend now," said the astonished Porthos.

"That's lucky," said Athos, shrugging his shoulders.

On their part the French, seeing the four friends return in common marching step, uttered cries of enthusiasm.

At length a fresh discharge was heard, and this time the balls came rattling among the stones around the friends and whistling sharply in their ears. The Rochellais had at last taken possession of the bastion.

"These Rochellais are bungling fellows," said Athos; "how many have we killed of them—a dozen?"

"Or fifteen."

"How many did we crush under the wall?"

"Eight or ten."

"And in exchange for all that, not even a scratch! Ah! but what is the matter with your hand, d'Artagnan? It bleeds, I think."

"Oh, it's nothing," said d'Artagnan.

"A spent ball?"

"Not even that."

"What is it, then?"

Athos loved d'Artagnan like a child, and this somber and inflexible character felt the anxiety of a parent for the young man.

"Only grazed a little," replied d'Artagnan; "my fingers were caught between two stones, that of the wall and that of my ring and the skin was broken."

"That comes from wearing diamonds, my master," said Athos disdainfully.

"Oh, to be sure," cried Porthos, "there is a diamond; why the devil, then, do we plague ourselves about money, when there is a diamond?"

"Stop a bit!" said Aramis.

"Well thought of, Porthos; this time you have an idea."

"Certainly I have," said Porthos, drawing himself up at Athos' compliment; "as there is a diamond, let us sell it."

"But," said d'Artagnan, "it is the Queen's diamond."

"The stronger reason why it should be sold," replied Athos; "the Queen saving M. de Buckingham, her lover, nothing more just; the Queen saving us, her friends, nothing more moral; let us sell the diamond. What says Monsieur l'Abbé? I don't ask Porthos; his opinion has been given."

"Why, I think," said Aramis, coloring as usual, "that, his ring not

147

coming from a mistress and, consequently, not being a love token, d'Artagnan may sell it."

"My dear Aramis, you speak like theology personified. Your opinion, then, is——"

"That the diamond may be sold."

"Well, then," said d'Artagnan gaily, "let us sell the diamond and say no more about it."

The fusillade continued, but the friends were out of reach and the Rochellais only fired to ease their consciences.

"Well! it was good that that idea came into Porthos' head—here we are at the camp; therefore, gentlemen, not a word more of this affair. We are observed—they are coming to meet us; we shall be borne inside in triumph."

In fact, the whole camp was in motion. More than two thousand persons had gazed, as at a spectacle, at this fortunate but wild undertaking of the four friends, an undertaking of which they were far from suspecting the real motive. Nothing was heard but cries of "Long live the Musketeers! long live the guards!" M. de Busigny was the first to come and shake Athos by the hand and acknowledge that the wager was lost. The dragoon and the Swiss followed him and all their comrades followed the dragoon and the Swiss. There was nothing but felicitations, pressures of the hand and embraces; there was no end to the inextinguishable laughter at the Rochellais. The tumult at length became so great that the Cardinal fancied there must be some riot and sent La Houdinière, his captain of the guard, to inquire what was going on.

The affair was described to the messenger with all the effervescence of enthusiasm.

"Well?" asked the Cardinal, on seeing La Houdinière return.

"Well, monseigneur," replied the latter, "three Musketeers and a guard laid a wager with M. de Busigny that they would go and breakfast in the bastion Saint-Gervais and, while breakfasting, they held it for two hours against the enemy and have killed I don't know how many Rochellais."

"Did you inquire the names of those three Musketeers?"

"Yes, monseigneur."

"What are their names?"

"Athos, Porthos, and Aramis."

"Still my three brave fellows!" murmured the Cardinal. "And the guard?"

148

"M. d'Artagnan."

"Still my young scapegrace. Positively, these four men must be mine."

That same evening, the Cardinal spoke to M. de Tréville of the exploit of the morning, which was the talk of the whole camp. M. de Tréville, who had received the account of the adventure from the mouths of the heroes themselves, related it in all its details to his Eminence, not forgetting the episode of the napkin.

"That's fine, Monsieur de Tréville," said the Cardinal; "let that napkin be sent to me. I will have three fleurs-de-lis embroidered on it in gold and will give it to your company as a standard."

"Monseigneur," said M. de Tréville, "that will hardly be doing justice to the guards; M. d'Artagnan is not mine; he serves under M. des Essarts."

"Well, then, take him," said the Cardinal; "when four men are so much attached to each other, it is only fair that they should serve in the same company."

That same evening, M. de Tréville announced this good news to the three Musketeers and d'Artagnan, inviting all four to breakfast with him next morning.

D'Artagnan was beside himself with joy. We know that the dream of his life had been to become a Musketeer. The three friends were likewise greatly delighted.

"Well, well," said d'Artagnan to Athos, "that was a triumphant idea of yours! As you said, we have acquired glory and were enabled to carry on a conversation of the greatest importance."

"Which we can resume now without anybody suspecting us, for, with the help of God, we shall henceforth pass for Cardinalists."

That evening d'Artagnan went to present his compliments to M. des Essarts and inform him of his promotion.

M. des Essarts, who esteemed d'Artagnan, offered him his services, as this change would bring on expenses for equipment.

D'Artagnan respectfully declined, but thinking the opportunity a good one, begged him to have the diamond he put into his hand valued, as he wished to turn it into money.

The next day by two o'clock, M. des Essarts' valet came to d'Artagnan's lodging and gave him a bag containing seven thousand livres.

This was the price of the Queen's diamond.

[*The four Musketeers dispatched letters to Lord de Winter in London, warning him against his sister-in-law, and to the "cousin" of Aramis, who was actually the Queen's sister, warning her that Buckingham was in danger. On her arrival in England, milady was intercepted by her brother-in-law's men and was imprisoned in his castle under the care of a young Puritan named John Felton. She cunningly made Felton believe that she, too, was a Puritan and told the trusting youth such a melodramatic tale of the wrongs she had suffered from Buckingham, that he became her partisan. He helped her to escape and then assassinated Buckingham.*

All this time Mme. Bonacieux had been safely concealed by the Queen's orders in a convent at Bethune. By a fatal coincidence, milady took refuge there on her flight from England. Recognizing Mme. Bonacieux, she tried, with the aid of the Count de Rochefort, to abduct her, and when the arrival of the Musketeers spoiled that plan, she poisoned the girl and fled. The Musketeers, in company with Lord de Winter and under the command of Athos, discovered that milady was in Armentières. Among the group which set out to put an end to milady's activity was a mysterious man in a red cloak, whom Athos had enlisted.]

Trial

IT WAS A STORMY AND DARK NIGHT; vast clouds covered the heavens, concealing the stars; the moon would not rise much before midnight.

Occasionally, by the light of a flash of lightning, which gleamed along the horizon, the road appeared before them, white and solitary; the flash extinct, all remained in darkness.

At every instant Athos was forced to restrain d'Artagnan, constantly in advance of the little troop, and to beg him to keep his rank, from which, at the end of a minute, he again departed. He had but one thought, which was to go forward, and forward he went.

They passed in silence through the little village of Festubert and then skirted the wood of Richebourg. When they arrived at Herlier, Planchet, who led the column, turned to the left.

Several times Lord de Winter, Porthos or Aramis endeavored to enter into conversation with the man in the red cloak; but to every interrogation put to him he bowed, without making any reply. The

travelers then comprehended that there must be some reason why
the unknown man preserved such a silence and they said no more
to him.

The storm came on, the flashes succeeded each other more rapidly, the thunder began to growl and the wind, the precursor of a
hurricane, whistled through the plumes and the hair of the horsemen.

The cavalcade trotted on more sharply.

A little before they came to Fromelles the storm burst in all its
fury upon them; they unfolded their cloaks. They had still three
leagues to travel and they traversed them amid torrents of rain.

D'Artagnan took off his hat and could not be persuaded to make
use of his cloak. He found ease in feeling the water trickle over his
burning brow and down his feverish body.

At the moment the little troop had passed Goskal, and was approaching the post-house, a man, sheltered beneath a tree, detached
himself from the trunk, with which he had been confounded in the
darkness and advanced into the middle of the road, with his finger
on his lips.

Athos recognized Grimaud.

"What's the matter?" cried Athos; "has she left Armentières?"

Grimaud made a sign in the affirmative. D'Artagnan ground his
teeth.

"Silence, d'Artagnan!" said Athos. "I have charged myself with
this affair; it is for me, then, to interrogate Grimaud."

"Where is she?" asked Athos.

Grimaud stretched out his hands in the direction of the River Lys.

"Far from here?" asked Athos.

Grimaud showed his master his forefinger bent.

"Alone?" asked Athos.

Grimaud made a sign that she was.

"Gentlemen," said Athos, "she is alone, within half a league of
us, in the direction of the river."

"That's well," said d'Artagnan; "lead us on, Grimaud."

Grimaud took his course across the country and acted as a guide
to the cavalcade.

At the end of about five hundred paces they came to a rivulet,
which they forded.

By the aid of the lightning they could perceive the village of
Enguinghem.

"Is she there?" asked d'Artagnan of Athos.

Grimaud shook his head negatively.

"Silence then!" said Athos.

And the troop continued on its route.

Another flash enlightened all around them; Grimaud extended his arm and, by the blue splendor of the serpent of fire, they distinguished a little isolated house on the banks of the river, within a hundred paces of a ferry.

A light was seen at one window.

"This is the place," said Athos.

At this moment a man, who had been crouching in a ditch, jumped up and came toward them. It was Mousqueton; he pointed with his finger to the window with the light in it.

"She is there," he said.

"And Bazin?" asked Athos.

"While I kept my eye on the window, he guarded the door."

"All is well!" said Athos; "you are good and faithful servants."

Athos sprang from his horse, gave the bridle to Grimaud and advanced toward the window, after having made a sign to the rest of the troop to go toward the door.

The little house was surrounded by a low, quickset hedge, two or three feet high; Athos sprang over the hedge and went up to the window, which was without shutters, but had the half-curtain drawn closely.

He got upon the skirting-stone to enable him to look over the curtain.

By the light of a lamp he saw a woman enveloped in a mantle of a dark color seated upon a stool near the dying embers of a fire; her elbows were placed upon a mean table and she bent her head upon her two hands, which were white as ivory.

He could not distinguish her countenance, but a sinister smile passed over the lips of Athos; he could not be deceived—it was the woman he sought.

At this moment one of the horses neighed. Milady raised her head, saw the pale face of Athos close to the window and screamed with terror.

Athos, perceiving that she knew him, pushed the window with his knee and hand; it yielded—the frame and glass were broken to slivers.

And Athos, like the specter of vengeance, sprang into the room.

152

Milady rushed to the door and opened it; but, still more pale and menacing than Athos, d'Artagnan stood on the sill.

Milady drew back, uttering a cry. D'Artagnan, believing she might have means of flight and fearing she should escape, drew a pistol from his belt; but Athos raised his hand.

"Put back that weapon, d'Artagnan," he said; "this woman must be judged, not assassinated. Wait but a little, my friend, and you shall be satisfied. Come in, gentlemen."

D'Artagnan obeyed, for Athos had the solemn voice and the powerful gesture of a judge sent by the Lord Himself. Behind d'Artagnan entered Porthos, Aramis, Lord de Winter and the man in the red cloak.

The four lackeys guarded the door and the window.

Milady had sunk into a chair, with her hands extended, as if to conjure away this terrible apparition. On perceiving her brother-in-law, an agonized cry of surprise and fright burst from her lips.

"What do you want?" screamed milady.

"We want," said Athos, "Charlotte Backson, who was first called Countess de la Fère, and afterward Lady de Winter, Baroness of Sheffield."

"That is I! that is I!" murmured milady, in extreme terror; "what do you want with me?"

"We want to judge you according to your crime," said Athos. "You shall be free to defend yourself; justify yourself if you can. Monsieur d'Artagnan, it is for you to accuse her first." D'Artagnan advanced.

"Before God and before men," said he, "I accuse this woman of having poisoned Constance Bonacieux, who died yesterday evening."

He turned toward Porthos and Aramis.

"We bear witness to this," said the two Musketeers, with one voice.

D'Artagnan continued:

"Before God and before men, I accuse this woman of having attempted to poison me with wine which she sent me from Villeroi, with a forged letter, as if that wine came from my friends. God preserved me, but another man died in my place."

"We bear witness to this," said Porthos and Aramis in the same manner as before.

"Before God and before men, I accuse this woman of having

urged me to murder the Baron de Wardes, and of having employed assassins to shoot me; from whom I was again preserved by God's providence, but as none can bear witness to these facts, I attest them myself. I have done," and d'Artagnan went to the other side of the room to take his place beside Porthos and Aramis.

"It is your turn, milord," said Athos.

The baron came forward.

"Before God and before men," he said, "I accuse this woman of having been the means of the assassination of the Duke of Buckingham."

"The Duke of Buckingham assassinated!" cried all present, with one voice.

"Yes," said the baron—"assassinated. Upon receiving the warning letter you wrote to me, I caused this woman to be arrested and gave her in charge to a loyal servant. She corrupted this man, she placed the poniard in his hand, she made him kill the duke; and at this moment, perhaps, the assassin is paying with his head for the crime of this fury."

A shudder crept through the judges at the revelation of such unheard-of crimes.

"That is not all," resumed Lord de Winter; "my brother, who made you his heir, died in three hours of a strange disorder which left livid traces behind it all over the body. Sister, how did your husband die?"

"Horror! horror!" cried Porthos and Aramis.

"Assassin of Buckingham, assassin of Felton, assassin of my brother, I demand justice upon you, and I swear that if it is not granted to me, I will execute it myself."

And Lord de Winter ranged himself by the side of d'Artagnan, leaving the place free for another accuser.

Milady let her head sink between her two hands, and endeavored to recall her ideas, which whirled about in a mortal vertigo.

"It is my turn," said Athos, himself, trembling as the lion trembles at the sight of the serpent; "it is my turn. I married that woman when she was a young girl; I married her in opposition to the wishes of all my family; I gave her my wealth, I gave her my name; and one day I discovered that this woman was branded; this woman was marked with a fleur-de-lis on her left shoulder."

"Oh!" said milady, "I defy you to find any tribunal which pro-

154

nounced such an infamous sentence against me. I defy you to find him who executed it."

"Silence!" cried a hollow voice. "It is for me to reply to that!" And the man in the red cloak came forward in his turn.

"What man is that? what man is that?" cried milady, suffocated by terror. Her hair tumbled down, then rose above her livid countenance as if alive.

All eyes were turned toward this man; for to all except Athos he was unknown. And even Athos looked at him with as much stupefaction as the rest, for he could not conceive how he could in any way be mixed up with the horrible drama which was then being unfolded.

After having approached milady with a slow and solemn step, so that the table alone separated them, the unknown man took off his mask.

Milady for some time examined with increasing terror that pale face, framed in its black hair, beard and whiskers, the only expression of which was icy impassibility. Then, all at once—

"Oh! no, no!" she cried, rising and retreating to the very wall; "no, no! it is an infernal apparition! It cannot be he! Help, help!" screamed she, turning toward the wall, as if she would tear an opening with her hands.

"Who are you then?" cried all the witnesses of this scene.

"Ask that woman," said the man in the red cloak, "for you may plainly see she knows me!"

"The executioner of Lille! the executioner of Lille!" cried milady, a prey to wild terror, and clinging with her hands to the wall to avoid falling.

Everyone drew back, and the man in the red cloak remained standing alone in the middle of the room.

"Oh! pardon! pardon!" cried the miserable woman, falling on her knees.

The unknown man waited for silence, and then resumed—

"I told you so; I was sure she would know me. Yes, I am the executioner of Lille, and this is my history."

All eyes were fixed upon this man, whose words were listened to with anxious attention.

"That woman was formerly a young maiden as beautiful as she is now. She was a nun in the convent of the Benedictines of Temple-mar. A young priest, of a simple and trustful heart, performed the duties of the church of that convent. She undertook his seduction, and succeeded: she would have seduced a saint.

"Their vows were sacred and irrevocable. Their connection could not last long without ruining both. She prevailed upon him to leave the country; but to leave the country, to fly together, to reach another part of France, where they might live at ease, because unknown, money was necessary; neither of them had any. The priest stole the sacred vessels and sold them; but as they were preparing to escape together, they were both arrested.

"Within a week she seduced the son of the jailer and got away. The young priest was condemned to ten years of imprisonment and to be branded. I was executioner of the city of Lille, as this woman has said, and the guilty man, gentlemen, was my brother!

"I then swore that this woman who had ruined him, who was more than his accomplice, since she had induced him to commit the crime, should at least share his punishment. I suspected where she was concealed. I followed her, I caught her, I bound her and I impressed the same disgraceful mark upon her that I had branded upon my poor brother.

"The day after my return to Lille, my brother, in his turn, succeeded in making his escape. I was accused of complicity and was condemned to remain in his place till he should be again a prisoner. My poor brother was ignorant of this sentence; he rejoined this woman; they fled together into Berry, and there he obtained a little curacy. This woman passed for his sister.

"The lord of the estate upon which the church of the curacy was situated saw this pretended sister and became enamored of her—so much so, that he offered to marry her. Then she left him she had ruined for him she was destined to ruin, and became the Countess de la Fère——"

All eyes were turned toward Athos, whose real name that was and who made a sign with his head that all was true that the executioner had said.

"Then," resumed the latter, "mad, desperate, determined to get rid of an existence from which she had taken away everything, both honor and happiness, my poor brother returned to Lille and, learning the sentence which had condemned me in his place, surrendered himself and hanged himself that same night from the iron bar in the loophole of his prison.

"To render justice to them who had condemned me, they kept their word. As soon as the identity of my brother was proved, I was set at liberty.

"That is the crime of which I accuse her; that is the cause of her being branded."

"Monsieur d'Artagnan," said Athos, "what is the penalty you demand against this woman?"

"The punishment of death," replied d'Artagnan.

"Milord de Winter," continued Athos, "what is the penalty you demand against this woman?"

"The punishment of death," replied Lord de Winter.

"Porthos and Aramis," again said Athos, "you who are her judges, what is the sentence you pronounce upon this woman?"

"The punishment of death," replied the Musketeers, in a stern, hollow voice.

Milady uttered a frightful shriek and dragged herself along several paces toward her judges upon her knees.

Athos stretched out his hand toward her.

"Charlotte Backson, Countess de la Fère, Milady de Winter," he said, "your crimes have wearied men on earth and God in Heaven. If you know any prayer, say it; for you are condemned and you shall die."

At these words, which left no hope, milady raised herself up to her full height, and endeavored to speak, but her strength failed her. She felt that a powerful and implacable hand seized her by the hair and dragged her away as irrevocably as fatality drags man: she did not, therefore, even attempt to make the least resistance and went out of the cottage.

Lord de Winter, d'Artagnan, Athos, Porthos, and Aramis went out close behind her and the executioner. The lackeys followed their masters and the chamber was left solitary, with its broken window, its open door and its smoky lamp burning dimly on the table.

Execution

IT WAS NEAR MIDNIGHT. The moon, sickle-shaped in its decline, and reddened by the last traces of the storm, arose behind the little town of Armentières, which showed against its pale light the dark silhouettes of its houses and the outline of its high belfry. In

157

front of them the Lys rolled its waters like a river of molten lead, while on the other side was a black mass of trees, cutting a stormy sky invaded by large coppery clouds, which created a sort of twilight amid the night. On the left was an old abandoned mill, with its motionless wings, from the ruins of which an owl threw out its shrill, periodical and monotonous cry. On the right and on the left of the road which the dismal cortege pursued, appeared a few low, stunted trees, which looked like deformed dwarfs crouching down to watch men traveling at this sinister hour.

From time to time a broad sheet of lightning opened the horizon in its whole width, darted like a serpent over the black mass of trees and, like a terrible scimitar, cleft asunder the heavens and the waters. Not a breath of wind now disturbed the heavy atmosphere. A deathlike silence oppressed all nature, the soil was humid and glittering with the rain which had recently fallen and the refreshed herbs threw forth their perfume with additional energy.

Two of the lackeys now led, or rather dragged, milady along by her arms; the executioner walked behind them and Lord de Winter, d'Artagnan, Athos, Porthos and Aramis walked behind the executioner. Planchet and Bazin came last.

The two lackeys led milady to the banks of the river. Her mouth was mute, but her eyes spoke with their inexpressible eloquence, supplicating by turns each of those she looked at. Being a few paces in advance, she whispered to the lackeys:

"A thousand pistoles to each of you, if you will help me to escape; but if you deliver me up to your masters, I have, near at hand, avengers who will make you pay for my death very dearly."

Grimaud hesitated; Mousqueton trembled in all his members.

Athos, who heard milady's voice, came sharply up; Lord de Winter did the same.

"Change these lackeys," he said; "she has spoken to them, they are no longer safe."

Planchet and Bazin were called forward, and took the places of Grimaud and Mousqueton.

When they arrived on the banks of the river, the executioner approached milady and bound her hands and feet.

Then she broke silence to cry out:

"You are base cowards, miserable assassins—ten men combined to murder one woman; beware! if I am not saved, I shall be avenged."

158

"You are not a woman," said Athos, coldly and sternly; "you do not belong to the human species: you are a demon escaped from hell, to which place we are going to send you back again."

"Ah! you virtuous men!" said milady, "but please remember that he who shall touch a hair of my head is himself an assassin."

"The executioner can kill, madame, without being on that account an assassin," said the man in the red cloak, striking upon his immense sword. "This is the last judge."

And as he bound her while saying these words, milady uttered two or three wild cries, which produced a strange and melancholy effect in flying away into the night and losing themselves in the depths of the woods.

"If I am guilty, if I have committed the crimes you accuse me of," shrieked milady, "take me before a tribunal; you are not judges, you cannot condemn me!"

"Why, I did offer you Tyburn," said Lord de Winter; "why did you not accept it?"

"Because I am not willing to die!" cried milady, struggling, "because I am too young to die!"

"The woman you poisoned at Bethune was still younger than you, madame, and yet she is dead," said d'Artagnan.

"I will enter a cloister. I will become a nun," said milady.

"You were in a cloister," said the executioner, "and you left it to destroy my brother."

Milady uttered a cry of terror and sank upon her knees.

The executioner took her up in his arms and was carrying her toward the boat.

"Oh! my God!" she cried, "my God! are you going to drown me?"

These cries had something so heartrending in them that d'Artagnan, who had been at first the most eager in pursuit of milady, sank down on the stump of a tree and leaned down his head, covering his ears with the palms of his hands; and yet, notwithstanding that, he could not help hearing her cries and threats.

D'Artagnan was the youngest of all these men; his heart failed him.

"Oh! I cannot behold this frightful spectacle!" he said; "I cannot consent that this woman should die thus!"

Milady heard these few words and caught at a shadow of hope.

"D'Artagnan! d'Artagnan!" she cried, "remember that I loved you!"

The young man rose and made a step toward her.

But Athos arose likewise, drew his sword and placed himself between them.

"One step further, M. d'Artagnan," he said, "and, dearly as I love you, we cross swords."

D'Artagnan sank on his knees and prayed.

"Come!" continued Athos, "executioner, do your duty."

"Willingly, monseigneur," said the executioner; "for, as I am a good Catholic, I firmly believe I am acting justly in performing my functions on this woman."

"That's well."

Athos made a step toward milady.

"I forgive you," he said, "the ill you have done me; I pardon you for my blasted future, my lost honor, my defiled love and my salvation forever compromised by the despair into which you have cast me. Die in peace."

Lord de Winter advanced in his turn.

"I forgive you," he said, "the poisoning of my brother, the assassination of the Duke of Buckingham; I forgive you the death of poor Felton; I forgive you the attempts upon my own person. Die in peace."

"And I," said d'Artagnan, "pardon me, madame, for having, by a trick unworthy of a gentleman, provoked your anger; and I, in exchange, pardon you for the murder of my poor love and your cruel vengeance against me. I pardon you and I weep for you. Die in peace."

"I am lost!" murmured milady, in English; "I must die!"

Then she rose up herself and cast around her one of those piercing looks which seemed to dart from an eye of flame.

She saw nothing.

She listened, and she heard nothing.

"Where am I to die?" said she.

"On the other bank," replied the executioner.

Then he placed her in the boat and, as he was going to set foot in it himself, Athos handed him a purse of gold.

"Here," he said, "is the pay for the execution, that it may be plain we act as judges."

"That is correct," said the executioner; "and now, in her turn, let this woman see that I am not fulfilling my trade, but my duty."

And he threw the money into the river.

160

The boat moved off toward the left-hand shore of the Lys, bearing the guilty woman and the executioner. All the others remained on the right-hand bank, where they fell on their knees.

The boat glided along the ferry-rope under the shadow of a pale cloud which hung over the water at the moment.

The troop of friends saw it gain the opposite bank; the figures in it cut the red-tinted horizon with a black shade.

Milady, during the passage, had contrived to untie the cord which fastened her feet; on coming near to the bank, she jumped lightly on shore and took to flight.

But the soil was moist: on gaining the top of the bank, she slipped and fell upon her knees.

She was struck, no doubt, with a superstitious idea: she conceived that Heaven denied its succor and remained in the attitude in which she had fallen, with her head drooping and her hands clasped.

Then they saw from the other bank the executioner raise both his arms slowly; a moonbeam fell upon the blade of the large sword; the two arms fell with a sudden force; they heard the hissing of the scimitar and the cry of the victim; then a truncated mass sank beneath the blow.

The executioner then took off his red cloak, spread it upon the ground, laid the body in it, threw in the head, tied all up with the four corners, lifted it to his back, and got into the boat again. When arrived in the middle of the stream, he stopped the boat, and, suspending his burden over the water—"Let the justice of God be done!" cried he, with a loud voice.

And he let the body drop into the depths of the waters, which closed over it.

Within three days the four Musketeers were in Paris. They had not exceeded their leave of absence and that same evening went to pay their customary visit to M. de Tréville.

"Well, gentlemen," said the brave captain, "I hope you have enjoyed your excursion."

"Prodigiously!" replied Athos, for himself and his companions.

Conclusion

O N THE SIXTH OF THE FOLLOWING MONTH, the King, in compliance with the promise he had made the Cardinal to return to La Rochelle, left his capital still in amazement at the news which began to spread of Buckingham's assassination.

Although warned that the man she had loved so much was in great danger, the Queen, when his death was announced to her, would not believe the fact and even imprudently exclaimed:

"It is false: he has just written to me!"

But the next day she was obliged to receive this fatal intelligence as truth. Laporte, detained in England, as everyone else had been, by the orders of Charles I, arrived and brought the duke's last dying present to the Queen.

The joy of the King was great; he did not even give himself the trouble to dissemble it and displayed it with affectation before the Queen. Louis XIII, like all weak minds, was miserably wanting in generosity.

But the King soon again became dull and indisposed; his brow was not one of those that are clear for long: he felt that by returning to his camp he was about to resume his state of slavery; nevertheless, he did return.

The Cardinal was for him the fascinating serpent and he was the bird which flies from branch to branch, without being able to escape.

The return to La Rochelle, therefore, was profoundly dull. Our four friends, in particular, astonished their comrades. They traveled together, side by side, with spiritless eyes, and heads depressed. Athos alone, from time to time, raised his expansive brow; a flash kindled in his eyes and a bitter smile passed over his lips; then, like his comrades, he sank again into his reveries.

As soon as the escort arrived in any city, when they had conducted the King to his quarters, the four friends either retired to their own or to some secluded cabaret, where they neither drank nor played. They only conversed in a low voice, looking around attentively to see that no one overheard them.

One day, when the King had halted to shoot birds, and the four friends, according to their custom, instead of following the sport, had stopped at a cabaret on the highway, a man coming from La Rochelle on horseback pulled up at the door to drink a glass of wine, and darted a searching glance into the chamber in which the four Musketeers were sitting.

"Hello! Monsieur d'Artagnan!" he said, "isn't that you I see yonder?"

D'Artagnan raised his head and uttered a cry of joy. It was the person he called his phantom; it was his unknown man of Meung, of the Rue des Fossoyeurs, and of Arras.

D'Artagnan drew his sword, and sprang toward the door.

But this time, instead of avoiding him, the unknown man jumped from his horse and advanced to meet d'Artagnan.

"Ah! monsieur!" said the young man, "I have met you, then, at last! This time, I will answer for it; you shall not escape me!"

"Neither is it my intention, monsieur, for this time I was seeking you; in the name of the King I arrest you."

"How! what do you say?" cried d'Artagnan.

"I say that you must surrender your sword to me, monsieur, and without resistance; the safety of your head depends upon your compliance."

"Who are you, then?" demanded d'Artagnan, lowering the point of his sword, but without yet surrendering it.

"I am the Count de Rochefort," answered the other, "the equerry of Cardinal Richelieu, and I have orders to conduct you to his Eminence."

"We are returning to his Eminence, Monsieur," said Athos, advancing; "and you will please accept d'Artagnan's word that he will go straight to La Rochelle."

"I must place him in the hands of guards who will take him to the camp."

"We will be his guards, monsieur, upon our words as noblemen; but, upon our words as noblemen, likewise," added Athos, knitting his brow, "M. d'Artagnan shall not leave us."

The Count de Rochefort cast a glance backward, and saw that Porthos and Aramis had placed themselves between him and the gate; he was convinced, therefore, that he was completely at the mercy of these four men.

"Gentlemen," he said, "if M. d'Artagnan will surrender his sword to me and join his word to yours, I will be satisfied with your promise to convey M. d'Artagnan to the quarters of the Cardinal."

"You have my word, monsieur, and here is my sword."

163

"This suits me better," said Rochefort, "as I wish to continue my journey."

"If it is for the purpose of rejoining milady," said Athos coolly, "it is useless; you will not find her."

"What has become of her, then?" asked Rochefort eagerly.

"Come back with us to the camp, and you shall know."

Rochefort remained for a moment undecided; then, as they were only a day's journey from Surgères, where the Cardinal was to come to meet the King, he resolved to follow Athos' advice and go with them.

Besides, this return presented him the advantage of watching over his prisoner.

They resumed their route.

On the morrow, at three o'clock in the afternoon, they arrived at Surgères. The Cardinal there awaited Louis XIII. The minister and the King exchanged numerous caresses, felicitating each other upon the fortunate chance which had freed France from the inveterate enemy who set all Europe against her. After which the Cardinal, who had been informed that d'Artagnan had been arrested, and who was anxious to see him, took leave of the King, inviting him to come the next day to view the dike, which had been completed.

On returning in the evening to his quarters at the bridge of La Pierre, the Cardinal found d'Artagnan, without his sword, and the three Musketeers, standing armed before the door of the house.

This time, as he was well attended, he looked at them sternly, and made a sign with his eye and hand for d'Artagnan to follow him.

D'Artagnan obeyed.

"We shall wait for you, d'Artagnan," said Athos, loud enough for the Cardinal to hear him.

His Eminence bent his brow, stopped for an instant and then kept on his way, without uttering a single word.

D'Artagnan entered after the Cardinal and behind d'Artagnan the door was guarded.

His Eminence went to the chamber which served him as a study and made a sign to Rochefort to bring in the young Musketeer.

Rochefort obeyed and retired.

D'Artagnan remained alone before the Cardinal. This was his second interview with Richelieu and he afterward confessed that he felt well assured it would be his last.

164

Richelieu remained standing, leaning against the mantelpiece; a table was between him and d'Artagnan.

"Monsieur," said the Cardinal, "you have been arrested by my orders."

"So I have been informed, monseigneur."

"Do you know why?"

"No, monseigneur, for the only thing for which I could be arrested is still unknown to your Eminence."

Richelieu looked steadfastly at the young man.

"Indeed!" he said, "what does that mean?"

"If monseigneur will have the goodness to tell me, in the first place, what crimes are imputed to me, I will then tell your Eminence what I have really done."

"Crimes are imputed to you that have brought down loftier heads than yours, monsieur," said the Cardinal.

"What are they, monseigneur?" said d'Artagnan, with a calmness that astonished the Cardinal himself.

"You are charged with having corresponded with the enemies of the kingdom; you are charged with having intercepted state secrets; you are charged with having endeavored to thwart the plans of your general."

"And who charges me with this, monseigneur?" said d'Artagnan, who had no doubt the accusation came from milady—"a woman branded by the justice of the country—a woman who has espoused one man in France and another in England—a woman who poisoned her second husband, and who attempted both to poison and assassinate me!"

"What is all this, monsieur?" cried the Cardinal, astonished; "and what woman are you speaking of thus?"

"Of Milady de Winter," replied d'Artagnan—"yes, of Milady de Winter, of whose crimes your Eminence is doubtless ignorant, because you have honored her with your confidence."

"Monsieur," said the Cardinal, "if Milady de Winter has committed the crimes you lay to her charge, she shall be punished."

"She has been punished, monseigneur."

"And who has punished her?"

"We have."

"Is she in prison?"

"She is dead."

165

"Dead!" repeated the Cardinal, who could not believe what he heard, "dead! Did you say she was dead?"

"Three times she attempted to kill me, and I pardoned her; but she murdered the woman I loved. Then my friends and I took her, tried her and condemned her."

D'Artagnan then related the poisoning of Madame Bonacieux in the convent of the Carmelites of Bethune, the trial in the solitary house and the execution on the banks of the Lys.

A shudder crept through the body of the Cardinal, who, it may be observed, was not easily made to shudder.

But all at once, as if undergoing the influence of a secret thought, the countenance of the Cardinal, till that moment gloomy, cleared up by degrees and recovered perfect serenity.

"So," said the Cardinal, in a tone that contrasted strongly with the severity of his words, "you have constituted yourselves judges, without remembering that they who punish without license to punish are assassins?"

"Monseigneur, I swear to you that I never for an instant had the intention of defending my head against you; I willingly will submit to any punishment your Eminence may please to inflict upon me; I do not hold life dear enough to be afraid of death."

"Yes, I know you are a man of a stout heart, monsieur," said the Cardinal, in an almost kind tone; "I can therefore tell you beforehand you shall be tried and even condemned."

"Another might reply that he had his pardon in his pocket. I will content myself with saying, 'Issue your orders, monseigneur; I am ready.' "

"Your pardon?" said Richelieu, surprised.

"Yes, monseigneur," said d'Artagnan.

"And signed by whom—by the King?"

The Cardinal pronounced these words with a singular expression of contempt.

"No; by your Eminence."

"By me? You must be mad, monsieur!"

"Monseigneur will doubtless recognize his own writing."

And d'Artagnan presented to the Cardinal the precious piece of paper which Athos had forced from milady and which he had given to d'Artagnan, to serve him as a safeguard.

His Eminence took the paper, and read it in a slow voice, dwelling upon every syllable.

166

The Cardinal then sank into a profound reverie; but he did not return the paper to d'Artagnan.

"He is meditating what sort of punishment he shall put me to death by," said d'Artagnan to himself. "Let him; indeed! he shall see how a nobleman can die!"

The young Musketeer was then in an excellent disposition to suffer heroically.

Richelieu still continued thinking, twisting and untwisting the paper in his hands.

At length he raised his head, fixed his eagle look upon that loyal, open and intelligent countenance, read upon that face, furrowed with tears, all the sufferings he had endured in the course of the last month and reflected for the third or fourth time how much that youth of twenty-one years had before him and what resources his activity, his courage and his shrewd understanding might offer to a good master.

On the other hand, the crimes, the strength of mind and the infernal genius of milady had more than once terrified him; he felt something like a secret joy at having got rid of this dangerous accomplice.

He slowly tore up the paper which d'Artagnan had generously placed in his hand.

"I am lost!" said d'Artagnan to himself.

And he bowed profoundly before the Cardinal, like a man who says, "Lord, Thy will be done!"

The Cardinal went to the table and, without sitting down, wrote a few lines upon a parchment of which two thirds were already filled up, and affixed his seal to it.

"That is my condemnation," thought d'Artagnan; "he will spare me the boredom of the Bastille, or the tediousness of a trial. That's very kind of him."

"Here, monsieur," said the Cardinal to the young man, "I have taken from you one signed blank to give you another. The name is wanting in this commission; you can write it yourself."

D'Artagnan took the paper hesitatingly, and cast his eyes over it; it was a lieutenant's commission in the Musketeers.

D'Artagnan fell at the feet of the Cardinal.

"Monseigneur," he said, "my life is yours—henceforward dispose of it. But this favor which you bestow upon me I do not merit; I have three friends who are more meritorious and more worthy——"

167

"You are a brave lad, d'Artagnan," interrupted the Cardinal, tapping him familiarly on the shoulder, charmed at having subdued this rebellious nature. "Do with this commission what you will; only remember that, though the name be a blank, it was to you that I gave it."

"I shall never forget it," replied d'Artagnan; "your Eminence may be certain of that."

The Cardinal turned around, and said in a loud voice:

"Rochefort!"

The count, who no doubt was near the door, entered immediately.

"Rochefort," said the Cardinal, "you see M. d'Artagnan—I receive him among the number of my friends; embrace, then, and be prudent, if you have any wish to preserve your heads."

Rochefort and d'Artagnan saluted coolly; but the Cardinal was there observing them with his vigilant eye.

They left the chamber at the same time.

"We shall meet again, shall we not, monsieur?"

"When you please," said d'Artagnan.

"An opportunity will offer itself," replied Rochefort.

"What's that?" said the Cardinal, opening the door.

The two men smiled at each other, shook hands and bowed to his Eminence.

"We were beginning to grow impatient," said Athos.

"Well, here I am, my friends," replied d'Artagnan, "not only free, but in favor."

"Tell us all about it."

"This evening."

Accordingly, that same evening d'Artagnan repaired to the quarters of Athos, whom he found in a fair way of emptying a bottle of Spanish wine, an occupation which he religiously went through every night.

He related all that had taken place between the Cardinal and himself and, drawing the commission from his pocket—

"Here, my dear Athos," said he, "this belongs to you."

Athos smiled one of his sweet and expressive smiles.

"My friend," he said, "for Athos this is too much, for the Count de la Fère it is too little. Keep the commission—it is yours; alas! you have purchased it dearly enough."

D'Artagnan left Athos' chamber and went to that of Porthos.

He found him clothed in a magnificent dress covered with splendid embroidery, admiring himself before a glass.

"Ah, ah! is that you, friend d'Artagnan?" exclaimed he. "How do you think these garments fit me, eh?"

"Wonderfully well," said d'Artagnan, "but I have come to offer you a dress which will become you still better."

"What's that?" asked Porthos.

"That of a lieutenant of Musketeers."

D'Artagnan related to Porthos the substance of his interview with the Cardinal, and, taking the commission from his pocket—

"Here, my friend," he said, "write your name upon it and become my officer."

Porthos cast his eyes over the commission and returned it to d'Artagnan, to the great astonishment of the young man.

"Yes," he said, "yes, that would flatter me very much; but I should not have time enough to enjoy the distinction. During our expedition to Bethune the husband of my duchess died, so that, my dear friend, the coffer of the defunct holding out its arms to me, I shall marry the widow; look here, at this moment I was trying on my wedding suit. No, keep the lieutenancy, my dear fellow, keep it."

And he returned the commission to d'Artagnan.

The young man then entered the apartment of Aramis.

He found him kneeling, with his head leaning upon an open book of prayer.

He described to him his interview with the Cardinal and, for the third time drawing his commission from his pocket—

"You, our friend, our intelligence, our invisible protector," he said, "accept this commission; you have merited it more than any of us by your wisdom and your counsels, always followed by such happy results."

"Alas! my dear friend," said Aramis, "our late adventures have disgusted me with life and with the sword; this time my determination is irrevocably taken: after the siege I shall enter the house of the Lazarists. Keep the commission, d'Artagnan—the profession of arms suits you; you will be a brave and adventurous captain."

D'Artagnan, his eye moist with gratitude, though beaming with joy, went back to Athos, whom he found still at table, contemplating the charms of his last glass of Malaga by the light of his lamp.

"Well," he said, "and they likewise have refused me!"

169

"That, my dear friend, is because nobody is more worthy than yourself."

And he took a pen, wrote the name of d'Artagnan on the commission and returned it to him.

"I shall, then, no longer have friends," said the young man; "alas! nothing but bitter recollections."

And he let his head sink upon his hands, while two large tears rolled down his cheeks.

"You are young," replied Athos, "and your bitter recollections have time to be changed into sweet remembrances."

Epilogue

LA ROCHELLE, deprived of the assistance of the English fleet and of the re-enforcements promised by Buckingham, surrendered after a siege of a year. On the twenty-eighth of October, 1628, the capitulation was signed.

The King made his entrance into Paris on the twenty-third of December of the same year. He was received in triumph, as if he came from conquering an enemy and not Frenchmen. He entered by the Faubourg St. Jacques, under verdant triumphal arches.

D'Artagnan took possession of his rank. Porthos left the service and in the course of the following year married Madame Coquenard; her so much coveted coffer contained 800,000 livres.

Mousqueton had a magnificent livery and enjoyed the satisfaction he had been ambitious of all his life—that of standing behind a gilded carriage.

Aramis, after a journey into Lorraine, disappeared all at once. and ceased to write to his friends. They learned, at a later period, through Madame de Chevreuse, who told it to two or three of her intimates, that he had taken the habit in a convent of Nancy.

Bazin became a lay brother.

Athos remained a Musketeer under the command of d'Artagnan till the year 1631, at which period, after a journey which he made to Touraine, he also quitted the service, under the pretext of having inherited a small property in Roussillon.

Grimaud followed Athos.

D'Artagnan fought three times with Rochefort and wounded him at each encounter.

"I shall most likely kill you the fourth time," he said to him, holding out his hand to assist him to rise.

"We had much better leave off as we are, both for you and for me," answered the wounded man. "I am much more your friend than you think; for, from our very first encounter, I could, by saying a word to the Cardinal, have had your throat cut!"

This time they embraced heartily, and without retaining any malice.

Planchet obtained from Rochefort the rank of sergeant in the guards.

M. Bonacieux lived on very quietly, perfectly ignorant of what had become of his wife and caring very little about the matter. One day he had the imprudence to intrude himself upon the memory of the Cardinal. The Cardinal had him informed that he would provide for him, so that he should never want for anything in future. In fact, M. Bonacieux, having left his house at seven o'clock in the evening to go to the Louvre, never appeared again in the Rue des Fossoyeurs. The opinion of those who seemed to be the best informed was that he was fed and lodged in some royal castle, at the expense of his generous Eminence.

WANDERING WILLIE'S TALE

by

Sir Walter Scott

HOME COURSE APPRECIATION

NEXT TO SHAKESPEARE'S HISTORY PLAYS, the novels of Scott have done more than any other works to give us the sense of history. That neither Shakespeare nor Scott was remarkably accurate hardly matters: they encouraged us to feel, perhaps even *made* us feel, that people in past times lived real lives and that the past, though different from the present, is intelligible and interesting.

When Sir Walter Scott was born, the attitude of the best minds toward any period earlier than their own was one of contempt. Dr. Samuel Johnson, for example, thought that Europe emerged from barbarism at about the time of his own birth. His remarks on Addison's contribution to English life show that he thought good style and good manners appeared in England only in the eighteenth century.

But even in so short a story as "Wandering Willie's Tale," Scott manages to suggest that barbarism, if these conditions of life represent barbarism, was a very interesting state of things. The story is suffused with nostalgia for a time when, if men were sometimes inconveniently rough, still, life was not so fatiguingly tame as many people may now find it. The passion for historical novels is a passion that Scott all but invented. One of its attributes is a view of the past as bigger, more brightly lit, clearer in its contrasts, intenser as to its hates and loves, its conflicts and its loyalties, than the world which we inhabit.

When Walter Scott was born, in 1771, the dying throes of ancient feudalism on the British island were still a matter of living memory. Bonnie Prince Charlie's last fine hopeless victory in assertion of his claims to the Scottish throne had taken place at Prestonpans in 1745. That ghost of a success had been followed six months later by a sound defeat at Culloden Moor, a defeat which put an end to the rule of the ancient clans and to Scottish nationalism as anything ex-

175

cept a sentiment until our own times. So Scott was perhaps justified in feeling that the old days, colorfully bad as they may have been, were better than the new, at least in Scotland.

And when he was a little boy with one leg hobbled by infantile paralysis, Walter Scott spent hours on the battlefield at Prestonpans hearing tales of Scottish valor from old people who had watched the battle. Because he was sickly, Scott lived on his grandfather's farm, which was near Prestonpans, rather than with his parents in Edin-

Sir Walter Scott (1771–1832).

burgh. There his grandmother told him the stories which she had heard as a girl, tales of the Border raids, legends which went back beyond the period of *Redgauntlet* (the novel in which this story is recounted), back to the time which the blind fiddler revives, the time of Steenie Steenson and the events of 1660. Members of the Scott family had been partisans in the struggles between England and Scotland since the history of the Border began. Walter Scott became Walter the Scot at an early age.

176

CHARACTERS WITH VITALITY

Scott's way with history is illustrated perfectly in "Wandering Willie's Tale": to place characters of vitality and temperamental interest in the midst of the kinds of action and conditions of life that can call forth their most brilliant definition and energy. Those actions, those conditions, become history; they animate the characters, and the characters animate them.

And in "Wandering Willie's Tale" we see with what energy the people live, these persons so unlike us and yet so real. In the first place, like the most delightful characters of Shakespeare or Dickens —Juliet's nurse or Mr. Micawber, for instance—they *talk* themselves alive. It is not just a matter of dialect, either, that convinces us that we are hearing the voices of real people from the past; indeed, a page of dialect is usually fatally daunting to the reader. No, the vitality of Scott's characters has to animate not only distant actions and customs, but unfamiliar modes of speech as well. The trick is— if we can call it a trick—that characters like Wandering Willie are natural poets, and they use the folk tongue the way a poet uses his own proper language—with momentary delight. Sir Robert Redgauntlet, Wandering Willie says, "lived in these parts *before the dear years . . . ;* our fathers used to *draw breath thick* if ever they heard him named."

The feelings of Scott's characters are true and lively, too. The current of response to the events of the story flows through the heart and nerves of Wandering Willie as he tells his tale. His family, he says in the third paragraph, had lived "under the Redgauntlets, since the riding days, and lang before. It was a pleasant bit; and I think the air is callerer and fresher there than ony where else in the country. It's a' deserted now; and I sat on the broken doorcheck three days since, and was glad I couldna see the plight the place was in; but that's a' wide o' the mark."

HISTORY COMES ALIVE

Of course, Willie's remark isn't wide of the mark at all; the blind fiddler's inward lamentation as he sat on the broken threshold is what makes us believe in what Scott has to tell us about the history of the Border. Because the feelings are real, we believe their stated causes are real.

That is what makes the story of Steenie Steenson itself so fine.

177

Everybody has heard stories about people who have sold their souls to the Devil and of poor innocent folk who have got mixed up with them to their dismay. The story itself, then, told as anybody not a born and developed master of story telling would tell it, could be just another of those boring pieces of incredibility in which folklore abounds. But because Wandering Willie is a person with a sense of delight in the intensest varieties of human expression, he makes his grandfather and the wicked laird intense and brilliant, too. Here they are confronted:

"Sir Robert gave my gudesire a look, as if he would have withered his heart in his bosom. . . .

" 'Are ye come light-handed, ye son of a toom whistle?' said Sir Robert. 'Zounds! if you are—'

"My gudesire, with as gude a countenance as he could put on, made a leg, and placed the bag of money on the table wi' a dash, like a man that does something clever. The Laird drew it to him hastily— 'Is it all here, Steenie, man?' "

Now, Scott doesn't have to say, "Thereupon, amused by grandfather's foolery, the nobleman relented, and the frown passed from his countenance." All that is communicated, as the imagination willingly conveys it, by the gentleness of " 'Is it all here, Steenie, man?' "

So not only has Wandering Willie told his story of ghosts and devils well, but he has brought it to bear upon Scottish history, too. He has suggested, in the first place, that the Episcopal party, to which Sir Robert belonged, the party favorable to the English, was the Devil's party. But then, he has softened this harsh judgment by showing the personal loyalty of Steenie Steenson to his old master, whose care for Steenie, even out of Hell, shows that devotion to be deserved. And in the contrast of the old master with the new one, who appears so chilly and business-like, Wandering Willie has suggested how the rough and ready, engagingly wicked old order holds its power over men's hearts, in a way that the new order, which Scott means to be recognized as that of the modern man of business, will be hard put to equal.

In such a way does Scott make history live.

Edwin Blois Barrett
Hamilton College

178

Ye maun have heard of Sir Robert Redgauntlet of that Ilk, who lived in these parts before the dear years. The country will lang mind him; and our fathers used to draw breath thick if ever they heard him named. He was out wi' the Hielandmen in Montrose's time; and again he was in the hills wi' Glencairn in the saxteen hundred and fifty-twa; and sae when King Charles the Second came in, wha was in sic favor as the Laird of Redgauntlet? He was knighted at Lonon court, wi' the King's ain sword; and being a redhot prelatist, he came down here, rampauging like a lion, with commissions of lieutenancy (and of lunacy, for what I ken) to put down a' the Whigs and Covenanters in the country. Wild wark they made of it; for the Whigs were as dour as the Cavaliers were fierce and it was which should first tire the other. Redgauntlet was aye for the strong hand; and his name is kend as wide in the country as Claverhouse's or Tam Dalyell's. Glen, nor dargle, nor mountain, nor cave, could hide the puir hill-folk when Redgauntlet was out with bugle and bloodhound after them, as if they had been sae mony deer. And troth when they fand them, they didna mak muckle mair ceremony than a Hielandman wi' a roebuck—It was just, "Will ye tak the test?"—if not, "Make ready—present—fire!" and there lay the recusant.

Far and wide was Sir Robert hated and feared. Men thought he had a direct compact with Satan—that he was proof against steel—and that bullets happed aff his buff-coat like hailstanes from a hearth

179

—that he had a mear that would turn a hare on the side of Carrifra-gawns—and muckle to the same purpose, of whilk mair anon. The best blessing they wared on him was, "Deil scowp wi' Redgauntlet!" He wasna a bad master to his ain folk, though, and was weel aneugh liked by his tenants; and as for the lackies and troopers that raid out wi' him to the persecutions, as the Whigs caa'd those killing times, they wad hae drunken themsells blind to his health at ony time.

Now you are to ken that my gudesire lived on Redgauntlet's grund—they ca' the place Primrose-Knowe. We had lived on the grund, and under the Redgauntlets, since the riding-days, and lang before. It was a pleasant bit; and I think the air is callerer and fresher there than ony where else in the country. It's a' deserted now; and I sat on the broken doorcheek three days since, and was glad I couldna see the plight the place was in; but that's a' wide o' the mark. There dwelt my gudesire, Steenie Steenson, a rambling, rattling chiel' he had been in his young days, and could play weel on the pipes; he was famous at "Hoopers and Girders"—a' Cumber-land couldna touch him at "Jockie Lattin"—and he had the finest finger for the backlilt between Berwick and Carlisle. The like o' Steenie wasna the sort that they made Whigs o'. And so he became a Tory, as they ca' it, which we now ca' Jacobites, just out of a kind of needcessity, that he might belang to some side or other. He had nae ill-will to the Whig bodies, and liked little to see the blude rin, though, being obliged to follow Sir Robert in hunting and hosting, watching and warding, he saw muckle mischief, and maybe did some, that he couldna avoid.

Now Steenie was a kind of favorite with his master, and kend a' the folks about the castle, and was often sent for to play the pipes when they were at their merriment. Auld Dougal MacCallum, the butler, that had followed Sir Robert through gude and ill, thick and thin, pool and stream, was specially fond of the pipes, and aye gae my gudesire his gude word wi' the Laird; for Dougal could turn his master round his finger.

Weel, round came the Revolution, and it had like to have broken the hearts baith of Dougal and his master. But the change was not a'thegether sae great as they feared, and other folk thought for. The Whigs made an unco crawing what they wad do with their auld ene-mies, and in special wi' Sir Robert Redgauntlet. But there were ower many great folks dipped in the same doings to mak a spick and span new warld. So **Parliament** passed it a' ower easy; and Sir Robert, bating that he was held to hunting foxes instead of Covenanters, remained just the man he was. His revel was as loud and his hall as weel lighted as ever it had been, though maybe he lacked the fines of the nonconformists, that used to come to stock his larder and cellar; for it is certain he began to be keener about the rents than his tenants used to find him before, and they behoved to be prompt to the rent-day, or else the Laird wasna pleased. And he was sic an awsome body, that naebody cared to anger him; for the oaths he swore, and the rage that he used to get into, and the looks that he put on, made men sometimes think him a devil incarnate.

Weel, my gudesire was nae manager—no that he was a very great misguider—but he hadna the saving gift and he got twa terms' rent in arrear. He got the first brash at Whitsunday put ower wi' fair word and piping; but when Martinmas came, there was a summons from the grund-officer to come wi' the rent on a day preceese, or else Steenie behoved to flit. Sair wark he had to get the siller; but he was weel-freended and at last he got the haill scraped thegether—a thousand merks—the maist of it was from a neighbor they caa'd Laurie Lapraik—a sly tod. Laurie had walth o' gear—could hunt wi' the hound and rin wi' the hare—and be Whig or Tory, saunt or sinner, as the wind stood. He was a professor in this Revolution warld, but he liked an orra sough of this warld, and a tune on the pipes weel aneugh at a bytime; and abune a', he thought he had gude security for the siller he lent my gudesire ower the stocking at Primrose-Knowe.

Away trots my gudesire to Redgauntlet Castle wi' a heavy purse and a light heart, glad to be out of the Laird's danger. Weel, the first thing he learned at the Castle was, that Sir Robert had fretted himsell into a fit of the gout, because he did not appear before twelve o'clock. It wasna a'thegether for sake of the money, Dougal thought; but because he didna like to part wi' my gudesire aff the grund. Dougal was glad to see Steenie, and brought him into the great oak parlor, and there sat the Laird his leesome lane, excepting that he had beside him a great, ill-favored jackanape, that was a special pet of his; a cankered beast it was, and mony an ill-natured trick it played—ill to please it was and easily angered—ran about the haill castle, chattering and yowling, and pinching and biting folk, specially before ill-weather, or disturbances in the State. Sir Robert caa'd it Major Weir,* after the warlock that was burnt; and few folk liked either the

* A celebrated wizard, executed at Edinburgh for sorcery and other crimes

181

name or the conditions of the creature—they thought there was something in it by ordinar—and my gudesire was not just easy in mind when the door shut on him and he saw himself in the room wi' naebody but the Laird, Dougal MacCallum and the Major, a thing that hadna chanced to him before.

Sir Robert sat, or, I should say, lay in a great armed chair, wi' his grand velvet gown, and his feet on a cradle; for he had baith gout and gravel and his face looked as gash and ghastly as Satan's. Major Weir sat opposite to him, in a red laced coat, and the Laird's wig on his head; and aye as Sir Robert girned wi' pain, the jackan-ape girned too, like a sheep's head between a pair of tangs—an ill-faur'd, fearsome couple they were. The Laird's buff-coat was hung on a pin behind him, and his broadsword and his pistols within reach; for he keepit up the auld fashion of having the weap-ons ready and a horse saddled day and night, just as he used to do when he was able to loup on horseback, and away after ony of the hill-folk he could get speerings of. Some said it was for fear of the Whigs taking vengeance, but I judge it was just his auld custom—he wasna gien to fear ony thing. The rental-book, wi' its black cover and brass clasps, was lying beside him; and a book of sculduddry sangs was put betwixt the leaves, to keep it open at the place where it bore evidence against the Goodman of Primrose-Knowe, as behind the hand with his mails and duties. Sir Robert gave my gudesire a look, as if he would have withered his heart in his bosom. Ye maun ken he had a way of bending his brows, that men saw the visible mark of a horseshoe in his forehead, deep dinted, as if it had been stamped there.

"Are ye come light-handed, ye son of a toom whistle?" said Sir Robert. "Zounds! if you are——"

My gudesire, with as gude a countenance as he could put on, made a leg and placed the bag of money on the table wi' a dash, like a man that does something clever. The Laird drew it to him hastily —"Is it all here, Steenie, man?"

"Your honor will find it right," said my gudesire.

"Here, Dougal," said the Laird, "gie Steenie a tass of brandy down stairs, till I count the siller and write the receipt."

But they werena weel out of the room, when Sir Robert gied a yelloch that garr'd the Castle rock. Back ran Dougal—in flew the liverymen—yell on yell gied the Laird, ilk ane mair awfu' than the ither. My gudesire knew not whether to stand or flee, but he ven-

tured back into the parlor, where a' was gaun hirdy-girdie—naebody to say "come in," or "gae out." Terribly the Laird roared
for cauld water to his feet and wine to cool his throat; and Hell, hell,
hell, and its flames, was aye the word in his mouth. They brought
him water, and when they plunged his swoln feet into the tub, he
cried out it was burning; and folk say that it *did* bubble and
sparkle like a seething caldron. He flung the cup at Dougal's head
and said he had given him blood instead of burgundy; and, sure
aneugh, the lass washed clotted blood aff the carpet the neist day.
The jackanape they caa'd Major Weir, it jibbered and cried as if
it was mocking its master; my gudesire's head was like to turn—
he forgot baith siller and receipt, and down stairs he banged; but
as he ran, the shrieks came faint and fainter; there was a deep-
drawn shivering groan, and word gaed through the Castle, that the
Laird was dead.

Weel, away came my gudesire, wi' his finger in his mouth, and
his best hope was that Dougal had seen the moneybag and heard
the Laird speak of writing the receipt. The young Laird, now Sir
John, came from Edinburgh, to see things put to rights. Sir John
and his father never gree'd weel. Sir John had been bred an advocate, and afterward sat in the last Scots Parliament and voted
for the Union, having gotten, it was thought, a rug of the compen-
sations—if his father could have come out of his grave, he would
have brained him for it on his awn hearthstane. Some thought it was
easier counting with the auld rough Knight than the fair-spoken
young ane—but mair of that anon.

Dougal MacCallum, poor body, neither grat nor grained, but
gaed about the house looking like a corpse, but directing, as was
his duty, a' the order of the grand funeral. Now, Dougal looked
aye waur and waur when night was coming, and was aye the last
to gang to his bed, whilk was in a little round, just opposite the
chamber of dais, whilk his master occupied while he was living
and where he now lay in state, as they caa'd it, weel-a-day! The
night before the funeral, Dougal could keep his awn counsel nae
langer; he came doun with his proud spirit and fairly asked auld
Hutcheon to sit in his room with him for an hour. When they were
in the round, Dougal took ae tass of brandy to himsell and gave
another to Hutcheon, and wished him all health and lang life, and said
that, for himsell, he wasna lang for this world; for that, every night
since Sir Robert's death, his silver call had sounded from the state

chamber, just as it used to do at nights in his lifetime, to call Dougal to help to turn him in his bed. Dougal said, that being alone with the dead on that floor of the tower (for naebody cared to wake Sir Robert Redgauntlet like another corpse), he had never daured to answer the call, but that now his conscience checked him for neglecting his duty; for "though death breaks service," said MacCallum, "it shall never break my service to Sir Robert; and I will answer his next whistle, so be you will stand by me, Hutcheon."

Hutcheon had nae will to the wark, but he had stood by Dougal in battle and broil and he wad not fail him at this pinch; so down the carles sat ower a stoup of brandy, and Hutcheon, who was something of a clerk, would have read a chapter of the Bible; but Dougal would hear naething but a blaud of Davie Lindsay, whilk was the waur preparation.

When midnight came, and the house was quiet as the grave, sure enough the silver whistle sounded as sharp and shrill as if Sir Robert was blowing it, and up got the twa auld servingmen and tottered into the room where the dead man lay. Hutcheon saw aneugh at the first glance; for there were torches in the room, which showed him the foul fiend, in his ain shape, sitting on the Laird's coffin! Ower he cowped as if he had been dead. He could not tell how lang he lay in a trance at the door, but when he gathered himself, he cried on his neighbor, and getting nae answer, raised the house, when Dougal was found lying dead within twa steps of the bed where his master's coffin was placed. As for the whistle, it was gane anes and aye; but mony a time was it heard at the top of the house on the bartizan, and amang the auld chimneys and turrets where the howlets have their nests. Sir John hushed the matter up and the funeral passed over without mair bogle-wark.

But when a' was ower, and the Laird was beginning to settle his affairs, every tenant was called up for his arrears, and my gudesire for the full sum that stood against him in the rental-book. Weel, away he trots to the Castle to tell his story, and there he is introduced to Sir John, sitting in his father's chair, in deep mourning, with weepers and hanging cravat and a small walking rapier by his side, instead of the auld broadsword that had a hundred-weight of steel about it, what with blade, chape and basket hilt. I have heard their communing so often tauld ower, that I almost think I was there mysell, though I couldna be born at the time. (In fact, Alan, my companion mimicked, with a good deal of humor, the flattering,

184

conciliating tone of the tenant's address, and the hypocritical melancholy of the Laird's reply. His grandfather, he said, had, while he spoke, his eye fixed on the rental-book, as if it were a mastiffdog that he was afraid would spring up and bite him.)

"I wuss ye joy, sir, of the head seat and the white loaf and the braid lairdship. Your father was a kind man to friends and followers; muckle grace to you, Sir John, to fill his shoon—his boots, I suld say, for he seldom wore shoon, unless it were muils when he had the gout."

"Ay, Steenie," quoth the Laird, sighing deeply and putting his napkin to his een, "his was a sudden call, and he will be missed in the country; no time to set his house in order—weel prepared Godward, no doubt, which is the root of the matter—but left us behind a tangled hesp to wind, Steenie.—Hem! hem! We maun go to business, Steenie; much to do and little time to do it in."

Here he opened the fatal volume. I have heard of a thing they call Doomsday Book—I am clear it has been a rental of backganging tenants.

"Stephen," said Sir John, still in the same soft, sleekit tone of voice—"Stephen Stevenson, or Steenson, ye are down here for a year's rent behind the hand—due at last term."

Stephen: "Please your honor, Sir John, I paid it to your father."

Sir John: "Ye took a receipt, then, doubtless, Stephen; and can produce it?"

Stephen: "Indeed, I hadna time, an it like your honor; for nae sooner had I set doun the siller, and just as his honor, Sir Robert, that's gaen, drew it till him to count it and write out the receipt, he was ta'en wi' the pains that removed him."

"That was unlucky," said Sir John, after a pause. "But ye maybe paid it in the presence of somebody. I want but a *talis qualis* evidence, Stephen. I would go ower strictly to work with no poor man."

Stephen: "Troth, Sir John, there was naebody in the room but Dougal MacCallum the butler. But, as your honor kens, he has e'en followed his auld master."

"Very unlucky again, Stephen," said Sir John, without altering his voice a single note. "The man to whom ye paid the money is dead—and the man who witnessed the payment is dead too—and the siller, which should have been to the fore, is neither seen nor heard tell of in the repositories. How am I to believe a' this?"

185

Stephen: "I dinna ken, your honor; but there is a bit memorandum note of the very coins; for, God help me! I had to borrow out of twenty purses; and I am sure that ilka man there set down will take his grit oath for what purpose I borrowed the money."

Sir John: "I have little doubt ye *borrowed* the money, Steenie. It is the *payment* to my father that I want to have some proof of."

Stephen: "The siller maun be about the house, Sir John. And since your honor never got it, and his honor that was canna have taen it wi' him, maybe some of the family may have seen it."

Sir John: "We will examine the servants, Stephen; that is but reasonable."

But lackey and lass, and page and groom, all denied stoutly that they had ever seen such a bag of money as my gudsire described. What was waur, he had unluckily not mentioned to any living soul of them his purpose of paying his rent. Ae quean had noticed something under his arm, but she took it for the pipes.

Sir John Redgauntlet ordered the servants out of the room, and them said to my gudesire, "Now, Steenie, ye see ye have fair play; and, as I have little doubt ye ken better where to find the siller than ony other body, I beg, in fair terms, and for your own sake, that you will end this fasherie; for, Stephen, ye maun pay or flit."

"The Lord forgie your opinion," said Stephen, driven almost to his wit's end. "I am an honest man."

"So am I, Stephen," said his honor; "and so are all the folks in the house, I hope. But if there be a knave amongst us, it must be he that tells the story he cannot prove." He paused, and then added, mair sternly, "If I understand your trick, sir, you want to take advantage of some malicious reports concernings things in this family, and particularly respecting my father's sudden death, thereby to cheat me out of the money, and perhaps take away my character, by insinuating that I have received the rent I am demanding. Where do you suppose this money to be? I insist upon knowing."

My gudesire saw every thing look so muckle against him, that he grew nearly desperate. However, he shifted from one foot to another, looked to every corner of the room, and made no answer.

"Speak out, sirrah," said the Laird, assuming a look of his father's, a very particular ane, which he had when he was angry— it seemed as if the wrinkles of his frown made that self-same fearful shape of a horse's shoe in the middle of his brow: "Speak out, sir! I *will* know your thoughts; do you suppose that I have this money?"

186

"Far be it frae me to say so," said Stephen.

"Do you charge any of my people with having taken it?"

"I wad be laith to charge them that may be innocent," said my gudesire; "and if there be any one that is guilty, I have nae proof."

"Somewhere the money must be, if there is a word of truth in your story," said Sir John; "I ask you where you think it is and demand a correct answer?"

"In hell, if you *will* have my thoughts of it," said my gudesire, driven to extremity, "in hell! with your father, his jackanape and his silver whistle."

Down the stairs he ran (for the parlor was nae place for him after such a word), and he heard the Laird swearing blood and wounds, behind him, as fast as ever did Sir Robert, and roaring for the bailie and the baron-officer.

Away rode my gudesire to his chief creditor (him they caa'd Laurie Lapraik), to try if he could make ony thing out of him; but when he tauld his story, he got but the warst word in his wame—thief, beggar, and dyvour, were the saftest terms; and to the boot of these hard terms, Laurie brought up the auld story of his dipping his hand in the blood of God's saunts, just as if a tenant could have helped riding with the Laird, and that a laird like Sir Robert Redgauntlet. My gudesire was, by this time, far beyond the bounds of patience and, while he and Laurie were at deil speed the liars, he was wanchancie aneugh to abuse Lapraik's doctrine as weel as the man, and said things that garr'd folks' flesh grue that heard them; he wasna just himsell, and he had lived wi' a wild set in his day.

At last they parted, and my gudesire was to ride hame through the wood of Pitmurkie, that is a' fou of black firs, as they say—I ken the wood, but the firs may be black or white for what I can tell—At the entry of the wood there is a wild common, and on the edge of the common, a little lonely change house, that was keepit then by an ostler wife, they suld hae caa'd her Tibbie Faw, and there puir Steenie cried for a mutchkin of brandy, for he had had no refreshment the haill day. Tibbie was earnest wi' him to take a bite of meat, but he couldna think o't, nor would he take his foot out of the stirrup, and took off the brandy wholely at twa draughts, and named a toast at each: the first was, the memory of Sir Robert Redgauntlet, and might he never lie quiet in his grave till he had righted his poor bondtenant; and the second was, a health to Man's Enemy, if he would but get him back the pock of siller, or tell him

187

what came o't, for he saw the haill world was like to regard him as a thief and a cheat, and he took that waur than even the ruin of his house and hauld.

On he rode, little caring where. It was a dark night turned, and the trees made it yet darker, and he let the beast take its ain road through the wood; when all of a sudden, from tired and wearied that it was before, the nag began to spring and flee and stend, that my gudesire could hardly keep the saddle. Upon the whilk, a horseman, suddenly riding up beside him, said, "That's a mettle beast of yours, freend; will you sell him?" So saying, he touched the horse's neck with his riding wand, and it fell into its auld heigh-ho of a stumbling trot. "But his spunk's soon out of him, I think," continued the stranger, "and that is like mony a man's courage, that thinks he wad do great things till he come to the proof."

My gudesire scarce listened to this, but spurred his horse, with "Gude e'en to you, freend."

But it's like the stranger was ane that doesna lightly yield his point; for, ride as Steenie liked, he was aye beside him at the selfsame pace. At last my gudesire, Steenie Steenson, grew half angry; and, to say the truth, half feared.

"What is it that ye want with me, freend?" he said, "If ye be a robber, I have nae money; if ye be a leal man, wanting company, I have nae heart to mirth or speaking; and if ye want to ken the road, I scarce ken it mysell."

"If you will tell me your grief," said the stranger, "I am one, that, though I have been sair miscaa'd in the world, am the only hand for helping my freends."

So my gudesire, to ease his ain heart, mair than from any hope of help, told him the story from beginning to end.

"It's a hard pinch," said the stranger; "but I think I can help you."

"If you could lend the money, sir, and take a lang day, I ken nae other help on earth," said my gudesire.

"But there may be some under the earth," said the stranger. "Come, I'll be frank wi' you; I could lend you the money on bond, but you would maybe scruple my terms. Now, I can tell you, that your auld Laird is disturbed in his grave by your curses, and the wailing of your family, and if ye daur venture to go to see him, he will give you the receipt."

My gudesire's hair stood on end at this proposal, but he thought

188

his companion might be some humorsome chield that was trying to frighten him, and might end with lending him the money. Besides, he was bauld wi' brandy, and desperate wi' distress; and he said he had courage to go to the gate of hell, and a step farther, for that receipt. The stranger laughed.

Weel, they rode on through the thickest of the wood, when, all of a sudden, the horse stopped at the door of a great house; and, but that he knew the place was ten miles off, my father would have thought he was at Redgauntlet Castle. They rode into the outer courtyard, through the muckle faulding yetts, and aneath the auld portcullis; and the whole front of the house was lighted, and there were pipes and fiddles, and as much dancing and deray within as used to be at Sir Robert's house at Pace and Yule, and such high seasons. They lap off, and my gudesire, as seemed to him, fastened his horse to the very ring he had tied him to that morning, when he gaed to wait on the young Sir John.

"God!" said my gudesire, "if Sir Robert's death be but a dream!"

He knocked at the ha' door just as he was wont, and his auld acquaintance, Dougal MacCallum—just after his wont, too—came to open the door, and said, "Piper Steenie, are ye there, lad? Sir Robert has been crying for you."

My gudesire was like a man in a dream. He looked for the stranger, but he was gane for the time. At last he just tried to say, "Ha! Dougal Driveower, are ye living? I thought ye had been dead."

"Never fash yoursell wi' me," said Dougal, "but look to yoursell; and see ye tak naething frae ony body here, neither meat, drink or siller, except just the receipt that is your ain."

So saying, he led the way out through halls and trances that were weel kend to my gudesire, and into the auld oak parlor; and there was as much singing of profane sangs, and birling of red wine, and speaking blasphemy and sculduddry, as had ever been in Red-gauntlet Castle when it was at the blithest.

But, Lord take us in keeping, what a set of ghastly revelers they were that sat around that table! My gudesire kend mony that had long before gane to their place, for often had he piped to the most part in the hall of Redgauntlet. There was the fierce Middleton and the dissolute Rothes and the crafty Lauderdale; and Dalyell, with his bauld head and a beard to his girdle; and Earlshall, with Cameron's blude on his hand; and wild Bonshaw, that tied blessed Mr. Cargill's limbs till the blude sprung; and Dunbarton Douglas, the twice-turned traitor baith to country and king. There was the Bluidy Advocate MacKenyie, who, for his worldly wit and wisdom, had been to the rest as a god. And there was Claverhouse, as beautiful as when he lived, with his long, dark, curled locks, streaming down over his laced buff-coat, and his left hand always on his right spule-blade, to hide the wound that the silver bullet had made. He sat apart from them all, and looked at them with a melancholy, haughty countenance; while the rest hallooed and sung and laughed, that the room rang. But their smiles were fearfully contorted from time to time; and their laughter passed into such wild sounds, as made my gudesire's very nails grow blue, and chilled the marrow in his banes.

They that waited at the table were just the wicked servingmen and troopers, that had done their work and cruel bidding on earth. There was the Lang Lad of the Nethertown, that helped to take Argyle; and the Bishop's summoner, that they called the Deil's Rattle-bag; and the wicked guardsmen in their laced coats; and the savage Highland Amorites, that shed blood like water; and many a proud servingman, haughty of heart and bloody of hand, cringing to the rich, and making them wickeder than they would be; grinding the poor to powder, when the rich had broken them to fragments. And mony, mony mair were coming and ganging, a' as busy in their vocation as if they had been alive.

Sir Robert Redgauntlet, in the midst of a' this fearful riot, cried, wi' a voice like thunder, on Steenie Piper to come to the boardhead where he was sitting; his legs stretched out before him and swathed up with flannel, with his holster pistols aside him, while the great broadsword rested against his chair, just as my gudesire had seen him the last time upon earth—the very cushion for the jackanape was close to him, but the creature itsell was not there—it wasna its hour, it's likely; for he heard them say, as he came forward, "Is not the Major come yet?" And another answered, "The jackanape will be here betimes the morn." And when my gudesire came forward, Sir Robert, or his ghaist, or the deevil in his likeness, said, "Weel, piper, hae ye settled wi' my son for the year's rent?"

With much ado my father gat breath to say, that Sir John would not settle without his honor's receipt.

"Ye shall hae that for a tune of the pipes, Steenie," said the appearance of Sir Robert. "Play us up, 'Weel hoddled, Luckie.' "

Now this was a tune my gudesire learned frae a warlock, that heard it when they were worshipping Satan at their meeting; and my gudesire had sometimes played it at the ranting suppers in Redgauntlet Castle, but never very willingly; and now he grew cauld at the very name of it and said, for excuse, he hadna his pipes wi' him.

"MacCallum, ye limb of Beelzebub," said the fearfu' Sir Robert, "bring Steenie the pipes that I am keeping for him!"

MacCallum brought a pair of pipes might have served the piper of Donald of the Isles. But he gave my gudesire a nudge as he offered them; and looking secretly and closely, Steenie saw that the chanter was of steel, and heated to a white heat; so he had fair warning not to trust his fingers with it. So he excused himself again, and said, he was faint and frightened and had not wind aneugh to fill the bag.

"Then ye maun eat and drink, Steenie," said the figure; "for we do little else here; and it's ill-speaking between a fou man and a fasting."

Now these were the very words that the bloody Earl of Douglas said to keep the King's messenger in hand, while he cut the head off MacLellan of Bombie, at the Threave Castle, and that put Steenie mair and mair on his guard. So he spoke up like a man, and said he came neither to eat or drink or make minstrelsy; but simply for his ain—to ken what was come o' the money he had paid, and to get a discharge for it; and he was so stout-hearted by this time, that he charged Sir Robert for conscience-sake (he had no power to say the holy name) and as he hoped for peace and rest, to spread no snares for him, but just to give him his ain.

The appearance gnashed its teeth and laughed, but it took from a large pocketbook the receipt, and handed it to Steenie. "There is your receipt, ye pitiful cur; and for the money, my dog-whelp of a son may go look for it in the Cat's Cradle."

My gudesire uttered mony thanks and was about to retire, when Sir Robert roared aloud, "Stop, though, thou sack-doudling son of a whore! I am not done with thee. HERE we do nothing for nothing; and you must return on this very day twelvemonth, to pay your master the homage that you owe me for my protection."

My father's tongue was loosed of a suddenty, and he said aloud, "I refer mysell to God's pleasure and not to yours."

He had no sooner uttered the word than all was dark around him; and he sunk on the earth with such a sudden shock, that he lost both breath and sense.

191

How lang Steenie lay there, he could not tell; but when he came to himsell, he was lying in the auld kirkyard of Redgauntlet parochine, just at the door of the family aisle, and the scutcheon of the auld knight, Sir Robert, hanging over his head. There was a deep morning fog on grass and gravestane around him, and his horse was feeding quietly beside the minister's twa cows. Steenie would have thought the whole was a dream, but he had the receipt in his hand, fairly written and signed by the auld Laird; only the last letters of his name were a little disorderly, written like one seized with sudden pain.

Sorely troubled in his mind, he left that dreary place, rode through the mist to Redgauntlet Castle, and with much ado he got speech of the Laird.

"Well, you dyvour bankrupt," was the first word, "have you brought me my rent?"

"No," answered my gudesire, "I have not; but I have brought your honor Sir Robert's receipt for it."

"How, sirrah? Sir Robert's receipt! You told me he had not given you one."

"Will your honor please to see if that bit line is right?"

Sir John looked at every line, and at every letter, with much attention; and at last, at the date, which my gudesire had not observed,—*"From my appointed place,"* he read, *"this twenty-fifth of November."* "What! That is yesterday! Villain, thou must have gone to hell for this!"

"I got it from your honor's father—whether he be in heaven or hell, I know not," said Steenie.

"I will delate you for a warlock to the Privy Council!" said Sir John. "I will send you to your master, the devil, with the help of a tar barrel and a torch!"

"I intend to delate mysell to the Presbytery," said Steenie, "and tell them all I have seen last night, whilk are things fitter for them to judge of than a borrel man like me."

Sir John paused, composed himself and desired to hear the full history; and my gudesire told it him from point to point, as I have told it you—word for word, neither more nor less.

Sir John was silent again for a long time, and at last he said, very composedly, "Steenie, this story of yours concerns the honor of many a noble family besides mine; and if it be a leasing-making, to keep yourself out of my danger, the least you can expect is to have a redhot iron driven through your tongue, and that will be as bad as scauding your fingers wi' a redhot chanter. But yet it may be true, Steenie; and if the money cast up, I shall not know what to think of it. But where shall we find the Cat's Cradle? There are cats enough about the old house, but I think they kitten without the ceremony of bed or cradle."

"We were best ask Hutcheon," said my gudesire; "he kens a' the odd corners about as weel as another serving man that is now gane, and that I wad not like to name."

Aweel, Hutcheon, when he was asked, told them, that a ruinous turret, lang disused, next to the clockhouse, only accessible by a ladder, for the opening was on the outside and far above the battle-ments, was called of old the Cat's Cradle.

"There will I go immediately," said Sir John; and he took (with what purpose, Heaven kens) one of his father's pistols from the hall table, where they had lain since the night he died, and hastened to the battlements.

It was a dangerous place to climb, for the ladder was auld and frail, and wanted ane or twa rounds. However, up got Sir John, and entered at the turret door, where his body stopped the only little light that was in the bit turret. Something flees at him wi' a vengeance, maist dang him back ower; bang gaed the knight's pistol, and Hutcheon, that held the ladder, and my gudesire that stood beside him, hears a loud skelloch. A minute after, Sir John flings the body of the jackanape down to them, and cries that the siller is fund and that they should come up and help him. And there was the bag of siller sure aneugh, and mony orra things besides, that had been missing for mony a day. And Sir John, when he had riped the turret weel, led my gudesire into the dining parlour, and took him by the hand and spoke kindly to him, and said he was sorry he should have doubted his word, and that he would hereafter be a good master to him, to make amends.

"And now, Steenie," said Sir John, "although this vision of yours tends, on the whole, to my father's credit, as an honest man, that he should, even after his death, desire to see justice done to a poor man like you, yet you are sensible that ill-dispositioned men might make bad constructions upon it, concerning his soul's health. So, I think, we had better lay the haill dirdum on that ill-deedie creature, Major Weir, and say naething about your dream in the wood of Pitmurkie. You had taken ower muckle brandy to be very certain

193

about ony thing; and, Steenie, this receipt," his hand shook while he held it out, "it's but a queer kind of document, and we will do best, I think, to put it quietly in the fire."

"Odd, but for as queer as it is, it's a' the voucher I have for my rent," said my gudesire, who was afraid, it may be, of losing the benefit of Sir Robert's discharge.

"I will bear the contents to your credit in the rentalbook, and give you a discharge under my own hand," said Sir John, "and that on the spot. And, Steenie, if you can hold your tongue about this matter, you shall sit, from this term downward, at an easier rent."

"Mony thanks to your honor," said Steenie, who saw easily in what corner the wind was; "doubtless I will be conformable to all your honor's commands; only I would willingly speak wi' some powerful minister on the subject, for I do not like the sort of soumons of appointment whilk your honor's father——"

"Do not call the phantom my father!" said Sir John, interrupting him.

"Weel, then, the thing that was so like him," said my gudesire; "he spoke of my coming back to him this time twelvemonth, and it's a weight on my conscience."

"Aweel, then," said Sir John, "if you be so much distressed in mind, you may speak to our minister of the parish; he is a douce man, regards the honor of our family, and the mair that he may look for some patronage from me."

Wi' that, my father readily agreed that the receipt should be burnt, and the Laird threw it into the chimney with his ain hand. Burn it would not for them, though; but away it flew up the lumb, wi' a lang train of sparks at its tail, and a hissing noise like a squib.

My gudesire gaed down to the Manse, and the minister, when he had heard the story, said, it was his real opinion, that though my gudesire had gaen very far in tampering with dangerous matters, yet, as he had refused the devil's arles, for such was the offer of meat and drink, and had refused to do homage by piping at his bidding, he hoped, that if he held a circumspect walk hereafter, Satan could take little advantage by what was come and gane. And, indeed, my gudesire, of his ain accord, lang foreswore baith the pipes and the brandy—it was not even till the year was out, and the fatal day past, that he would so much as take the fiddle or drink usquebaugh or tippenny.

Sir John made up his story about the jackanape as he liked himsell; and some believe till this day there was no more in the matter than the filching nature of the brute. Indeed, ye'll no hinder some to threap, that it was nane o' the auld Enemy that Dougal and my gudesire saw in the Laird's room, but only that wanchancy creature, the Major, capering on the coffin; and that, as to the blawing on the Laird's whistle that was heard after he was dead, the filthy brute could do that as weel as the Laird himsell, if no better. But Heaven kens the truth, whilk first came out by the minister's wife, after Sir John and her ain gudeman were baith in the molds. And then my gudesire, wha was failed in his limbs, but not in his judgment or memory—at least nothing to speak of—was obliged to tell the real narrative to his freends, for the credit of his good name. He might else have been charged for a warlock.

The shades of evening were growing thicker around us as my conductor finished his long narrative with this moral: "You see, birkie, it is nae chancy thing to tak' a stranger traveler for a guide, when ye are in an uncouth land."

"I should not have made that inference," said I. "Your grandfather's adventure was fortunate for himself, whom it saved from ruin and distress; and fortunate for his landlord also, whom it prevented from committing a gross act of injustice."

"Ay, but they had baith to sup the sauce o't sooner or later," said Wandering Willie, "what was fristed wasna forgiven. Sir John died before he was much over threescore; and it was just like of a moment's illness. And for my gudesire, though he departed in fulness of life, yet there was my father, a yauld man of forty-five, fell down betwixt the stilts of his pleugh, and raise never again, and left nae bairn but me, a puir sightless, fatherless, motherless creature, could neither work nor want. Things gaed weel aneugh at first; for Sir Redwald Redgauntlet, the only son of Sir John, and the oye of auld Sir Robert, and, waes me! the last of the honorable house, took the farm aff our hands, and brought me into his household to have care of me. He liked music and I had the best teachers baith England and Scotland could gie me. Mony a merry year was I wi' him; but waes me! he gaed out with other pretty men in the forty-five. I'll say nae mair about it. My head never settled weel since I lost him; and if I say another word about it, deil a bar will I have the heart to play the night. Look out, my gentle chap," he resumed in a different tone, "ye should see the lights in Brokenburn Glen by this time."

LIVES
OF THE
POETS

by

Samuel Johnson

A CONDENSATION

HOME COURSE APPRECIATION

S IR," SAID DOCTOR JOHNSON, "the biographical part of literature
is what I love most." And he was a happy man in his likes,
certainly. He himself was the subject of the greatest biography
ever written, and among his own productions the *Lives of the English
Poets,* if not the most famous, are the most loved and are sure to be
the longest read.

The publishers of a set of the works of the major English poets
commissioned Doctor Johnson to write these short biographies and
critical sketches. They no doubt hoped that the volumes would sell
better with the great man's name upon the covers, but Doctor Johnson obviously took the occasion to produce a set of small master-
pieces of moralized biography.

We do not read them today primarily for the biographies, however, nor even for the moral teaching, but for Samuel Johnson, who
stands plainly and firmly behind them. Johnson says of Milton in
this book that "he can please when pleasure is required; but it is
his peculiar power to astonish." That is precisely the quality we seek
in Samuel Johnson himself, the power of astonishing us with the
individuality and force of his own character. Probably no one else
in history can so well convince us that it may be worthwhile to listen
to extravagantly opinionated persons. Only because Johnson convinces us at once of his own personal distinction, can we manage not
to hoot when we find him making judgments like this one on Milton's
Lycidas: "One of the poems on which much praise has been bestowed is *Lycidas,* of which the diction is harsh, the rhymes uncertain, and the numbers unpleasing. . . . Its form is that of a
pastoral, easy, vulgar, and therefore disgusting." No modern critic,
certainly, could urge such a view without being laughed at, and no
other critic of Johnson's day could have, either, without the same
reproach.

But when Doctor Johnson so delivers himself, we are at first

199

Samuel Johnson, greatest literary personality of his age.

astonished, and then to our shock is added delight. We are glad, in a world where dissent is most often merely petulant, to see him stand upon his principles so squarely. We are the more glad when we realize that his principles all resolve themselves to sturdy common sense, which he *will* apply even in places where, as here, we think some other principle might well be invoked. Here is what he says further about Milton's sublime elegy on the death of his friend: ". . . What image of tenderness can be excited by these lines?—

> *We drove a field, and both together heard*
> *What time the grey fly winds her sultry horn,*
> *Battening our flocks with the fresh dews of night.*

We know that they never drove a field, and that they had no flocks to batten; and though it be allowed that the representation may be allegorical, the true meaning is so uncertain and remote that it is never sought because it cannot be known when it is found."

Of course Milton could have been more direct, but he was concerned not with making his sense easy but with making his feelings beautifully exact. Johnson's mistake is in supposing we care more about Milton's feelings outside the poem than about the expression he gives them inside the poem. The choice does not often have to

200

be made between what is sensible and what is fine, but when the choice is presented, Doctor Johnson can be trusted to come down firmly on the side of common sense. And often he almost convinces us that common sense is really common and that we share it.

JOHNSON THE MORALIST

JOHNSON AS A MORALIST is probably more impressive through his style than through his arguments. He seems confident that every man can, if he chooses, live his life with intelligence and economy of energy. This assurance certainly outweighs Johnson's own example: he stands before us as a great moral teacher despite the fact that he failed dismayingly as a schoolmaster and that his own habits were extravagantly crotchety.

His remarks on Addison show what he thought characterizes the moral teacher. Addison, he tells us, as a teacher of wisdom "may be confidently followed. His religion has nothing in it enthusiastic or superstitious: he appears neither weakly credulous, nor wantonly skeptical; his morality is neither dangerously lax, nor impractically rigid. All the enchantment of fancy, and all the cogency of argument, are employed to recommend to the reader his real interest, the care of pleasing the Author of his being."

Johnson's terms of praise here, one notices, are all terms of limitation. Addison, he implies, maintains a position of suitable moderation between unbecoming extremes; by dignified adjustment he masters life. Addison's purpose, Johnson had said earlier, "was to infuse literary curiosity by gentle and unsuspected conveyance into the gay, the idle, and the wealthy: he therefore presented knowledge in the most alluring form, not lofty and austere, but accessible and familiar. When he showed them their defects, he showed them likewise that they might be easily supplied. His attempt succeeded; inquiry was awakened, and comprehension expanded. An emulation of intellectual elegance was excited, and from this time to our own, life has been gradually exalted, and conversation purified and enlarged."

Here, too, Addison is praised for his careful intention and moderation, and Johnson shows himself suspicious of the inordinate, the excessive—as he does wherever he finds it.

JOHNSON THE WRITER

Surely his belief in balance is what causes Johnson's sentences to fall into a rhythm that we never forget once it has caught our ear.

201

Some of England's most illustrious poets, left to right: Congreve,
Swift, Milton, Addison, Thomson, Gray, Dryden, Pope.

A typical sentence in Johnson will be constructed somewhat in the fashion of this one: "The account [Dryden's] of Shakespeare may stand as a perpetual model of encomiastic criticism; exact without minuteness, and lofty without exaggeration." Johnson's own loftiness, which often sounds exaggerated today, is partly to be recognized by terms like *encomiastic*. But the real distinguishing characteristic of his style is the way he defines his ideas by first stating them and then mentioning what they might become but don't: Dryden is exact, he says, without falling into the error that the wish to be exact may lead to, and lofty without being carried away into pomposity. This device gives his style the air of careful judiciousness without, at the same time, furnishing a great deal of concrete information.

Yet that is to identify Johnson's style in biography as approaching nearer to the moralist's manner than to that of the formal historian. And, after all, the moralist is what he set out to be. The morality of common sense does not usually seek the particulars in a case brought before it, but rather searches out the general truth which the case may illustrate. It seeks not the personal but the typical, not the detailed but the instructive.

When Johnson astonishes us, he does so by the vigor with which he sweeps away what he thinks unworthy of notice. Here he comments on Pope's habit of choosing great noblemen to dedicate his books to; Pope was not, he says, "very happy in his choice; for, except Lord Bathurst, none of his noble friends were such as that a good man would wish to have his intimacy with them known to posterity: he can derive little honor from the notice of Cobham, Burlington, or Bolingbroke." When Johnson puts so much of the world beneath his notice, and can drop a prime minister into the wastebasket with so majestic an unconcern, we are as much delighted as impressed.

To be worldly-wise often means to be cynical, but although all the follies and most of the sins of mankind fall under his notice, Johnson's familiarity with men's motives never leads him into merely blackening human nature.

Johnson's wisdom is, one decides at last, the noblest kind of worldly wisdom. Its limits are narrow, and its greatest effort is to preserve its limits, but within those bounds there is the possibility of great insight and a princely calm that encourages us to be grander beings in this world.

Yet he can be very damaging when he chooses, and without either

204

the loss of the judicious tone or seemingly too exact a reference; in fact, a good deal of the pleasure one gets from reading Johnson may come from observing his tact when he is faced with serious embarrassments. In this line, he is best when he is writing about men he thinks great and when his honesty requires him to insert some small doubt about them. Their lapses in taste or sense do not embarrass him—one sees how outspoken he could be in condemning "Lycidas" —but, when he suspects their moral integrity or constancy, his ponderous delicacy is impressive indeed. His treatment of Pope as a letter-writer is typical.

JOHNSON THE FRIEND

IN THE "LIFE OF SAVAGE," the longest of the lives in this edition and the one which Johnson wrote for separate publication several years before the rest, the most various qualities of the biographer are brought out. Here, to the duties of the moralist had to be added those of the friend. Savage was a thorough rogue *and* Johnson's friend *and* the author of poems of which Johnson approved—though no one today need be led from reading the "Life" to reading Savage's works.

Johnson had a great fund of benevolence for victims of deep misfortune, and Savage appeared to him in that guise. Subsequent critics point out that the probabilities are that Savage was not, as he claimed, the disavowed and persecuted bastard son of the Countess of Macclesfield. So his claims to being one whom a wolfish world has run to earth may have been simply a brash fraud, a sympathy device. And even if Johnson had good reasons for believing Savage was what he claimed to be, by the time he has told everything about Savage that he feels he must, Johnson has shown him to be something that looks like a desperate hypocrite, flatterer, liar, libertine, and time server. So why, we are moved to ask, does Johnson bother to defend Savage at all? Why is the "Life of Savage" a work written in sorrow rather than indignation?

JOHNSON THE MAN

The reasons for Johnson's defense of Savage lie, no doubt, in the character of Johnson himself. Joseph Wood Krutch, whose *Samuel Johnson* is one of the most recent biographies, suggests that Johnson really saw some qualities of his own in Savage. Mr. Krutch enumerates: both were talkers first and scholars or writers only second, and

205

neither could bear to break up the party before dawn; both were capable of gestures of haughty self-assertion in the face of poverty and condescension; both were, when out of company, subject to melancholia. Both had, too, that quality of lively concentration upon the present moment which the true genius may share with the perverted genius, with the rascal.

But surely more important in Johnson's affection for Savage than any of these rather superficial similarities between them is the quality which most distinguishes Johnson as a moralist and perhaps as a man as well—his love of life in its intensity and its variety. The best recommendation of a moralist is that he knows life; the second-best recommendation is that he loves it. London, in Johnson's time a city more dangerous and more abominably filthy than any in a civilized nation today, seemed a kind of heaven to him, and in it he rapturously contemplated, as he said, "the full tide of human existence." When he wrote the *Lives,* Johnson was on the crest of that flood; he was the greatest man in London, the most sought-after companion and the most respected intellect. But he had been in its depths, where the human tide drew along harsh rocks. Before the poems that won him respect, before the moral essays that won him admiration, before the great *Dictionary* that won him adulation were more than remotely projected, Samuel Johnson had been a gross, ill-formed, slovenly, proud and sensitive fellow, a hack-writer when magazine journalism was just being invented. And once, at least, he had walked the streets of London the whole of a night in hunger because he had no money and no acquaintance to take him in. And the companion of that night, turning the terrors of the London streets into living brilliance with his talk, was the rascal Savage.

Edwin Blois Barrett
Hamilton College

JOHN MILTON

1608–1674

* * *

I N THE EXAMINATION of Milton's poetical works I shall pay so much regard to time as to begin with his juvenile productions. For his early pieces he seems to have had had a degree of fondness not very laudable; what he has once written he resolves to preserve, and gives to the public an unfinished poem, which he broke off because he was *nothing satisfied with what he had done,* supposing his readers less nice than himself. These preludes to his future labors are in Italian, Latin and English. Of the Italian I cannot pretend to speak as a critic, but I have heard them commended by a man well qualified to decide their merit. The Latin pieces are lusciously elegant, but the delight which they afford is rather by the exquisite imitation of the ancient writers, by the purity of the diction and the harmony of the numbers, than by any power of invention or vigor of sentiment. They are not all of equal value; the elegies excel the odes and some of the exercises on *Gunpowder Treason* might have been spared.

The English poems, though they make no promises of *Paradise Lost,* have this evidence of genius, that they have a cast original and unborrowed. But their peculiarity is not excellence: if they differ from verses of others, they differ for the worse, for they are too often distinguished by repulsive harshness; the combinations of words are new, but they are not pleasing; the rhymes and epithets seem to be laboriously sought and violently applied. . . .

Those who admire the beauties of this great poet sometimes

force their own judgment into false approbation of his little pieces, and prevail upon themselves to think that admirable which is only singular. All that short compositions can commonly attain is neatness and elegance. Milton never learned the art of doing little things with grace; he overlooked the milder excellence of suavity and softness; he was a *lion* that had no skill *in dandling the kid*.

One of the poems on which much praise has been bestowed is *Lycidas,* of which the diction is harsh, the rhymes uncertain and the numbers unpleasing. What beauty there is we must therefore seek in the sentiments and images. It is not to be considered as the effusion of real passion, for passion runs not after remote allusions and obscure opinions. Passion plucks no berries from the myrtle and ivy, nor calls upon Arethusa and Mincius,* nor tells of rough *satyrs* and *fauns with cloven heel*. Where there is leisure for fiction there is little grief.

In this poem there is no nature, for there is nothing new. Its form is that of a pastoral, easy, vulgar and therefore disgusting; whatever images it can supply are long ago exhausted, and its inherent improbability always forces dissatisfaction on the mind. When Cowley tells of Harvey,† that they studied together, it is easy to suppose how much he must miss the companion of his labors, and the partner of his discoveries; but what image of tenderness can be excited by these lines?

> *We drove a field, and both together heard*
> *What time the gray fly winds her sultry horn,*
> *Battening our flocks with the fresh dews of night.*

We know that they never drove a field and that they had no flocks to batten; and though it be allowed that the representation may be allegorical, the true meaning is so uncertain and remote that it is never sought because it cannot be known when it is found.

Among the flocks and copses and flowers, appear the heathen deities—Jove and Phoebus, Neptune and Aeolus, with a long train of mythological imagery, such as a college easily supplies. Nothing can less display knowledge or less exercise invention, than to tell how a shepherd has lost his companion and must now feed his flocks alone, without any judge of his skill in piping; and how one

---

* Mincius, a river god, son of Benacus (Lake Garda)
† Abraham Cowley wrote an elegy on the death of William Harvey. Similarly Milton wrote *Lycidas* in memory of Edward King.

god asks another god what is become of Lycidas and how neither god can tell. He who thus grieves will excite no sympathy; he who thus praises will confer no honor.

This poem has yet a grosser fault. With these trifling fictions are mingled the most awful and sacred truths, such as ought never to be polluted with such irreverend combinations. The shepherd likewise is now a feeder of sheep, and afterward an ecclesiastical pastor, a superintendent of a Christian flock. Such equivocations are always unskillful; but here they are indecent, and at least approach to impiety, of which, however, I believe the writer not to have been conscious.

Such is the power of reputation justly acquired, that its blaze drives away the eye from nice examination. Surely no man could have fancied that he read *Lycidas* with pleasure had he not known its author.

Of the two pieces, *L'Allegro* and *Il Penseroso,* I believe opinion is uniform; every man that reads them reads them with pleasure. The author's design is not, what Theobald * has remarked, merely to show how objects derive their colors from the mind, by representing the operation of the same things upon the gay and the melancholy temper, or upon the same man as he is differently disposed; but rather how, among the successive variety of appearances, every disposition of mind takes hold on those by which it may be gratified.

The *cheerful* man hears the lark in the morning; the *pensive* man hears the nightingale in the evening. The *cheerful* man sees the cock strut and hears the horn and hounds echo in the wood; then walks, *not unseen,* to observe the glory of the rising sun, or listen to the singing milkmaid and view the labors of the ploughman and the mower; then casts his eyes about him over scenes of smiling plenty and looks up to the distant tower, the residence of some fair inhabitant; thus he pursues rural gaiety through a day of labor or of play and delights himself at night with the fanciful narratives of superstitious ignorance.

The *pensive* man, at one time, walks *unseen* to muse at midnight, and at another hears the sullen curfew. If the weather drives him home, he sits in a room lighted only by *glowing embers,* or by a lonely lamp outwatches the north star, to discover the habitation of separate souls, and varies the shades of meditation by contem-

* Lewis Theobald, English playwright and critic

209

plating the magnificent or pathetic scenes of tragic and epic poetry. When the morning comes, a morning gloomy with rain and wind, he walks into the dark trackless woods, falls asleep by some murmuring water and with melancholy enthusiasm expects some dream of prognostication, or some music played by aerial performers.

Both Mirth and Melancholy are solitary, silent inhabitants of the breast, that neither receive nor transmit communication; no mention is therefore made of a philosophical friend or a pleasant companion. The seriousness does not arise from any participation of calamity, nor the gaiety from the pleasures of the bottle.

The man of *cheerfulness,* having exhausted the country, tries what *towered cities* will afford, and mingles with scenes of splendor, gay assemblies and nuptial festivities; but he mingles a mere spectator as, when the learned comedies of Jonson or the wild dramas of Shakespeare are exhibited, he attends the theater.

The *pensive* man never loses himself in crowds, but walks the cloister or frequents the cathedral. Milton probably had not yet forsaken the Church.

Both his characters delight in music; but he seems to think that cheerful notes would have obtained from Pluto a complete dismission of Eurydice, of whom solemn sounds only procured a conditional release.

For the old age of Cheerfulness he makes no provision; but Melancholy he conducts with great dignity to the close of life. His cheerfulness is without levity, and his pensiveness without asperity.

Through these two poems the images are properly selected and nicely distinguished; but the colors of the diction seem not sufficiently discriminated. I know not whether the characters are kept sufficiently apart. No mirth can indeed be found in his melancholy; but I am afraid that I always meet some melancholy in his mirth. They are two noble efforts of imagination.

The greatest of his juvenile performances is the *Masque of Comus,* in which may very plainly be discovered the dawn or twilight of *Paradise Lost.* Milton appears to have formed very early that system of diction and mode of verse, which his maturer judgment approved, and from which he never endeavored nor desired to deviate.

Nor does *Comus* afford only a specimen of his language; it exhibits likewise his power of description and his vigor of sentiment employed in the praise and defence of virtue. A work more truly poetical is rarely found; allusions, images and descriptive epithets embellish almost every period with lavish decoration. As a series of lines, therefore, it may be considered as worthy of all the admiration with which the votaries have received it.

As a drama it is deficient. The action is not probable. A masque, in those parts where supernatural intervention is admitted, must indeed be given up to all the freaks of imagination; but, so far as the action is merely human, it ought to be reasonable, which can hardly be said of the conduct of the two brothers, who, when their sister sinks with fatigue in a pathless wilderness, wander both away together in search of berries too far to find their way back and leave a helpless Lady to all the sadness and danger of solitude. This, however, is a defect overbalanced by its convenience.

What deserves more reprehension is that the prologue spoken in the wild wood by the attendant Spirit is addressed to the audience; a mode of communication so contrary to the nature of dramatic representation, that no precedents can support it.

The discourse of the Spirit is too long—an objection that may be made to almost all the following speeches; they have not the sprightliness of a dialogue animated by reciprocal contention, but seem rather declamations deliberately composed, and formally repeated, on a moral question. The auditor therefore listens as to a lecture, without passion, without anxiety.

The song of Comus has airiness and jollity; but, what may recommend Milton's morals as well as his poetry, the invitations to pleasure are so general, that they excite no distinct images of corrupt enjoyment and take no dangerous hold on the fancy.

The following soliloquies of Comus and the Lady are elegant, but tedious. The song must owe much to the voice, if it ever can delight. At last the Brothers enter, with too much tranquillity; and when they have feared lest their sister should be in danger, and hoped that she is not in danger, the Elder makes a speech in praise of chastity and the Younger finds how fine it is to be a philosopher.

Then descends the Spirit in form of a shepherd and the Brother, instead of being in haste to ask his help, praises his singing and inquires his business in that place. It is remarkable that at this interview the Brother is taken with a short fit of rhyming. The Spirit relates that the Lady is in the power of Comus; the Brother moral-

211

izes again; and the Spirit makes a long narration, of no use because it is false, and therefore unsuitable to a good being.

In all these parts the language is poetical and the sentiments are generous; but there is something wanting to allure attention.

The dispute between the Lady and Comus is the most animated and affecting scene of the drama, and wants nothing but a brisker reciprocation of objections and replies to invite attention and detain it.

The songs are vigorous and full of imagery, but they are harsh in their diction and not very musical in their numbers.

Throughout the whole the figures are too bold and the language too luxuriant for dialogue. It is a drama in the epic style, inelegantly splendid and tediously instructive.

The *Sonnets* were written in different parts of Milton's life, upon different occasions. They deserve not any particular criticism; for of the best it can only be said that they are not bad; and perhaps only the eighth and twenty-first are truly entitled to this slender commendation. The fabric of a sonnet, however adapted to the Italian language, has never succeeded in ours, which, having greater variety of termination, requires the rhymes to be often changed.

Those little pieces may be despatched without much anxiety; a greater work calls for greater care. I am now to examine *Paradise Lost;* a poem which, considered with respect to design, may claim the first place, and with respect to performance, the second, among the productions of the human mind.

By the general consent of critics the first praise of genius is due to the writer of an epic poem, as it requires an assemblage of all the powers which are singly sufficient for other compositions. Poetry is the art of uniting pleasure with truth, by calling imagination to the help of reason. Epic poetry undertakes to teach the most important truths by the most pleasing precepts, and therefore relates some great event in the most affecting manner. History must supply the writer with the rudiments of narration, which he must improve and exalt by a nobler art, must animate by dramatic energy, and diversify by retrospection and anticipation; morality must teach him the exact bounds, and different shades, of vice and virtue; from policy and the practice of life, he has to learn the discriminations of character and the tendency of the passions, either single or combined; and physiology must supply him with illustrations and images.

212

To put these materials to poetical use, is required an imagination capable of painting nature and realizing fiction. Nor is he yet a poet till he has attained the whole extension of his language, distinguished all the delicacies of phrase and all the colors of words, and learned to adjust their different sounds to all the varieties of metrical modulation.

Bossu * is of opinion that the poet's first work is to find a *moral,* which his fable is afterward to illustrate and establish. This seems to have been the process only of Milton; the moral of other poems is incidental and consequent; in Milton's only it is essential and intrinsic. His purpose was the most useful and the most arduous; *to vindicate the ways of God to man;* to show the reasonableness of religion, and the necessity of obedience to the Divine Law.

To convey this moral, there must be a *fable,* a narration artfully constructed, so as to excite curiosity and surprise expectation. In this part of his work Milton must be confessed to have equaled every other poet. He has involved in his account of the Fall of Man the events which preceded, and those that were to follow it: he has interwoven the whole system of theology with such propriety, that every part appears to be necessary; and scarcely any recital is wished shorter for the sake of quickening the progress of the main action.

The subject of an epic poem is naturally an event of great importance. That of Milton is not the destruction of a city, the conduct of a colony or the foundation of an empire. His subject is the fate of worlds, the revolutions of heaven and of earth; rebellion against the Supreme King, raised by the highest order of created beings; the overthrow of their host and the punishment of their crime; the creation of a new race of reasonable creatures; their original happiness and innocence, their forfeiture of immortality and their restoration to hope and peace.

Great events can be hastened or retarded only by persons of elevated dignity. Before the greatness displayed in Milton's poem, all other greatness shrinks away. The weakest of his agents are the highest and noblest of human beings, the original parents of mankind; with whose actions the elements consented; on whose rectitude, or deviation of will, depended the state of terrestrial nature and the condition of all the future inhabitants of the globe.

* René Le Bossu, French author of a treatise on epic poetry

Of the other agents in the poem, the chief are such as it is ir-
reverence to name on slight occasions. The rest were lower powers

> ——*of which the least could wield*
> *Those elements, and arm him with the force*
> *Of all their regions;*

powers which only the control of Omnipotence restrains from laying
creation waste, and filling the vast expanse of space with ruin and
confusion. To display the motives and actions of beings thus superior, so far as human reason can examine them, or human imagination represent them, is the task which this mighty poet has
undertaken and performed.

In the examination of epic poems much speculation is commonly employed upon the *characters*. The characters in the *Paradise Lost,* which admit of examination, are those of angels and of
man; of angels good and evil; of man in his innocent and sinful
state.

Among the angels, the virtue of Raphael is mild and placid, of
easy condescension and free communication; that of Michael is
regal and lofty and, as may seem, attentive to the dignity of his
own nature. Abdiel and Gabriel appear occasionally and act as
every incident requires; the solitary fidelity of Abdiel is very ami-
ably painted.

Of the evil angels the characters are more diversified. To Satan,
as Addison observes, such sentiments are given as suit *the most
exalted and most depraved being.* Milton has been censured by
Clarke * for the impiety which sometimes breaks from Satan's
mouth. For there are thoughts, as he justly remarks, which no observation of character can justify, because no good man would willingly permit them to pass, however transiently, through his own
mind. To make Satan speak as a rebel, without any such expressions as might taint the reader's imagination, was indeed one of the
greatest difficulties in Milton's undertaking, and I cannot but think
that he has extricated himself with great happiness. There is in
Satan's speeches little that can give pain to a pious ear. The language of rebellion cannot be the same with that of obedience. The
malignity of Satan foams in haughtiness and obstinacy, but his expressions are commonly general, and no otherwise offensive than as
they are wicked.

* Samuel Clarke, English divine

214

The other chiefs of the celestial rebellion are very judiciously discriminated in the first and second books; and the ferocious character of Moloch appears, both in the battle and the council, with exact consistency.

To Adam and to Eve are given, during their innocence, such sentiments as innocence can generate and utter. Their love is pure benevolence and mutual veneration; their repasts are without luxury, and their diligence without toil. Their addresses to their Maker have little more than the voice of admiration and gratitude. Fruition left them nothing to ask, and Innocence left them nothing to fear.

But with guilt enter distrust and discord, mutual accusation and stubborn self-defense; they regard each other with alienated minds and dread their Creator as the avenger of their transgression. At last they seek shelter in his mercy, soften to repentance and melt in supplication. Both before and after the Fall the superiority of Adam is diligently sustained.

Of the *probable* and the *marvelous,* two parts of a vulgar epic poem which immerge the critic in deep consideration, the *Paradise Lost* requires little to be said. It contains the history of a miracle, of Creation and Redemption; it displays the power and the mercy of the Supreme Being; the probable therefore is marvelous, and the marvelous is probable. The substance of the narrative is truth; and as truth allows no choice, it is, like necessity, superior to rule. To the accidental or adventitious parts, as to everything human, some slight exceptions may be made. But the main fabric is immovably supported.

It is justly remarked by Addison, that this poem has, by the nature of its subject, the advantage above all others, that it is universally and perpetually interesting. All mankind will, through all ages, bear the same relation to Adam and to Eve, and must partake of that good and evil which extend to themselves. . . .

To the completeness or *integrity* of the design nothing can be objected; it has distinctly and clearly what Aristotle requires, a beginning, a middle and an end. There is perhaps no poem, of the same length, from which so little can be taken without apparent mutilation. Here are no funeral games, nor is there any long description of a shield. The short digressions at the beginning of the third, seventh and ninth books might doubtless be spared; but superfluities so beautiful, who would take away? or who does not wish that the author of the *Iliad* had gratified succeeding ages with a

215

little knowledge of himself? Perhaps no passages are more frequently or more attentively read than those extrinsic paragraphs; and, since the end of poetry is pleasure, that cannot be unpoetical with which all are pleased.

The questions, whether the action of the poem be strictly *one,* whether the poem can be properly termed *heroic,* and who is the hero, are raised by such readers as draw their principles of judgment rather from books than from reason. Milton, though he entitled *Paradise Lost* only a *poem,* yet calls it himself *heroic song.* Dryden, petulantly and indecently, denies the heroism of Adam, because he was overcome; but there is no reason why the hero should not be unfortunate, except established practice, since success and virtue do not go necessarily together. Cato is the hero of Lucan *; but Lucan's authority will not be suffered by Quintilian to decide. However, if success be necessary, Adam's deceiver was at last crushed; Adam was restored to his Maker's favor, and therefore may securely resume his human rank.

After the scheme and fabric of the poem, must be considered its component parts, the sentiments and the diction.

The *sentiments,* as expressive of manners, or appropriated to characters, are for the greater part unexceptionally just.

Splendid passages containing lessons of morality or precepts of prudence occur seldom. Such is the original formation of this poem, that as it admits no human manners till the Fall, it can give little assistance to human conduct. Its end is to raise the thoughts above sublunary cares or pleasures. Yet the praise of that fortitude with which Abdiel maintained his singularity of virtue against the scorn of multitudes, may be accommodated to all times; and Raphael's reproof of Adam's curiosity after the planetary motions, with the answer returned by Adam, may be confidently opposed to any rule of life which any poet has delivered.

The thoughts which are occasionally called forth in the progress are such as could only be produced by an imagination in the highest degree fervid and active, to which materials were supplied by incessant study and unlimited curiosity. The heat of Milton's mind might be said to sublimate his learning, to throw off into his work the spirit of science, unmingled with its grosser parts.

He had considered creation in its whole extent and his descriptions are therefore learned. He had accustomed his imagination to

* Roman poet

unrestrained indulgence and his conceptions therefore were extensive. The characteristic quality of his poem is sublimity. He sometimes descends to the elegant, but his element is the great. He can occasionally invest himself with grace, but his natural port is gigantic loftiness. He can please when pleasure is required, but it is his peculiar power to astonish.

He seems to have been well acquainted with his own genius and to know what it was that nature had bestowed upon him more bountifully than upon others; the power of displaying the vast, illuminating the splendid, enforcing the awful, darkening the gloomy and aggravating the dreadful; he therefore chose a subject on which too much could not be said, on which he might tire his fancy without the censure of extravagance.

The appearances of nature, and the occurrences of life, did not satiate his appetite of greatness. To paint things as they are requires a minute attention, and employs the memory rather than the fancy. Milton's delight was to sport in the wide regions of possibility; reality was a scene too narrow for his mind. He sent his faculties out upon discovery, into worlds where only imagination can travel, and delighted to form new modes of existence, and furnish sentiment and action to superior beings, to trace the counsels of hell or accompany the choirs of heaven.

But he could not be always in other worlds; he must sometimes revisit earth and tell of things visible and known. When he cannot raise wonder by the sublimity of his mind, he gives delight by its fertility.

Whatever be his subject, he never fails to fill the imagination. But his images and descriptions of the scenes or operations of nature do not seem to be always copied from original form, nor to have the freshness, raciness and energy of immediate observation. He saw nature, as Dryden expresses it, *through the spectacles of books;* and on most occasions calls learning to his assistance. The garden of Eden brings to his mind the vale of Enna, where Proserpine was gathering flowers. Satan makes his way through fighting elements, like Argo between the Cyanean rocks, or Ulysses between the two Sicilian whirlpools, when he shunned Charybdis on the *larboard.* The mythological allusions have been justly censured, as not being always used with notice of their vanity; but they contribute variety to the narration, and produce an alternate exercise of the memory and the fancy.

217

His similes are less numerous and more various than those of his predecessors. But he does not confine himself within the limits of rigorous comparison: his great excellence is amplitude, and he expands the adventitious image beyond the dimensions which the occasion required. Thus, comparing the shield of Satan to the orb of the moon, he crowds the imagination with the discovery of the telescope and all the wonders which the telescope discovers.

Of his moral sentiments it is hardly praise to affirm that they excel those of all other poets; for this superiority he was indebted to his acquaintance with the sacred writings. The ancient epic poets, wanting the light of revelation, were very unskillful teachers of virtue: their principal characters may be great, but they are not amiable. The reader may rise from their works with a greater degree of active or passive fortitude, and sometimes of prudence; but he will be able to carry away few precepts of justice and none of mercy.

From the Italian writers it appears that the advantages of even Christian knowledge may be possessed in vain. Ariosto's pravity is generally known; and though the *Deliverance of Jerusalem* may be considered as a sacred subject, the poet has been very sparing of moral instruction.

In Milton every line breathes sanctity of thought and purity of manners, except when the train of the narration requires the introduction of the rebellious spirits; and even they are compelled to acknowledge their subjection to God, in such a manner as excites reverence and confirms piety.

Of human beings there are but two; but those two are the parents of mankind, venerable before their fall for dignity and innocence and amiable after it for repentance and submission. In their first state their affection is tender without weakness, and their piety sublime without presumption. When they have sinned, they show how discord begins in mutual frailty and how it ought to cease in mutual forbearance, how confidence of the Divine favor is forfeited by sin, and how hope of pardon may be obtained by penitence and prayer. A state of innocence we can only conceive, if indeed in our present misery it be possible to conceive it; but the sentiments and worship proper to a fallen and offending being we have all to learn, as we have all to practice.

The poet, whatever be done, is always great. Our progenitors in

218

their first state conversed with angels; even when folly and sin had degraded them, they had not in their humiliation *the port of mean suitors;* and they rise again to reverential regard when we find that their prayers were heard.

As human passions did not enter the world before the Fall, there is in the *Paradise Lost* little opportunity for the pathetic; but what little there is has not been lost. That passion which is peculiar to rational nature, the anguish arising from the consciousness of transgression, and the horrors attending the sense of the Divine displeasure, are very justly described and forcibly impressed. But the passions are moved only on one occasion; sublimity is the general and prevailing quality of this poem; sublimity variously modified, sometimes descriptive, sometimes argumentative.

The defects and faults of *Paradise Lost*—for faults and defects every work of man must have—it is the business of impartial criticism to discover. As, in displaying the excellence of Milton, I have not made long quotations, because of selecting beauties there had been no end, I shall in the same general manner mention that which seems to deserve censure; for what Englishman can take delight in transcribing passages which, if they lessen the reputation of Milton, diminish in some degree the honor of our country?

The generality of my scheme does not admit the frequent notice of verbal inaccuracies; which Bentley,* perhaps better skilled in grammar than poetry, has often found, though he sometimes made them, and which he imputed to the obtrusions of a reviser, whom the author's blindness obliged him to employ; a supposition rash and groundless if he thought it true, and vile and pernicious if, as is said, he in private allowed it to be false.

The plan of *Paradise Lost* has this inconvenience, that it comprises neither human actions nor human manners. The man and woman who act and suffer are in a state which no other man or woman can ever know. The reader finds no transaction in which he can by any effort of imagination place himself; he has therefore little natural curiosity or sympathy.

We all, indeed, feel the effects of Adam's disobedience; we all sin like Adam, and like him must all bewail our offences: we have restless and insidious enemies in the fallen angels, and in the blessed spirits we have guardians and friends; in the redemption of man-

* Richard Bentley, clergyman and critic

219

kind we hope to be included; in the description of heaven and hell we are surely interested, as we are all to reside hereafter either in the regions of horror or bliss.

But these truths are too important to be new; they have been taught to our infancy; they have mingled with our solitary thoughts and familiar conversation, and are habitually interwoven with the whole texture of life. Being therefore not new, they raise no unaccustomed emotion in the mind; what we knew before, we cannot learn; what is not unexpected, cannot surprise.

Of the idea suggested by these awful scenes, from some we recede with reverence, except when stated hours require their association; and from others we shrink with horror, or admit them only as salutary inflictions, as counterpoises to our interests and passions. Such images rather obstruct the career of fancy than incite it.

Pleasure and terror are indeed the genuine sources of poetry; but poetical pleasure must be such as human imagination can at least conceive, and poetical terrors such as human strength and fortitude may combat. The good and evil of eternity are too ponderous for the wings of wit; the mind sinks under them in passive helplessness, content with calm belief and humble adoration.

Known truths, however, may take a different appearance, and be conveyed to the mind by a new train of intermediate images. This Milton has undertaken and performed with pregnancy and vigor of mind peculiar to himself. Whoever considers the few radical positions which the Scriptures afforded him, will wonder by what energetic operation he expanded them to such extent, and ramified them to so much variety, restrained as he was by religious reverence from licentiousness of fiction.

Here is a full display of the united force of study and genius; of a great accumulation of materials, with judgment to digest and fancy to combine them: Milton was able to select from nature or from story, from an ancient fable or from modern science, whatever could illustrate or adorn his thoughts. An accumulation of knowledge impregnated his mind, fermented by study and exalted by imagination.

It has been therefore said, without an indecent hyperbole, by one of his encomiasts, that in reading *Paradise Lost* we read a book of universal knowledge.

But original deficiency cannot be supplied. The want of human interest is always felt. *Paradise Lost* is one of the books which the reader admires and lays down and forgets to take up again. None ever wished it longer than it is. Its perusal is a duty rather than a pleasure. We read Milton for instruction, retire harassed and over-burdened and look elsewhere for recreation; we desert our master and seek for companions.

Another inconvenience of Milton's design is, that it requires the description of what cannot be described, the agency of spirits. He saw that immateriality supplied no images, and that he could not show angels acting but by instruments of action; he therefore invested them with form and matter. This, being necessary, was therefore defensible; and he should have secured the consistency of his system by keeping immateriality out of sight and enticing his reader to drop it from his thoughts. But he has unhappily perplexed his poetry with his philosophy. His infernal and celestial powers are sometimes pure spirit, and sometimes animated body. When Satan walks with his lance upon the *burning marle,* he has a body; when, in his passage between hell and the new world, he is in danger of sinking in the vacuity and is supported by a gust of rising vapors, he has a body; when he animates the toad, he seems to be mere spirit, that can penetrate matter at pleasure; when he *starts up in his own shape,* he has at least a determined form; and when he is brought before Gabriel, he has *a spear and a shield,* which he had the power of hiding in the toad, though the arms of the contending angels are evidently material.

The vulgar inhabitants of Pandemonium, being *incorporal spirits,* are *at large, though without number,* in a limited space: yet in the battle, when they were overwhelmed by mountains, their armor hurt them, *crushed in upon their substance, now grown gross by sinning.* This likewise happened to the uncorrupted angels, who were over-thrown the *sooner for their arms, for unarmed they might easily as spirits have evaded by contraction or remove.* Even as spirits they are hardly spiritual; for *contraction* and *remove* are images of matter; but if they could have escaped without their armor, they might have escaped from it, and left only the empty cover to be battered. Uriel, when he rides on a sunbeam, is material; Satan is material when he is afraid of the prowess of Adam.

The confusion of spirit and matter which pervades the whole narration of the war of heaven fills it with incongruity; and the book in which it is related is, I believe, the favorite of children and gradually neglected as knowledge is increased.

After the operation of immaterial agents, which cannot be ex-

221

plained, may be considered that of allegorical persons, which have no real existence. To exalt causes into agents, to invest abstract ideas with form and animate them with activity, has always been the right of poetry. But such airy beings are, for the most part, suffered only to do their natural office and retire. Thus Fame tells a tale and Victory hovers over a general or perches on a standard; but Fame and Victory can do more. To give them any real employment, or ascribe to them any material agency, is to make them allegorical no longer, but to shock the mind by ascribing effects to nonentity. In the *Prometheus* of Aeschylus we see Violence and Strength, and in the *Alcestis* of Euripides we see Death brought upon the stage, all as active persons of the drama; but no precedents can justify absurdity.

Milton's allegory of Sin and Death is undoubtedly faulty. Sin is indeed the mother of Death, and may be allowed to be the portress of hell; but when they stop the journey of Satan, a journey described as real, and when Death offers him battle, the allegory is broken. That Sin and Death should have shown the way to hell, might have been allowed; but they cannot facilitate the passage by building a bridge, because the difficulty of Satan's passage is described as real and sensible, and the bridge ought to be only figurative. The hell assigned to the rebellious spirits is described as not less local than the residence of man. It is placed in some distant part of space, separated from the regions of harmony and order by a chaotic waste and an unoccupied vacuity; but Sin and Death worked up a *mole* of *aggravated soil,* cemented with *asphaltus;* a work too bulky for ideal architects.

This unskillful allegory appears to me one of the greatest faults of the poem; and to this there was no temptation but the author's opinion of its beauty.

To the conduct of the narrative some objection may be made. Satan is with great expectation brought before Gabriel in Paradise, and is suffered to go away unmolested. The creation of man is represented as the consequence of the vacuity left in heaven by the expulsion of the rebels; yet Satan mentions it as a report *rife in heaven* before his departure.

To find sentiments for the state of innocence was very difficult; and something of anticipation perhaps is now and then discovered. Adam's discourse of dreams seems not to be the speculation of a new-created being. I know not whether his answer to the angel's reproof for curiosity does not want something of propriety; it is the speech of a man acquainted with many other men. Some philosophical notions, especially when the philosophy is false, might have been better omitted. The angel, in a comparison, speaks of *timorous deer* before deer were yet timorous and before Adam could understand the comparison.

Dryden remarks that Milton has some flats among his elevations. This is only to say that all the parts are not equal. In every work one part must be for the sake of others; a palace must have passages; a poem must have transitions. It is no more to be required that wit should always be blazing than that the sun should always stand at noon. In a great work there is a vicissitude of luminous and opaque parts, as there is in the world a succession of day and night. Milton, when he has expatiated in the sky, may be allowed sometimes to revisit earth; for what other author ever soared so high, or sustained his flight so long?

Milton, being well versed in the Italian poets, appears to have borrowed often from them; and as every man catches something from his companions, his desire of imitating Ariosto's levity has disgraced his work with the "Paradise of Fools"—a fiction not in itself ill-imagined, but too ludicrous for its place.

His play on words, in which he delights too often; his equivocations, which Bentley endeavors to defend by the example of the ancients; his unnecessary and ungraceful use of terms of art, it is not necessary to mention, because they are easily remarked, and generally censured, and at last bear so little proportion to the whole that they scarcely deserve the attention of a critic.

Such are the faults of that wonderful performance *Paradise Lost,* which he who can put in balance with its beauties must be considered not as nice but as dull, as less to be censured for want of candor, than pitied for want of sensibility.

Of *Paradise Regained,* the general judgment seems now to be right, that it is in many parts elegant and everywhere instructive. It was not to be supposed that the writer of *Paradise Lost* could ever write without great effusions of fancy and exalted precepts of wisdom. The basis of *Paradise Regained* is narrow: a dialogue without action can never please like a union of the narrative and dramatic powers. Had this poem been written not by Milton, but by some imitator, it would have claimed and received universal praise.

If *Paradise Regained* has been too much depreciated, *Samson*

Agonistes has in requital been too much admired. It could only be by long prejudice, and the bigotry of learning, that Milton could prefer the ancient tragedies, with their encumbrance of a chorus, to the exhibitions of the French and English stages; and it is only by a blind confidence in the reputation of Milton that a drama can be praised in which the intermediate parts have neither cause nor consequence, neither hasten nor retard the catastrophe.

In this tragedy are however many particular beauties, many just sentiments and striking lines; but it wants that power of attracting the attention which a well-connected plan produces.

Milton would not have excelled in dramatic writing; he knew human nature only in the gross, and had never studied the shades of character, nor the combinations of concurring, or the perplexity of contending, passions. He had read much, and knew what books could teach, but had mingled little in the world, and was deficient in the knowledge which experience must confer. . . .

JOHN DRYDEN
1631–1700

* * *

O F THE PERSON of Dryden I know not any account; of his mind, the portrait which has been left by Congreve, who knew him with great familiarity, is such as adds our love of his manners to our admiration of his genius. "He was," we are told, "of a nature exceedingly humane and compassionate, ready to forgive injuries, and capable of a sincere reconciliation with those that had offended him. His friendship, where he professed it, went beyond his professions. He was of a very easy, of very pleasing access; but somewhat slow and, as it were, diffident in his advances to others; he had that in his nature which abhorred intrusion into any society whatever. He was therefore less known, and consequently his character became more liable to misapprehensions and misrepresentations: he was very modest and very easily to be discountenanced in his approaches to his equals or superiors. As his reading had been very extensive, so was he very happy in a memory tenacious of everything that he had

224

read. He was not more possessed of knowledge than he was communicative of it; but then his communication was by no means pedantic or imposed upon the conversation, but just such, and went so far as, by the natural turn of the conversation in which he was engaged, it was necessarily promoted or required. He was extremely ready and gentle in his correction of the errors of any writer who thought fit to consult him, and full as ready and patient to admit the reprehensions of others, in respect of his own oversights or mistakes."

To this account of Congreve nothing can be objected but the fondness of friendship; and to have excited that fondness in such a mind is no small degree of praise. The disposition of Dryden, however, is shown in this character rather as it exhibited itself in cursory conversation, than as it operated on the more important parts of life. His placability and his friendship indeed were solid virtues; but courtesy and good humor are often found with little real worth. Since Congreve, who knew him well, has told us no more, the rest must be collected as it can from other testimonies and particularly from those notices which Dryden has very liberally given us of himself.

The modesty which made him so slow to advance, and so easy to be repulsed, was certainly no suspicion of deficient merit, or unconsciousness of his own value; he appears to have known, in its whole extent, the dignity of his own character and to have set a very high value on his own powers and performances. He probably did not offer his conversation, because he expected it to be solicited; and he retired from a cold reception, not submissive but indignant, with such reference of his own greatness as made him unwilling to expose it to neglect or violation.

His modesty was by no means inconsistent with ostentatiousness; he is diligent enough to remind the world of his merit and expresses with very little scruple his high opinion of his own powers; but his self-condemnations are read without scorn or indignation; we allow his claims and love his frankness.

Tradition, however, has not allowed that his confidence in himself exempted him from jealousy of others. He is accused of envy and insidiousness; and is particularly charged with inciting Creech * to translate Horace, that he might lose the reputation which Lucretius had given him.

* Thomas Creech, classical scholar and translator

225

Of this charge we immediately discover that it is merely conjec-, tural; the purpose was such as no man would confess; and a crime that admits no proof, why should we believe?

He has been described as magisterially presiding over the younger writers and assuming the distribution of poetical fame; but he who excels has a right to teach and he whose judgment is incontestable may without usurpation examine and decide.

Congreve represents him as ready to advise and instruct; but there is reason to believe that his communication was rather useful than entertaining. He declares of himself that he was saturnine and not one of those whose sprightly sayings diverted company; and one of his censurers makes him say:

> *Nor wine nor love could ever see me gay;*
> *To writing bred, I knew not what to say.*

There are men whose powers operate only at leisure and in retirement, and whose intellectual vigor deserts them in conversation; whom merriment confuses and objection disconcerts; whose bashfulness restrains their exertion and suffers them not to speak till the time of speaking is past; or whose attention to their own character makes them unwilling to utter at hazard what has not been considered and cannot be recalled.

Of Dryden's sluggishness in conversation it is vain to search or to guess the cause. He certainly wanted neither sentiments nor language: his intellectual treasures were great, though they were locked up from his own use. "His thoughts," when he wrote, "flowed in upon him so fast, that his only care was which to choose, and which to reject." Such rapidity of composition naturally promises a flow of talk; yet we must be content to believe what an enemy says of him, when he likewise says it of himself. But whatever was his character as a companion, it appears that he lived in familiarity with the highest persons of his time. It is related by Carte * of the Duke of Ormond, that he used often to pass a night with Dryden and those with whom Dryden consorted: who they were, Carte has not told, but certainly the convivial table at which Ormond sat was not surrounded with a plebeian society. He was indeed reproached with boasting of his familiarity with the great; and Horace will support him in the opinion, that to please superiors is not the lowest kind of merit.

* Thomas Carte, historian

LIVES OF THE POETS

The merit of pleasing must, however, be estimated by the means. Favor is not always gained by good actions or laudable qualities. Caresses and preferments are often bestowed on the auxiliaries of vice, the procurers of pleasure or the flatterers of vanity. Dryden has never been charged with any personal agency unworthy of a good character: he abetted vice and vanity only with his pen. One of his enemies has accused him of lewdness in his conversation; but, if accusation without proof be credited, who shall be innocent?

His works afford too many examples of dissolute licentiousness and abject adulation; but they were probably, like his merriment, artificial and constrained; the effects of study and meditation and his trade rather than his pleasure.

Of the mind that can trade in corruption, and can deliberately pollute itself with ideal wickedness for the sake of spreading the contagion in society, I wish not to conceal or excuse the depravity. Such degradation of the dignity of genius, such abuse of superlative abilities, cannot be contemplated but with grief and indignation. What consolation can be had, Dryden has afforded, by living to repent, and to testify his repentance.

Of dramatic immorality he did not want examples among his predecessors, or companions among his contemporaries; but in the meanness and servility of hyperbolical adulation, I know not whether, since the days in which the Roman emperors were deified, he has been ever equaled, except by Aphra Behn * in an address to Eleanor Gwyn.† When once he has undertaken the task of praise, he no longer retains shame in himself, nor supposes it in his patron. As many odoriferous bodies are observed to diffuse perfumes from year to year, without sensible diminution of bulk or weight, he appears never to have impoverished his mint of flattery by his expenses, however lavish. He had all the forms of excellence, intellectual and moral, combined in his mind, with endless variation; and when he had scattered on the hero of the day the golden shower of wit and virtue, he had ready for him whom he wished to court on the morrow, new wit and virtue with another stamp. Of this kind of meanness he never seems to decline the practice, or lament the necessity: he considers the great as entitled to encomiastic homage, and brings praise rather as a tribute than a gift, more delighted with the fertility of his invention, than mortified by the prostitution of his judgment.

* First female professional writer in England
† Nell Gwyn, favorite of Charles II

It is indeed not certain that on these occasions his judgment much rebelled against his interest. There are minds which easily sink into submission, that look on grandeur with undistinguishing reverence, and discover no defect where there is elevation of rank and affluence of riches.

With his praises of others and of himself is always intermingled a strain of discontent and lamentation, a sullen growl of resentment, or querulous murmur of distress. His works are undervalued, his merit is unrewarded and "he has few thanks to pay his stars that he was born among Englishmen." To his critics he is sometimes contemptuous, sometimes resentful and sometimes submissive. The writer who thinks his works formed for duration, mistakes his interest when he mentions his enemies. He degrades his own dignity by showing that he was affected by their censures, and gives lasting importance to names which, left to themselves, would vanish from remembrance. From this principle Dryden did not often depart; his complaints are for the greater part general; he seldom pollutes his page with an adverse name. . . .

Dryden may be properly considered as the father of English criticism, as the writer who first taught us to determine upon principles the merit of composition. Of our former poets, the greatest dramatist wrote without rules, conducted through life and nature by a genius that rarely misled and rarely deserted him. Of the rest, those who knew the laws of propriety had neglected to teach them.

Two *Arts of English Poetry* were written in the days of Elizabeth by Webbe and Puttenham,* from which something might be learned, and a few hints had been given by Jonson and Cowley; but Dryden's *Essay on Dramatic Poetry* was the first regular and valuable treatise on the art of writing.

He who, having formed his opinions in the present age of English literature, turns back to peruse this dialogue, will not perhaps find much increase of knowledge, or much novelty of instruction; but he is to remember that critical principles were then in the hands of a few, who had gathered them partly from the ancients and partly from the Italians and French. The structure of dramatic poems was then not generally understood. Audiences applauded by instinct; and poets perhaps often pleased by chance.

* William Webbe and George Puttenham

A writer who obtains his full purpose loses himself in his own luster. Of an opinion which is no longer doubted, the evidence ceases to be examined. Of an art universally practiced, the first teacher is forgotten. Learning once made popular is no longer learning; it has the appearance of something which we have bestowed upon ourselves, as the dew appears to rise from the field which it refreshes.

To judge rightly of an author, we must transport ourselves to his time, and examine what were the wants of his contemporaries, and what were his means of supplying them. That which is easy at one time was difficult at another. Dryden at least imported his science and gave his country what it wanted before; or, rather, he imported only the materials and manufactured them by his own skill.

The *Dialogue on the Drama* was one of his first essays of criticism, written when he was yet a timorous candidate for reputation, and therefore labored with that diligence which he might allow himself somewhat to remit, when his name gave sanction to his positions, and his awe of the public was abated, partly by custom and partly by success. It will not be easy to find, in all the opulence of our language, a treatise so artfully variegated with successive representations of opposite probabilities, so enlivened with imagery, so brightened with illustrations. His portraits of the English dramatists are wrought with great spirit and diligence. The account of Shakespeare may stand as a perpetual model of encomiastic criticism; exact without minuteness and lofty without exaggeration. The praise lavished by Longinus,* on the attestation of the heroes of Marathon, by Demosthenes, fades away before it. In a few lines is exhibited a character, so extensive in its comprehension, and so curious in its limitations, that nothing can be added, diminished or reformed; nor can the editors and admirers of Shakespeare, in all their emulation of reverence, boast of much more than of having diffused and paraphrased this epitome of excellence, of having changed Dryden's gold for baser metal, of lower value though of greater bulk. . . .

* Greek philosopher and critic

JOSEPH ADDISON
1672–1719

I T IS NOT UNCOMMON for those who have grown wise by the labor of others to add a little of their own and overlook their masters. Addison is now despised by some who perhaps would never have seen his defects but by the lights which he afforded them. That he always wrote as he would think it necessary to write now, cannot be affirmed; his instructions were such as the characters of his readers made proper. That general knowledge which now circulates in common talk, was in his time rarely to be found. Men not professing learning were not ashamed of ignorance; and, in the female world, any acquaintance with books was distinguished only to be censured. His purpose was to infuse literary curiosity by gentle and unsuspected conveyance into the gay, the idle and the wealthy: he therefore presented knowledge in the most alluring form, not lofty and austere, but accessible and familiar. When he showed them their defects, he showed them likewise that they might be easily supplied. His attempt succeeded; inquiry was awakened and comprehension expanded. An emulation of intellectual elegance was excited, and from this time to our own, life has been gradually exalted, and conversation purified and enlarged.

Dryden had, not many years before, scattered criticism over his prefaces with very little parsimony; but though he sometimes condescended to be somewhat familiar, his manner was in general too scholastic for those who had yet their rudiments to learn, and found it not easy to understand their master. His observations were framed rather for those that were learning to write, than for those that read only to talk.

An instructor like Addison was now wanting, whose remarks being superficial might be easily understood and being just might prepare the mind for more attainments. Had he presented *Paradise Lost* to the public with all the pomp of system and severity of science, the criticism would perhaps have been admired, and the poem still have been neglected; but by the blandishments of gentleness and

230

facility, he has made Milton a universal favorite, with whom readers of every class think it necessary to be pleased.

He descended now and then to lower disquisitions; and by a serious display of the beauties of *Chevy Chase* * exposed himself to the ridicule of Wagstaffe † who bestowed a like pompous character on *Tom Thumb;* and to the contempt of Dennis,‡ who, considering the fundamental position of his criticism, that *Chevy Chase* pleases, and ought to please, because it is natural, observes, "that there is a way of deviating from nature, by bombast or tumor, which soars above nature, and enlarges images beyond their real bulk; by affectation, which forsakes nature in quest of something unsuitable; and by imbecility, which degrades nature by faintness and diminution, by obscuring its appearances, and weakening its effects." In *Chevy Chase* there is not much of either bombast or affectation, but there is chill and lifeless imbecility. The story cannot possibly be told in a manner that shall make less impression on the mind.

Before the profound observers of the present race repose too securely on the consciousness of their superiority to Addison, let them consider his *Remarks on Ovid,* in which may be found specimens of criticism sufficiently subtle and refined; let them peruse likewise his essays on Wit and on the Pleasures of Imagination, in which he founds art on the base of nature, and draws the principles of invention from dispositions inherent in the mind of man with skill and elegance, such as his contemners will not easily attain.

As a describer of life and manners, he must be allowed to stand perhaps the first of the first rank. His humor, which, as Steele ** observes, is peculiar to himself, is so happily diffused as to give the grace of novelty to domestic scenes and daily occurrences. He never "outsteps the modesty of nature," nor raises merriment or wonder by the violation of truth. His figures neither divert by distortion, nor amaze by aggravation. He copies life with so much fidelity, that he can be hardly said to invent; yet his exhibitions have an air so much original, that it is difficult to suppose them not merely the product of imagination.

As a teacher of wisdom, he may be confidently followed. His religion has nothing in it enthusiastic or superstitious: he appears

* Ancient ballad
† William Wagstaffe, author of *A Commentary on the History of Tom Thumb,* which ridiculed Addison's praise of *Chevy Chase*
‡ John Dennis, critic
** Richard Steele, essayist

neither weakly credulous, nor wantonly sceptical; his morality is neither dangerously lax, nor impracticably rigid. All the enchantment of fancy and all the cogency of argument are employed to recommend to the reader his real interest, the care of pleasing the Author of his being. Truth is shown sometimes as the phantom of a vision; sometimes appears half veiled in an allegory; sometimes attracts regard in the robes of fancy; and sometimes steps forth in the confidence of reason. She wears a thousand dresses and in all is pleasing.

Mille habet ornatus, mille decenter habet.

His prose is the model of the middle style; on grave subjects not formal, on light occasions not groveling; pure without scrupulosity and exact without apparent elaboration; always equable and always easy, without glowing words or pointed sentences. Addison never deviates from his track to snatch a grace; he seeks no ambitious ornaments, and tries no hazardous innovations. His page is always luminous, but never blazes in unexpected splendor.

It was apparently his principal endeavor to avoid all harshness and severity of diction; he is therefore sometimes verbose in his transitions and connections, and sometimes descends too much to the language of conversation; yet if his language had been less idiomatical, it might have lost somewhat of its genuine Anglicism. What he attempted, he performed: he is never feeble and he did not wish to be energetic; he is never rapid, and he never stagnates. His sentences have neither studied amplitude, nor affected brevity; his periods, though not diligently rounded, are voluble and easy. Whoever wishes to attain an English style, familiar but not coarse, and elegant but not ostentatious, must give his days and nights to the volumes of Addison.

WILLIAM CONGREVE

1670—1728–29

WILLIAM CONGREVE DESCENDED from a family in Staffordshire, of so great antiquity that it claims a place among the few that extend their line beyond the Norman Conquest . . . Neither the time nor place of his birth are certainly known; if the inscription upon his monument be true, he was born in 1672. For the place, it was said by himself that he owed his nativity to England, and by everybody else that he was born in Ireland. . . .

Wherever Congreve was born, he was educated first at Kilkenny, and afterward at Dublin, his father having some military employment that stationed him in Ireland: but after having passed through the usual preparatory studies, as may be reasonably supposed, with great celerity and success, his father thought it proper to assign him a profession, by which something might be gotten; and about the time of the Revolution sent him, at the age of sixteen, to study law in the Middle Temple, where he lived for many years, but with very little attention to Statutes or Reports.

His disposition to become an author appeared very early, as he very early felt that force of imagination, and possessed that copiousness of sentiment, by which intellectual pleasure can be given. His first performance was a novel, called *Incognita, or Love and Duty reconciled*. It is praised by the biographers, who quote some part of the Preface, that is indeed, for such a time of life, uncommonly judicious. I would rather praise it than read it.

His first dramatic labor was the *Old Bachelor;* of which he says, in his defence against Collier,* "that comedy was written, as several know, some years before it was acted. When I wrote it, I had little thought of the stage; but did it, to amuse myself in a slow recovery from a fit of sickness. Afterward, through my indiscretion, it was seen, and in some little time more it was acted; and I, through the remainder of my indiscretion, suffered myself to be drawn in to the prosecution of a difficult and thankless study, and to be involved in a perpetual war with knaves and fools."

There seems to be a strange affectation in authors of appearing to have done everything by chance. The *Old Bachelor* was written for amusement, in the languor of convalescence. Yet it is apparently composed with great elaborateness of dialogue and incessant ambition of wit. The age of the writer considered, it is indeed a very wonderful performance; for, whenever written, it was acted (January 1692–3) when he was not more than twenty-one [four] years old; and was then recommended by Mr. Dryden, Mr. Southerne, and Mr. Maynwaring.† Dryden said that he never had seen such a

* Jeremy Collier attacked the "immorality" of the stage
† Thomas Southerne and Arthur Maynwaring

first play; but they found it deficient in some things requisite to the success of its exhibition, and by their greater experience fitted it for the stage. Southerne used to relate of one comedy, probably of this, that when Congreve read it to the players, he pronounced it so wretchedly, that they had almost rejected it; but they were afterward so well persuaded of its excellence, that, for half a year before it was acted, the manager allowed its author the privilege of the house. . . .

Next year he gave another specimen of his abilities in *The Double Dealer,* which was not received with equal kindness. He writes to his patron the Lord Halifax a Dedication, in which he endeavors to reconcile the reader to that which found few friends among the audience. These apologies are always useless: *de gustibus non est disputandum;* men may be convinced, but they cannot be pleased against their will. But though taste is obstinate, it is very variable, and time often prevails when arguments have failed.

Queen Mary conferred upon both those plays the honor of her presence; and when she died, soon after, Congreve testified his gratitude by a despicable effusion of elegiac pastoral; a composition in which all is unnatural, and yet nothing is new.

In another year (1695) his prolific pen produced *Love for Love;* a comedy of nearer alliance to life, and exhibiting more real manners, than either of the former. . . .

With this play was opened the New Theatre, under the direction of Betterton the tragedian; where he exhibited two years afterward (1697) *The Mourning Bride,* a tragedy, so written as to show him sufficiently qualified for either kind of dramatic poetry.

In this play, of which, when he afterward revised it, he reduced the versification to greater regularity, there is more bustle than sentiment; the plot is busy and intricate, and the events take hold on the attention; but, except a very few passages, we are rather amused with noise, and perplexed with stratagem, than entertained with any true delineation of natural characters. This, however, was received with more benevolence than any other of his works and still continues to be acted and applauded.

Congreve's last play was *The Way of the World;* which, though as he hints in his dedication it was written with great labor and much thought, was received with so little favor, that, being in a high degree offended and disgusted, he resolved to commit his quiet and his fame no more to the caprices of an audience.

234

From this time his life ceased to be public; he lived for himself and for his friends; and among his friends was able to name every man of his time whom wit and elegance had raised to reputation. It may be therefore reasonably supposed that his manners were polite and his conversation pleasing. . . .

Congreve has merit of the highest kind; he is an original writer, who borrowed neither the models of his plot, nor the manner of his dialogue. Of his plays I cannot speak distinctly; for since I inspected them many years have passed; but what remains upon my memory is, that his characters are commonly fictitious and artificial, with very little of nature and not much of life. He formed a peculiar idea of comic excellence, which he supposed to consist in gay remarks and unexpected answers; but that which he endeavored, he seldom failed of performing. His scenes exhibit not much of humor, imagery or passion: his personages are a kind of intellectual gladiators; every sentence is to ward or strike; the contest of smartness is never intermitted; his wit is a meteor playing to and fro with alternate coruscations. His comedies have therefore, in some degree, the operation of tragedies; they surprise rather than divert, and raise admiration oftener than merriment. But they are the works of a mind replete with images, and quick in combination. . . .

JOHN GAY

1688–1732

JOHN GAY, DESCENDED from an old family that had been long in possession of the manor of Goldworthy in Devonshire, was born in 1688, at or near Barnstaple, where he was educated by Mr. Luck, who taught the school of that town with good reputation, and, a little before he retired from it, published a volume of Latin and English verses. Under such a master he was likely to form a taste for poetry. Being born without prospect of hereditary riches, he was sent to London in his youth, and placed apprentice with a silk mercer. . . .

The report is, that he was soon weary of either the restraint or servility of his occupation, and easily persuaded his master to discharge him.

235

The Duchess of Monmouth, remarkable for inflexible persever-ance in her demand to be treated as a princess, in 1712 took Gay into her service as secretary: by quitting a shop for such service, he might gain leisure, but he certainly advanced little in the boast of independence. Of his leisure he made so good use, that he pub-lished next year a poem on *Rural Sports,* and inscribed it to Mr. Pope, who was then rising fast into reputation. Pope was pleased with the honor; and when he became acquainted with Gay, found such attractions in his manners and conversation, that he seems to have received him into his inmost confidence; and a friendship was formed between them which lasted to their separation by death, with-out any known abatement on either part. Gay was the general fa-vorite of the whole association of wits; but they regarded him as a playfellow rather than a partner, and treated him with more fond-ness than respect.

Next year (1714) he published *The Shepherd's Week,* six English pastorals, in which the images are drawn from real life, such as it appears among the rustics in parts of England remote from London. . . . These pastorals became popular, and were read with delight as just representations of rural manners and occupations. . . .

In 1713 he brought a comedy, called *The Wife of Bath,* upon the stage, but it received no applause: he printed it, however; and sev-enteen years after, having altered it, and, as he thought, adapted it more to the public taste, he offered it again to the town; but . . . he had the mortification to see it again rejected.

In the last year of Queen Anne's life (1714) Gay was made sec-retary to the Earl of Clarendon, ambassador to the court of Hanover. This was a station that naturally gave him hopes of kindness from every party; but the Queen's death put an end to her favors. . . .

He did not, however, omit to improve the right which his office had given him to the notice of the royal family. On the arrival of the Princess of Wales [1714–15], he wrote a poem, and obtained so much favor, that both the Prince and Princess went to see his *What d'ye call it,* a kind of mock-tragedy, in which the images were comic and the action grave; so that, as Pope relates, Mr. Cromwell,* who could not hear what was said, was at a loss how to reconcile the laughter of the audience with the solemnity of the scene. . . .

Gay is represented as a man easily incited to hope, and deeply

* Henry Cromwell, a deaf friend of Pope

236

depressed when his hopes were disappointed. This is not the character of a hero; but it may naturally imply something more generally welcome, a soft and civil companion. Whoever is apt to hope good from others is diligent to please them; but he that believes his power strong enough to force their own way, commonly tries only to please himself.

He had been simple enough to imagine that those who laughed at the *What d'ye call it* would raise the fortune of its author; and, finding nothing done, sunk into dejection. His friends endeavored to divert him. The Earl of Burlington [the architect] sent him (1716) into Devonshire; the year after, Mr. Pulteney [afterwards Earl of Bath] took him to Aix; and in the following year Lord Harcourt invited him to his seat [in Oxfordshire], where, during his visit, two rural lovers were killed with lightning, as is particularly told in Pope's Letters.

Being now generally known, he published (1720) his Poems by subscription with such success, that he raised a thousand pounds; and called his friends to a consultation, what use might be best made of it. Lewis, the steward of Lord Oxford, advised him to intrust it to the funds, and live upon the interest; Arbuthnot * bade him intrust it to Providence, and live upon the principal; Pope directed him, and was seconded by Swift, to purchase an annuity.

Gay in that disastrous year had a present from young Craggs † of some South Sea stock, and once supposed himself to be master of 20,000*l*. His friends persuaded him to sell his share; but he dreamed of dignity and splendor, and could not bear to obstruct his own fortune. He was then importuned to sell as much as would purchase a hundred a year for life, "which," says Fenton, "will make you sure of a clean shirt and a shoulder of mutton every day." This counsel was rejected: the profit and principal were lost, and Gay sunk under the calamity so low that his life became in danger.

By the care of his friends, among whom Pope appears to have shown particular tenderness, his health was restored; and, returning to his studies, he wrote a tragedy called *The Captives,* which he was invited to read before the Princess of Wales. When the hour came, he saw the Princess and her ladies all in expectation, and advancing with reverence, too great for any other attention, stumbled at a stool, and falling forward threw down a weighty Japan

* John Arbuthnot, Scottish doctor and writer
† James Craggs, English statesman

237

screen. The Princess started, the ladies screamed, and poor Gay, after all the disturbance, was still to read his play.

The fate of *The Captives,* which was acted at Drury Lane in 1723–4, I know not; but he now thought himself in favor, and undertook (1726) to write a volume of Fables for the improvement of the young Duke of Cumberland. For this he is said to have been promised a reward, which he had doubtless magnified with all the wild expectations of indigence and vanity.

Next year [1727] the Prince and Princess became King and Queen, and Gay was to be great and happy; but on the settlement of the household he found himself appointed gentleman usher to the Princess Louisa. By this offer he thought himself insulted, and sent a message to the Queen that he was too old for the place. There seem to have been many machinations employed afterwards in his favor; and diligent court was paid to Mrs. Howard, afterwards Countess of Suffolk, who was much beloved by the King and Queen, to engage her interest for his promotion; but solicitations, verses, and flatteries were thrown away; the lady heard them, and did nothing.

All the pain which he suffered from neglect or, as he perhaps termed it, the ingratitude of the Court, may be supposed to have been driven away by the unexampled success of the *Beggar's Opera.* This play, written in ridicule of the musical Italian Drama, was first offered to Cibber * and his brethren at Drury Lane, and rejected; it being then carried to Rich, had the effect, as was ludicrously said, of *making* Gay *rich* and Rich *gay*.

Of this lucky piece, as the reader cannot but wish to know the original and progress, I have inserted the relation which Spence † has given in Pope's words:

"Dr. Swift had been observing once to Mr. Gay, what an odd pretty sort of a thing a Newgate Pastoral might make. Gay was inclined to try at such a thing for some time; but afterward thought it would be better to write a comedy on the same plan. This was what gave rise to the *Beggar's Opera.* He began on it; and when first he mentioned it to Swift, the Doctor did not much like the project. As he carried it on, he showed what he wrote to both of us, and we now and then gave a correction, or a word or two of advice; but it was wholly of his own writing. When it was done, neither

* Colley Cibber, playwright and actor
† Joseph Spence, friend of Pope

of us thought it would succeed. We showed it to Congreve; who, after reading it over, said, 'It would either take greatly, or be damned confoundedly.' We were all, at the first night of it, in great uncertainty of the event; till we were very much encouraged by overhearing the Duke of Argyle, who sat in the next box to us, say, 'It will do—it must do! I see it in the eyes of them.' This was a good while before the first act was over, and so gave us ease soon; for that Duke (besides his own good taste) has a more particular knack than anyone now living in discovering the taste of the public. He was quite right in this, as usual; the good nature of the audience appeared stronger and stronger every act, and ended in a clamor of applause."

Its reception is thus recorded in the notes to the *Dunciad:*

"The vast success of it was unprecedented and almost incredible. . . . It was acted in London sixty-three days uninterrupted, and renewed the next season with equal applauses. It spread into all the great towns of England; was played in many places to the thirtieth and fortieth time; at Bath and Bristol fifty, etc. It made its progress into Wales, Scotland, and Ireland, where it was performed twenty-four days together. It was at last acted in Minorca. The fame of it was not confined to the author only; the ladies carried about with them the favorite songs of it in fans, and houses were furnished with it in screens. The person who acted Polly,* till then obscure, became all at once the favorite of the town; her pictures were engraved, and sold in great numbers; her life written, books of letters and verses to her published, and pamphlets made even of her sayings and jests. Furthermore, it drove out of England (for that season) the Italian Opera, which had carried all before it for ten years."

Of this performance, when it was printed, the reception was different according to the different opinion of its readers. Swift commended it for the excellence of its morality, as a piece that "placed vices of all kinds in the strongest and most odious light"; but others, and among them Dr. Herring, afterward Archbishop of Canterbury, censured it as giving encouragement not only to vice but to crimes, by making a highwayman the hero, and dismissing him at last unpunished. It has been even said that, after the exhibition of the *Beggar's Opera,* the gangs of robbers were evidently multiplied.

Both these decisions are surely exaggerated. The play, like many others, was plainly written only to divert, without any moral pur-

* Lavinia Fenton became Duchess of Bolton.

239

pose, and is therefore not likely to do good; nor can it be conceived, without more speculation than life requires or admits, to be productive of much evil. Highwaymen and housebreakers seldom frequent the playhouse or mingle in any elegant diversion; nor is it possible for anyone to imagine that he may rob with safety, because he sees Macheath reprieved upon the stage. . . .

As a poet he cannot be rated very high. He was, as I once heard a female critic remark, "of a lower order." He had not in any great degree the *mens divinior,* the dignity of genius. Much however must be allowed to the author of a new species of composition, though it be not of the highest kind. We owe to Gay the ballad opera; a mode of comedy which at first was supposed to delight only by its novelty, but has now by the experience of half a century been found so well accommodated to the disposition of a popular audience, that it is likely to keep long possession of the stage. Whether this new drama was the product of judgment or of luck, the praise of it must be given to the inventor; and there are many writers read with more reverence, to whom such merit of originality cannot be attributed. . . .

RICHARD SAVAGE
1697–98—1743

IT HAS BEEN OBSERVED in all ages that the advantages of nature or of fortune have contributed very little to the promotion of happiness; and that those whom the splendor of their rank, or the extent of their capacity, have placed upon the summit of human life have not often given any just occasion to envy in those who look up to them from a lower station; whether it be that apparent superiority incites great designs, and great designs are naturally liable to fatal miscarriages; or that the general lot of mankind is misery, and the misfortunes of those whose eminence drew upon them a universal attention have been more carefully recorded because they were more generally observed, and have in reality been only more conspicuous than those of others, not more frequent, or more severe.

That affluence and power, advantages extrinsic and adventitious, and therefore easily separable from those by whom they are possessed, should very often flatter the mind with expectations of felicity which they cannot give, raises no astonishment; but it seems rational to hope that intellectual greatness should produce better effects; that minds qualified for great attainments should first endeavor their own benefit; and that they who are most able to teach others the way to happiness should with most certainty follow it themselves.

But this expectation, however plausible, has been very frequently disappointed. The heroes of literary as well as civil history have been very often no less remarkable for what they have suffered than for what they have achieved; and volumes have been written only to enumerate the miseries of the learned, and relate their unhappy lives and untimely deaths.

To these mournful narratives I am about to add the Life of Richard Savage, a man whose writings entitle him to an eminent rank in the classes of learning, and whose misfortunes claim a degree of compassion not always due to the unhappy, as they were often the consequences of the crimes of others rather than his own.

In the year 1697, Anne, Countess of Macclesfield, having lived some time upon very uneasy terms with her husband, thought a public confession of adultery the most obvious and expeditious method of obtaining her liberty; and therefore declared that the child with which she was then great was begotten by the Earl Rivers. This, as may be imagined, made her husband no less desirous of a separation than herself, and he prosecuted his design in the most effectual manner; for he applied not to the ecclesiastical courts for a divorce, but to the parliament for an act by which his marriage might be dissolved, the nuptial contract annulled, and the children of his wife illegitimated. This act, after the usual deliberation, he obtained, though without the approbation of some, who considered marriage as an affair only cognizable by ecclesiastical judges; and, on March 3rd, was separated from his wife, whose fortune, which was very great, was repaid her, and who having, as well as her husband, the liberty of making another choice, was in a short time married to Colonel Brett.

While the Earl of Macclesfield was prosecuting this affair, his wife was, on the 10th of January, 1697–8, delivered of a son; and the Earl Rivers, by appearing to consider him as his own, left none any reason to doubt of the sincerity of her declaration; for he was his godfather and gave him his own name, which was by his direction inserted in the register of St. Andrew's parish in Holborn; but, un-

241

fortunately, left him to the care of his mother, whom, as she was now set free from her husband, he probably imagined likely to treat with great tenderness the child that had contributed to so pleasing an event. It is not indeed easy to discover what motives could be found to overbalance that natural affection of a parent, or what interest could be promoted by neglect or cruelty. The dread of shame or of poverty, by which some wretches have been incited to abandon or to murder their children, cannot be supposed to have affected a woman who had proclaimed her crimes and solicited reproach, and on whom the clemency of the legislature had undeservedly bestowed a fortune, which would have been very little diminished by the expenses which the care of her child could have brought upon her. It was therefore not likely that she would be wicked without temptation; that she would look upon her son from his birth with a kind of resentment and abhorrence; and instead of supporting, assisting and defending him, delight to see him struggling with misery, or that she would take every opportunity of aggravating his misfortunes and obstructing his resources, and with an implacable and restless cruelty continue her persecution from the first hour of his life to the last.

But, whatever were her motives, no sooner was her son born than she discovered a resolution of disowning him; and in a very short time removed him from her sight by committing him to the care of a poor woman, whom she directed to educate him as her own, and enjoined never to inform him of his true parents.

Such was the beginning of the life of Richard Savage. Born with a legal claim to honor and to affluence, he was in two months illegitimated by the parliament, and disowned by his mother, doomed to poverty and obscurity and launched upon the ocean of life only that he might be swallowed by its quicksands or dashed upon its rocks.

His mother could not indeed infect others with the same cruelty. As it was impossible to avoid the inquiries which the curiosity or tenderness of her relations made after her child, she was obliged to give some account of the measures she had taken; and her mother, the Lady Mason, whether in approbation of her design or to prevent more criminal contrivances, engaged to transact with the nurse, to pay her for her care, and to superintend the education of the child.

In this charitable office she was assisted by his godmother, Mrs. Lloyd, who while she lived always looked upon him with that tenderness which the barbarity of his mother made peculiarly necessary; but her death, which happened in his tenth year, was another of the misfortunes of his childhood; for though she kindly endeavored to alleviate his loss by a legacy of 300*l.*, yet, as he had none to prosecute his claim, to shelter him from oppression, or call in law to the assistance of justice, her will was eluded by the executors, and no part of the money was ever paid.

He was, however, not yet wholly abandoned. The Lady Mason still continued her care and directed him to be placed at a small grammar school near St. Alban's, where he was called by the name of his nurse, without the least intimation that he had a claim to any other.

Here he was initiated in literature, and passed through several of the classes, with what rapidity or with what applause cannot now be known. As he always spoke with respect of his master, it is probable that the mean rank in which he then appeared did not hinder his genius from being distinguished, or his industry from being rewarded; and if in so low a state he obtained distinction and rewards, it is not likely that they were gained but by genius and industry.

It is very reasonable to conjecture that his application was equal to his abilities, because his improvement was more than proportioned to the opportunities which he enjoyed; nor can it be doubted that, if his earliest productions had been preserved like those of happier students, we might in some have found vigorous sallies of that sprightly humor which distinguishes *The Author to be Let,* and in others strong touches of that imagination which painted the solemn scenes of *The Wanderer.*

While he was thus cultivating his genius, his father, the Earl Rivers, was seized with a distemper which in a short time put an end to his life. He had frequently inquired after his son, and had always been amused with fallacious and evasive answers; but, being now in his own opinion on his deathbed, he thought it his duty to provide for him among his other natural children, and therefore demanded a positive account of him, with an importunity not to be diverted or denied. His mother, who could no longer refuse an answer, determined at least to give such as should cut him off forever from that happiness which competence affords, and therefore declared that he was dead; which is perhaps the first instance of a lie invented by a mother to deprive her son of a provision which was designed him by another, and which she could not expect herself though he should lose it.

This was therefore an act of wickedness which could not be de-

243

feated, because it could not be suspected; the Earl did not imagine there could exist in a human form a mother that would ruin her son without enriching herself, and therefore bestowed upon some other person 6000*l.* which he had in his will bequeathed to Savage.

The same cruelty which incited his mother to intercept this provision which had been intended him prompted her in a short time to another project, a project worthy of such a disposition. She endeavored to rid herself from the danger of being at any time made known to him, by sending him secretly to the American Plantations.

By whose kindness this scheme was counteracted, or by whose interposition she was induced to lay aside her design, I know not: it is not improbable that the Lady Mason might persuade or compel her to desist; or perhaps she could not easily find accomplices wicked enough to concur in so cruel an action; for it may be conceived that those who had by a long gradation of guilt hardened their hearts against the sense of common wickedness would yet be shocked at the design of a mother to expose her son to slavery and want, to expose him without interest and without provocation; and Savage might on this occasion find protectors and advocates among those who had long traded in crimes, and whom compassion had never touched before.

Being hindered, by whatever means, from banishing him into another country, she formed soon after a scheme for burying him in poverty and obscurity in his own; and, that his station of life, if not the place of his residence, might keep him forever at a distance from her, she ordered him to be placed with a shoemaker in Holborn, that, after the usual time of trial, he might become his apprentice.

It is generally reported that this project was for some time successful, and that Savage was employed at the awl longer than he was willing to confess; nor was it perhaps any great advantage to him that an unexpected discovery determined him to quit his occupation.

About this time his nurse, who had always treated him as her own son, died; and it was natural for him to take care of those effects which by her death were, as he imagined, become his own: he therefore went to her house, opened her boxes and examined her papers, among which he found some letters written to her by the Lady Mason, which informed him of his birth, and the reasons for which it was concealed.

He was no longer satisfied with the employment which had been allotted him, but thought he had a right to share the affluence of his mother; and therefore, without scruple, applied to her as her son and made use of every art to awaken her tenderness and attract her regard. But neither his letters nor the interposition of those friends which his merit or his distress procured him made any impression upon her mind. She still resolved to neglect, though she could no longer disown him.

It was to no purpose that he frequently solicited her to admit him to see her; she avoided him with the most vigilant precaution, and ordered him to be excluded from her house, by whomsoever he might be introduced, and what reason soever he might give for entering it.

Savage was at the same time so touched with the discovery of his real mother that it was his frequent practice to walk in the dark evenings for several hours before her door, in hopes of seeing her as she might come by accident to the window or cross her apartment with a candle in her hand.

But all his assiduity and tenderness were without effect, for he could neither soften her heart nor open her hand, and was reduced to the utmost miseries of want while he was endeavoring to awaken the affection of a mother. He was therefore obliged to seek some other means of support; and, having no profession, became by necessity an author.

At this time the attention of the literary world was engrossed by the Bangorian controversy,* which filled the press with pamphlets, and the coffeehouses with disputants. Of this subject, as most popular, he made choice for his first attempt and, without any other knowledge of the question than he had casually collected from conversation, published [1717] a poem against the Bishop.

What was the success or merit of this performance I know not; it was probably lost among the innumerable pamphlets to which that dispute gave occasion. Mr. Savage was himself in a little time ashamed of it, and endeavored to suppress it by destroying all the copies that he could collect.

He then attempted a more gainful kind of writing, and in his eighteenth year offered to the stage a comedy borrowed from a Spanish plot, which was refused by the players, and was therefore given by him to Mr. Bullock,† who, having more interest, made some slight alterations, and brought it upon the stage under the title of *Woman's*

* A theological dispute started by Dr. Hoadley, Bishop of Bangor
† Christopher Bullock, actor and dramatist

a Riddle, but allowed the unhappy author no part of the profit.

Not discouraged, however, at his repulse, he wrote, two years afterward, *Love in a Veil,* another comedy, borrowed likewise from the Spanish, but with little better success than before; for though it was received and acted, yet it appeared so late in the year that the author obtained no other advantage from it than the acquaintance of Sir Richard Steele and Mr. Wilks,* by whom he was pitied, caressed and relieved.

Sir Richard Steele, having declared in his favor with all the ardor of benevolence which constituted his character, promoted his interest with the utmost zeal, related his misfortunes, applauded his merit, took all the opportunities of recommending him, and asserted that "the inhumanity of his mother had given him a right to find every good man his father."

Nor was Mr. Savage admitted to his acquaintance only, but to his confidence, of which he sometimes related an instance too extraordinary to be omitted, as it affords a very just idea of his patron's character.

He was once desired by Sir Richard, with an air of the utmost importance, to come very early to his house the next morning. Mr. Savage came as he had promised, found the chariot at the door and Sir Richard waiting for him and ready to go out. What was intended and whither they were to go, Savage could not conjecture and was not willing to inquire; but immediately seated himself with Sir Richard. The coachman was ordered to drive, and they hurried with the utmost expedition to Hyde Park Corner, where they stopped at a petty tavern and retired to a private room. Sir Richard then informed him that he intended to publish a pamphlet, and that he had desired him to come thither that he might write for him. He soon sat down to the work. Sir Richard dictated and Savage wrote till the dinner that had been ordered was put upon the table. Savage was surprised at the meanness of the entertainment, and after some hesitation ventured to ask for wine, which Sir Richard, not without reluctance, ordered to be brought. They then finished their dinner and proceeded in their pamphlet, which they concluded in the afternoon.

Mr Savage then imagined his task over and expected that Sir Richard would call for the reckoning and return home; but his expectations deceived him, for Sir Richard told him that he was with-

* Robert Wilks, actor

246

out money, and that the pamphlet must be sold before the dinner could be paid for; and Savage was therefore obliged to go and offer their new production to sale for two guineas, which with some difficulty he obtained. Sir Richard then returned home, having retired that day only to avoid his creditors, and composed the pamphlet only to discharge his reckoning.

Mr. Savage related another fact equally uncommon, which, though it has no relation to his life, ought to be preserved. Sir Richard Steele having one day invited to his house a great number of persons of the first quality, they were surprised at the number of liveries which surrounded the table; and, after dinner, when wine and mirth had set them free from the observation of a rigid ceremony, one of them inquired of Sir Richard how such an expensive train of domestics could be consistent with his fortune. Sir Richard very frankly confessed that they were fellows of whom he would very willingly be rid. And being then asked why he did not discharge them, declared that they were bailiffs, who had introduced themselves with an execution, and whom, since he could not send them away, he had thought it convenient to embellish with liveries, that they might do him credit while they stayed.

His friends were diverted with the expedient and by paying the debt discharged their attendants, having obliged Sir Richard to promise that they should never again find him graced with a retinue of the same kind.

Under such a tutor, Mr. Savage was not likely to learn prudence or frugality; and perhaps many of the misfortunes which the want of those virtues brought upon him in the following parts of his life might be justly imputed to so unimproving an example.

Nor did the kindness of Sir Richard end in common favors. He proposed to have established him in some settled scheme of life, and to have contracted a kind of alliance with him by marrying him to a natural daughter, on whom he intended to bestow a thousand pounds. But though he was always lavish of future bounties, he conducted his affairs in such a manner that he was very seldom able to keep his promises or execute his own intentions; and, as he was never able to raise the sum which he had offered, the marriage was delayed. In the meantime he was officiously informed that Mr. Savage had ridiculed him; by which he was so much exasperated that he withdrew the allowance which he had paid him, and never afterward admitted him to his house.

247

It is not indeed unlikely that Savage might, by his imprudence, expose himself to the malice of a talebearer; for his patron had many follies, which, as his discernment easily discovered, his imagination might sometimes incite him to mention too ludicrously. A little knowledge of the world is sufficient to discover that such weakness is very common, and that there are few who do not sometimes, in the wantonness of thoughtless mirth, or the heat of transient resentment, speak of their friends and benefactors with levity and contempt, though in their cooler moments they want neither sense of their kindness nor reverence for their virtue. The fault therefore of Mr. Savage was rather negligence than ingratitude: but Sir Richard must likewise be acquitted of severity; for who is there that can patiently bear contempt from one whom he has relieved and supported, whose establishment he has labored, and whose interest he has promoted?

He was now again abandoned to fortune without any other friend than Mr. Wilks; a man who, whatever were his abilities or skill as an actor, deserves at least to be remembered for his virtues, which are not often to be found in the world, and perhaps less often in his profession than in others. To be humane, generous and candid, is a very high degree of merit in any case; but those qualities deserve still greater praise when they are found in that condition which makes almost every other man, for whatever reason, contemptuous, insolent, petulant, selfish and brutal.

As Mr. Wilks was one of those to whom calamity seldom complained without relief, he naturally took an unfortunate wit into his protection, and not only assisted him in any casual distresses, but continued an equal and steady kindness to the time of his death.

By his interposition Mr. Savage once obtained from his mother 50*l.* and a promise of 150*l.* more; but it was the fate of this unhappy man that few promises of any advantage to him were performed. His mother was infected, among others, with the general madness of the South Sea traffic; and, having been disappointed in her expectations, refused to pay what perhaps nothing but the prospect of sudden affluence prompted her to promise.

Being thus obliged to depend upon the friendship of Mr. Wilks, he was consequently an assiduous frequenter of the theaters; and in a short time the amusements of the stage took such possession of his mind that he never was absent from a play in several years.

This constant attendance naturally procured him the acquaintance of the players and, among others, of Mrs. Oldfield, who was so

248

much pleased with his conversation, and touched with his misfortunes, that she allowed him a settled pension of 50*l.* a year, which was during her life regularly paid.

That this act of generosity may receive its due praise, and that the good actions of Mrs. Oldfield may not be sullied by her general character, it is proper to mention that Mr. Savage often declared in the strongest terms, that he never saw her alone, or in any other place than behind the scenes. At her death [23rd Oct., 1730] he endeavored to show his gratitude in the most decent manner, by wearing mourning as for a mother. . . .

The kindness of his friends not affording him any constant supply, and the prospect of improving his fortune by enlarging his acquaintance necessarily leading him to places of expense, he found it necessary to endeavor once more at dramatic poetry, for which he was now better qualified by a more extensive knowledge and longer observation. But having been unsuccessful in comedy, though rather for want of opportunities than genius, he resolved now to try whether he should not be more fortunate in exhibiting a tragedy.

The story which he chose for the subject was that of Sir Thomas Overbury,* a story well adapted to the stage, though perhaps not far enough removed from the present age to admit properly the fictions necessary to complete the plan: for the mind, which naturally loves truth, is always most offended with the violation of those truths of which we are most certain; and we of course conceive those facts most certain which approach nearest to our own time.

Out of this story he formed a tragedy, which, if the circumstances in which he wrote it be considered, will afford at once an uncommon proof of strength of genius and evenness of mind, of a serenity not to be ruffled and an imagination not to be suppressed.

During a considerable part of the time in which he was employed upon this performance he was without lodging and often without meat; nor had he any other conveniences for study than the fields or the streets allowed him; there he used to walk and form his speeches, and afterward step into a shop, beg for a few moments the use of the pen and ink, and write down what he had composed upon paper which he had picked up by accident.

If the performance of a writer thus distressed is not perfect, its faults ought surely to be imputed to a cause very different from want of genius, and must rather excite pity than provoke censure.

* Poisoned in the Tower

But when under these discouragements the tragedy was finished, there yet remained the labor of introducing it on the stage—an undertaking which, to an ingenuous mind, was in a very high degree vexatious and disgusting; for, having little interest or reputation, he was obliged to submit himself wholly to the players and admit, with whatever reluctance, the emendations of Mr. Cibber, which he always considered as the disgrace of his performance.

He had indeed in Mr. Hill * another critic of a very different class, from whose friendship he received great assistance on many occasions, and whom he never mentioned but with the utmost tenderness and regard. He had been for some time distinguished by him with very particular kindness, and on this occasion it was natural to apply to him as an author of an established character. He therefore sent this tragedy to him, with a short copy of verses, in which he desired his correction. Mr. Hill, whose humanity and politeness are generally known, readily complied with his request; but as he is remarkable for singularity of sentiment, and bold experiments in language, Mr. Savage did not think his play much improved by his innovation, and had even at that time the courage to reject several passages which he could not approve; and, what is still more laudable, Mr. Hill had the generosity not to resent the neglect of his alterations, but wrote the Prologue and Epilogue, in which he touches on the circumstances of the author with great tenderness.

After all these obstructions and compliances he was only able to bring his play upon the stage in the summer, when the chief actors had retired, and the rest were in possession of the house for their own advantage. Among these Mr. Savage was admitted to play the part of Sir Thomas Overbury, by which he gained no great reputation, the theater being a province for which nature seemed not to have designed him; for neither his voice, look nor gesture were such as were expected on the stage; and he was so much ashamed of having been reduced to appear as a player, that he always blotted out his name from the list when a copy of his tragedy was to be shown to his friends.

In the publication of his performance he was more successful, for the rays of genius that glimmered in it, that glimmered through all the mists which poverty and Cibber had been able to spread over it,

* Aaron Hill, poet and playwright

procured him the notice and esteem of many persons eminent for their rank, their virtue and their wit.

Of this play, acted, printed and dedicated, the accumulated profits arose to 100*l.*, which he thought at that time a very large sum, having been never master of so much before. . . .

Soon afterward [11th June, 1727] the death of the King * furnished a general subject for a poetical contest, in which Mr. Savage engaged, and is allowed to have carried the prize of honor from his competitors: but I know not whether he gained by his performance any other advantage than the increase of his reputation; though it must certainly have been with farther views that he prevailed upon himself to attempt a species of writing of which all the topics had been long before exhausted, and which was made at once difficult by the multitudes that had failed in it, and those that had succeeded.

He was now advancing in reputation, and though frequently involved in very distressful perplexities, appeared however to be gaining upon mankind, when both his fame and his life were endangered by an event, of which it is not yet determined whether it ought to be mentioned as a crime or a calamity.

On the 20th of November 1727, Mr. Savage came from Richmond, where he then lodged, that he might pursue his studies with less interruption, with an intent to discharge another lodging which he had in Westminster; and accidentally meeting two gentlemen, his acquaintances, whose names were Merchant and Gregory, he went in with them to a neighboring coffeehouse, and sat drinking till it was late, it being in no time of Mr. Savage's life any part of his character to be the first of the company that desired to separate. He would willingly have gone to bed in the same house; but there was not room for the whole company, and therefore they agreed to ramble about the streets and divert themselves with such amusements as should offer themselves till morning.

In this walk they happened unluckily to discover a light in Robinson's coffeehouse, near Charing Cross, and therefore went in. Merchant with some rudeness demanded a room and was told that there was a good fire in the next parlor, which the company were about to leave, being then paying their reckoning. Merchant, not satisfied with this answer, rushed into the room and was followed by his compan-

* George I

ions. He then petulantly placed himself between the company and the fire, and soon after kicked down the table. This produced a quarrel, swords were drawn on both sides and one Mr. James Sinclair was killed. Savage having likewise wounded a maid that held him, forced his way with Merchant out of the house, but being intimidated and confused, without resolution either to fly or stay, they were taken in a back court by one of the company and some soldiers, whom he had called to his assistance.

Being secured and guarded that night, they were in the morning carried before three justices, who committed them to the Gatehouse [at Westminster], from whence, upon the death of Mr. Sinclair, which happened the same day, they were removed in the night to Newgate, where they were however treated with some distinction, exempted from the ignominy of chains, and confined, not among the common criminals, but in the press yard.

When the day of trial came the court was crowded in a very unusual manner, and the public appeared to interest itself as in a cause of general concern. The witnesses against Mr. Savage and his friends were the woman who kept the house, which was a house of ill-fame, and her maid, the men who were in the room with Mr. Sinclair and a woman of the town, who had been drinking with them, and with whom one of them had been seen in bed. They swore in general that Merchant gave the provocation, which Savage and Gregory drew their swords to justify; that Savage drew first, and that he stabbed Sinclair when he was not in a posture of defense, or while Gregory commanded his sword; that after he had given the thrust he turned pale, and would have retired, but the maid clung round him, and one of the company endeavored to detain him, from whom he broke, by cutting the maid on the head, but was afterward taken in a court.

There was some difference in their depositions: one did not see Savage give the wound, another saw it given when Sinclair held his point toward the ground; and the woman of the town asserted that she did not see Sinclair's sword at all: this difference however was very far from amounting to inconsistency; but it was sufficient to show that the hurry of the dispute was such, that it was not easy to discover the truth with relation to particular circumstances, and that therefore some deductions were to be made from the credibility of the testimonies.

Sinclair had declared several times before his death that he received his wound from Savage; nor did Savage at his trial deny the

fact, but endeavored partly to extenuate it, by urging the sudden-
ness of the whole action, and the impossibility of any ill-design or
premeditated malice; and partly to justify it by the necessity of self-
defense and the hazard of his own life, if he had lost that opportunity
of giving the thrust: he observed that neither reason nor law obliged
a man to wait for the blow which was threatened, and which, if he
should suffer it, he might never be able to return; that it was always
allowable to prevent an assault, and to preserve life by taking away
that of the adversary by whom it was endangered.

With regard to the violence with which he endeavored to escape,
he declared that it was not his design to fly from justice, or decline a
trial, but to avoid the expenses and severities of a prison; and that he
intended to have appeared at the bar without compulsion.

This defense, which took up more than an hour, was heard by the
multitude that thronged the court with the most attentive and respectful silence: those who thought he ought not to be acquitted, owned
that applause could not be refused him; and those who before pitied
his misfortunes, now reverenced his abilities.

The witnesses which appeared against him were proved to be
persons of characters which did not entitle them to much credit; a
common strumpet, a woman by whom strumpets were entertained
and a man by whom they were supported; and the character of
Savage was by several persons of distinction asserted to be that of a
modest, inoffensive man, not inclined to broils or to insolence, and
who had, to that time, been only known for his misfortunes and
his wit.

Had his audience been his judges, he had undoubtedly been acquitted; but Mr. Page, who was then upon the bench, treated him
with his usual insolence and severity, and when he had summed up
the evidence, endeavored to exasperate the jury, as Mr. Savage used
to relate it, with this eloquent harangue:

"Gentlemen of the jury, you are to consider that Mr. Savage is a
very great man, a much greater man than you or I, gentlemen of the
jury; that he wears very fine clothes, much finer clothes than you or
I, gentlemen of the jury; that he has abundance of money in his
pocket, much more money than you or I, gentlemen of the jury; but,
gentlemen of the jury, is it not a very hard case, gentlemen of the
jury, that Mr. Savage should therefore kill you or me, gentlemen
of the jury?"

Mr. Savage hearing his defense thus misrepresented, and the men

253

who were to decide his fate incited against him by invidious comparisons, resolutely asserted that his cause was not candidly explained, and began to recapitulate what he had before said with regard to his condition, and the necessity of endeavoring to escape the expenses of imprisonment; but the judge having ordered him to be silent, and repeated his orders without effect, commanded that he should be taken from the bar by force.

The jury then heard the opinion of the judge that good characters were of no weight against positive evidence, though they might turn the scale where it was doubtful; and that though, when two men attack each other, the death of either is only manslaughter; but where one is the aggressor, as in the case before them and, in pursuance of his first attack, kills the other, the law supposes the action, however sudden, to be malicious. They then deliberated upon their verdict, and determined that Mr. Savage and Mr. Gregory were guilty of murder; and Mr. Merchant, who had no sword, only of manslaughter.

Thus ended this memorable trial, which lasted eight hours. Mr. Savage and Mr. Gregory were conducted back to prison, where they were more closely confined, and loaded with irons of fifty pounds weight: four days afterward they were sent back to the court to receive sentence; on which occasion Mr. Savage made, as far as it could be retained in memory, the following speech:

"It is now, my Lord, too late to offer anything by way of defense or vindication; nor can we expect aught from your Lordships in this court but the sentence which the law requires you, as judges, to pronounce against men of our calamitous condition. But we are also persuaded, that as mere men, and out of this seat of rigorous justice, you are susceptive of the tender passions and too humane not to commiserate the unhappy situation of those whom the law sometimes, perhaps, exacts from you to pronounce upon. No doubt you distinguish between offenses which arise out of premeditation and a disposition habituated to vice or immorality, and transgressions which are the unhappy and unforeseen effects of a casual absence of reason and sudden impulse of passion: we therefore hope you will contribute all you can to an extension of that mercy which the gentlemen of the jury have been pleased to show Mr. Merchant, who (allowing facts as sworn against us by the evidence) has led us into this our calamity. I hope this will not be construed as if we meant to reflect upon that gentleman, or remove anything from us upon him, or that we repine the more at our fate because he has no participation of it: No, my Lord! For my part I declare nothing could more soften my grief than to be without any companion in so great a misfortune."

Mr. Savage had now no hopes of life but from the mercy of the Crown, which was very earnestly solicited by his friends, and which, with whatever difficulty the story may obtain belief, was obstructed only by his mother.

To prejudice the Queen [Caroline, Queen of George II] against him, she made use of an incident which was omitted in the order of time, that it might be mentioned together with the purpose which it was made to serve. Mr. Savage, when he had discovered his birth, had an incessant desire to speak to his mother, who always avoided him in public and refused him admission into her house. One evening walking, as it was his custom, in the street that she inhabited, he saw the door of her house by accident open, he entered it and, finding no person in the passage to hinder him, went upstairs to salute her. She discovered him before he entered her chamber, alarmed the family with the most distressful outcries and when she had by her screams gathered them about her, ordered them to drive out of the house that villain who had forced himself in upon her and endeavored to murder her. Savage, who had attempted with the most submissive tenderness to soften her rage, hearing her utter so detestable an accusation, thought it prudent to retire and, I believe, never attempted afterward to speak to her.

But, shocked as he was with her falsehood and her cruelty, he imagined that she intended no other use of her lie than to set herself free from his embraces and solicitations, and was very far from suspecting that she would treasure it in her memory as an instrument of future wickedness, or that she would endeavor for this fictitious assault to deprive him of his life.

But when the Queen was solicited for his pardon and informed of the severe treatment which he had suffered from his judge, she answered, that however unjustifiable might be the manner of his trial, or whatever extenuation the action for which he was condemned might admit, she could not think that man a proper object of the King's mercy who had been capable of entering his mother's house in the night with an intent to murder her.

By whom this atrocious calumny had been transmitted to the Queen; whether she that invented had the front to relate it; whether she found anyone weak enough to credit it, or corrupt enough to concur with her in her hateful design, I know not; but methods had

255

been taken to persuade the Queen so strongly of the truth of it, that she for a long time refused to hear anyone of those who petitioned for his life.

Thus had Savage perished by the evidence of a bawd, a strumpet and his mother, had not justice and compassion procured him an advocate of rank too great to be rejected unheard, and of virtue too eminent to be heard without being believed. His merit and his calamities happened to reach the ear of the Countess of Hertford, who engaged in his support with all the tenderness that is excited by pity and all the zeal which is kindled by generosity; and, demanding an audience of the Queen, laid before her the whole series of his mother's cruelty, exposed the improbability of an accusation by which he was charged with an intent to commit a murder that could produce no advantage, and soon convinced her how little his former conduct could deserve to be mentioned as a reason for extraordinary severity.

The interposition of this lady was so successful that he was soon after admitted to bail and, on the 9th of March 1728, pleaded the King's pardon.

It is natural to inquire upon what motives his mother could persecute him in a manner so outrageous and implacable; for what reason she could employ all the arts of malice and all the snares of calumny to take away the life of her own son, of a son who never injured her, who was never supported by her expense, nor obstructed any prospect of pleasure or advantage; why she should endeavor to destroy him by a lie—a lie which could not gain credit, but must vanish of itself at the first moment of examination, and of which only this can be said to make it probable, that it may be observed from her conduct that the most execrable crimes are sometimes committed without apparent temptation.

This mother is still alive, and may perhaps even yet, though her malice was so often defeated, enjoy the pleasure of reflecting that the life which she often endeavored to destroy was at last shortened by her maternal offices; that though she could not transport her son to the plantations, bury him in the shop of a mechanic, or hasten the hand of the public executioner, she has yet had the satisfaction of embittering all his hours and forcing him into exigences that hurried on his death.

It is by no means necessary to aggravate the enormity of this woman's conduct by placing it in opposition to that of the Countess of Hertford; no one can fail to observe how much more amiable it is to relieve than to oppress, and to rescue innocence from destruction than to destroy without an injury.

Mr. Savage, during his imprisonment, his trial, and the time in which he lay under sentence of death, behaved with great firmness and equality of mind, and confirmed by his fortitude the esteem of those who before admired him for his abilities. The peculiar circumstances of his life were made more generally known by a short account, which was then published, and of which several thousands were in a few weeks dispersed over the nation: and the compassion of mankind operated so powerfully in his favor, that he was enabled by frequent presents not only to support himself, but to assist Mr. Gregory in prison; and when he was pardoned and released, he found the number of his friends not lessened.

The nature of the act for which he had been tried was in itself doubtful; of the evidences which appeared against him, the character of the man was not unexceptionable, that of the women notoriously infamous; she whose testimony chiefly influenced the jury to condemn him, afterward retracted her assertions. He always himself denied that he was drunk, as had been generally reported. Mr. Gregory, who is now (1744) Collector of Antigua, is said to declare him far less criminal than he was imagined, even by some who favored him; and Page himself afterward confessed that he had treated him with uncommon rigor. When all these particulars are rated together, perhaps the memory of Savage may not be much sullied by his trial.

Some time after he obtained his liberty, he met in the street the woman that had sworn with so much malignity against him. She informed him that she was in distress and, with a degree of confidence not easily attainable, desired him to relieve her. He, instead of insulting her misery, and taking pleasure in the calamities of one who had brought his life into danger, reproved her gently for her perjury; and changing the only guinea that he had, divided it equally between her and himself.

This is an action which in some ages would have made a saint, and perhaps in others a hero, and which, without any hyperbolical encomiums, must be allowed to be an instance of uncommon generosity, an act of complicated virtue; by which he at once relieved the poor, corrected the vicious and forgave an enemy; by which he at once remitted the strongest provocations, and exercised the most ardent charity.

Compassion was indeed the distinguishing quality of Savage; he never appeared inclined to take advantage of weakness, to attack the defenseless, or to press upon the falling: whoever was distressed, was certain at least of his good wishes; and when he could give no assistance to extricate them from misfortunes, he endeavored to soothe them by sympathy and tenderness.

But when his heart was not softened by the sight of misery, he was sometimes obstinate in his resentment and did not quickly lose the remembrance of an injury. He always continued to speak with anger of the insolence and partiality of Page and a short time before his death revenged it by a satire.

It is natural to inquire in what terms Mr. Savage spoke of this fatal action when the danger was over, and he was under no necessity of using any art to set his conduct in the fairest light. He was not willing to dwell upon it; and, if he transiently mentioned it, appeared neither to consider himself as a murderer, nor as a man wholly free from the guilt of blood. How much and how long he regretted it, appeared in a poem which he published many years afterward. On occasion of a copy of verses, in which the failings of good men were recounted, and in which the author had endeavored to illustrate his position, that "the best may sometimes deviate from virtue," by an instance of murder committed by Savage in the heat of wine, Savage remarked, that it was no very just representation of a good man, to suppose him liable to drunkenness and disposed in his riots to cut throats.

He was now indeed at liberty, but was, as before, without any other support than accidental favors and uncertain patronage afforded him; sources by which he was sometimes very liberally supplied and which at other times were suddenly stopped; so that he spent his life between want and plenty; or, what was yet worse, between beggary and extravagance; for, as whatever he received was the gift of chance, which might as well favor him at one time as another, he was tempted to squander what he had, because he always hoped to be immediately supplied.

Another cause of his profusion was the absurd kindness of his friends, who at once rewarded and enjoyed his abilities by treating him at taverns and habituating him to pleasures which he could not afford to enjoy, and which he was not able to deny himself, though he purchased the luxury of a single night by the anguish of cold and hunger for a week.

The experience of these inconveniences determined him to endeavor after some settled income, which, having long found submission and entreaties fruitless, he attempted to extort from his mother by rougher methods. He had now, as he acknowledged, lost that tenderness for her which the whole series of her cruelty had not been able wholly to repress, till he found, by the efforts which she made for his destruction, that she was not content with refusing to assist him, and being neutral in his struggles with poverty, but was as ready to snatch every opportunity of adding to his misfortunes; and that she was now to be considered as an enemy implacably malicious, whom nothing but his blood could satisfy. He therefore threatened to harass her with lampoons, and to publish a copious narrative of her conduct unless she consented to purchase an exemption from infamy by allowing him a pension.

This expedient proved successful. Whether shame still survived, though virtue was extinct, or whether her relations had more delicacy than herself and imagined that some of the darts which satire might point at her would glance upon them, Lord Tyrconnel, whatever were his motives, upon his promise to lay aside his design of exposing the cruelty of his mother, received him into his family, treated him as his equal, and engaged to allow him a pension of 200*l.* a year.

This was the golden part of Mr. Savage's life and for some time he had no reason to complain of fortune; his appearance was splendid, his expenses large, and his acquaintance extensive. He was courted by all who endeavored to be thought men of genius and caressed by all who valued themselves upon a refined taste. To admire Mr. Savage was a proof of discernment, and to be acquainted with him was a title to poetical reputation. His presence was sufficient to make any place of public entertainment popular and his approbation and example constituted the fashion. So powerful is genius when it is invested with the glitter of affluence! Men willingly pay to fortune that regard which they owe to merit and are pleased when they have an opportunity at once of gratifying their vanity and practising their duty.

This interval of prosperity furnished him with opportunities of enlarging his knowledge of human nature, by contemplating life from

259

its highest gradations to its lowest; and, had he afterward applied to dramatic poetry, he would perhaps not have had many superiors; for as he never suffered any scene to pass before his eyes without notice, he had treasured in his mind all the different combinations of passions and the innumerable mixtures of vice and virtue, which distinguish one character from another; and, as his conception was strong, his expressions were clear, he easily received impressions from objects and very forcibly transmitted them to others.

Of his exact observations on human life he has left a proof, which would do honor to the greatest names, in a small pamphlet, called *The Author to be Let,* where he introduces Iscariot Hackney, a prostitute scribbler, giving an account of his birth, his education, his disposition and morals, habits of life and maxims of conduct. In the Introduction are related many secret histories of the petty writers of that time, but sometimes mixed with ungenerous reflections on their birth, their circumstances, or those of their relations; nor can it be denied that some passages are such as Iscariot Hackney might himself have produced.

He was accused likewise of living in an appearance of friendship with some whom he satirized, and of making use of the confidence which he gained by a seeming kindness, to discover failings and expose them: it must be confessed that Mr. Savage's esteem was no very certain possession, and that he would lampoon at one time those whom he had praised at another.

It may be alleged, that the same man may change his principles; and that he who was once deservedly commended, may be afterward satirized with equal justice; or that the poet was dazzled with the appearance of virtue, and found the man whom he had celebrated, when he had an opportunity of examining him more narrowly, unworthy of the panegyric which he had too hastily bestowed; and that, as a false satire ought to be recanted for the sake of him whose reputation may be injured, false praise ought likewise to be obviated, lest the distinction between vice and virtue should be lost, lest a bad man should be trusted upon the credit of his encomiast, or lest others should endeavor to obtain the like praises by the same means.

But though these excuses may be often plausible, and sometimes just, they are very seldom satisfactory to mankind; and the writer who is not constant to his subject quickly sinks into contempt, his satire loses its force, and his panegyric its value, and he is only considered at one time as a flatterer, and as a calumniator at another.

To avoid these imputations, it is only necessary to follow the rules of virtue, and to preserve an unvaried regard to truth. For though it is undoubtedly possible that a man, however cautious, may be sometimes deceived by an artful appearance of virtue, or by false evidences of guilt, such errors will not be frequent; and it will be allowed, that the name of an author would never have been made contemptible, had no man ever said what he did not think, or misled others but when he was himself deceived.

The Author to be Let was first published in a single pamphlet, and afterward inserted in a collection of pieces relating to the *Dunciad,** which were addressed by Mr. Savage to the Earl of Middlesex, in a Dedication which he was prevailed upon to sign, though he did not write it, and in which there are some positions that the true author would perhaps not have published under his own name, and on which Mr. Savage afterward reflected with no great satisfaction. The enumeration of the bad effects of the "uncontrolled freedom of the press," and the assertion that the "liberties taken by the writers of journals with their superiors were exorbitant and unjustifiable," very ill became men who have themselves not always shown the exactest regard to the laws of subordination in their writings, and who have often satirized those that at least thought themselves their superiors, as they were eminent for their hereditary rank, and employed in the highest offices of the kingdom. But this is only an instance of that partiality which almost every man indulges with regard to himself: the liberty of the press is a blessing when we are inclined to write against others and a calamity when we find ourselves overborne by the multitude of our assailants; as the power of the Crown is always thought too great by those who suffer by its influence and too little by those in whose favor it is exerted; and a standing army is generally accounted necessary by those who command, and dangerous and oppressive by those who support it.

Mr. Savage was likewise very far from believing that the letters annexed to each species of bad poets in the Bathos were, as he was directed to assert, "set down at random"; for when he was charged by one of his friends with putting his name to such an improbability, he had no other answer to make, than that "he did not think of it"; and his friend had too much tenderness to reply, that next to the

* A biting satire, full of literary gossip, in which Pope attacked some of his fellow "men of letters"

crime of writing contrary to what he thought, was that of writing without thinking.

After having remarked what is false in this Dedication, it is proper that I observe the impartiality which I recommend, by declaring what Savage asserted; that the account of the circumstances which attended the publication of the *Dunciad,* however strange and improbable, was exactly true.

The publication of this piece at this time raised Mr. Savage a great number of enemies among those that were attacked by Mr. Pope, with whom he was considered as a kind of confederate, and whom he was suspected of supplying with private intelligence and secret incidents: so that the ignominy of an informer was added to the terror of a satirist.

That he was not altogether free from literary hypocrisy and that he sometimes spoke one thing and wrote another, cannot be denied; because he himself confessed that, when he lived with great familiarity with Dennis, he wrote an epigram against him.

Mr. Savage, however, set all the malice of all the pigmy writers at defiance, and thought the friendship of Mr. Pope cheaply purchased by being exposed to their censure and their hatred; nor had he any reason to repent of the preference, for he found Mr. Pope a steady and unalienable friend almost to the end of his life. . . .

In this gay period (1729) of his life, while he was surrounded by affluence and pleasure, he published *The Wanderer,* a moral poem, of which the design is comprised in these lines:

> *I fly all public care, all venal strife,*
> *To try the still, compar'd with active, life;*
> *To prove, by these, the sons of men may owe*
> *The fruits of bliss to bursting clouds of woe;*
> *That ev'n calamity, by thought refin'd,*
> *Inspirits and adorns the thinking mind.*

And more distinctly in the following passages:

> *By woe, the soul to daring action swells;*
> *By woe, in plaintless patience it excels;*
> *From patience, prudent clear experience springs,*
> *And traces knowledge thro' the course of things!*
> *Thence hope is form'd, thence fortitude, success,*
> *Renown—whate'er men covet and caress.*

262

This performance was always considered by himself as his masterpiece; and Mr. Pope, when he asked his opinion of it, told him, that he read it once over and was not displeased with it; that it gave him more pleasure at the second perusal, and delighted him still more at the third.

It has been generally objected to *The Wanderer,* that the disposition of the parts is irregular; that the design is obscure, and the plan perplexed; that the images, however beautiful, succeed each other without order; and that the whole performance is not so much a regular fabric, as a heap of shining materials thrown together by accident, which strikes rather with the solemn magnificence of a stupendous ruin, than the elegant grandeur of a finished pile.

This criticism is universal, and therefore it is reasonable to believe it at least in a great degree just; but Mr. Savage was always of a contrary opinion, and thought his drift could only be missed by negligence or stupidity, and that the whole plan was regular, and the parts distinct.

It was never denied to abound with strong representations of nature and just observations upon life; and it may easily be observed, that most of his pictures have an evident tendency to illustrate his first great position, "that good is the consequence of evil." The sun that burns up the mountains, fructifies the vales; the deluge that rushes down the broken rocks with dreadful impetuosity, is separated into purling brooks; and the rage of the hurricane purifies the air.

Even in this poem he has not been able to forbear one touch upon the cruelty of his mother, which, though remarkably delicate and tender, is a proof how deep an impression it had upon his mind.

This must be at least acknowledged, which ought to be thought equivalent to many other excellences, that this poem can promote no other purposes than those of virtue, and that it is written with a very strong sense of the efficacy of religion.

But my province is rather to give the history of Mr. Savage's performances than to display their beauties, or to obviate the criticisms which they have occasioned; and therefore I shall not dwell upon the particular passages which deserve applause: I shall neither show the excellence of his descriptions, nor expatiate on the terrific portrait of suicide, nor point out the artful touches by which he has

263

distinguished the intellectual features of the rebels, who suffer death in his last canto. It is, however, proper to observe, that Mr. Savage always declared the characters wholly fictitious, and without the least allusion to any real persons or actions.

From a poem so diligently labored, and so successfully finished, it might be reasonably expected that he should have gained considerable advantage; nor can it, without some degree of indignation and concern, be told, that he sold the copy for ten guineas, of which he afterward returned two, that the two last sheets of the work might be reprinted, of which he had in his absence intrusted the correction to a friend, who was too indolent to perform it with accuracy.

A superstitious regard to the correction of his sheets was one of Mr. Savage's peculiarities: he often altered, revised, recurred to his first reading or punctuation, and again adopted the alteration; he was dubious and irresolute without end, as on a question of the last importance, and at last was seldom satisfied: the intrusion or omission of a comma was sufficient to discompose him and he would lament an error of a single letter as a heavy calamity. In one of his letters relating to an impression of some verses, he remarks, that he had, with regard to the correction of the proof, "a spell upon him"; and indeed the anxiety with which he dwelt upon the minutest and most trifling niceties deserved no other name than that of fascination.

That he sold so valuable a performance for so small a price, was not to be imputed either to necessity, by which the learned and ingenious are often obliged to submit to very hard conditions; or to avarice, by which the booksellers are frequently incited to oppress that genius by which they are supported; but to that intemperate desire of pleasure, and habitual slavery to his passions, which involved him in many perplexities. He happened at that time to be engaged in the pursuit of some trifling gratification and, being without money for the present occasion, sold his poem to the first bidder, and perhaps for the first price that was proposed, and would probably have been content with less if less had been offered him.

This poem was addressed to the Lord Tyrconnel, not only in the first lines, but in a formal Dedication filled with the highest strains of panegyric, and the warmest professions of gratitude, but by no means remarkable for delicacy of connection or elegance of style.

These praises in a short time he found himself inclined to retract, being discarded by the man on whom he had bestowed them, and whom he then immediately discovered not to have deserved them. Of this quarrel, which every day made more bitter, Lord Tyrconnel and Mr. Savage assigned very different reasons, which might perhaps all in reality concur, though they were not all convenient to be alleged by either party. Lord Tyrconnel affirmed that it was the constant practice of Mr. Savage to enter a tavern with any company that proposed it, drink the most expensive wines with great profusion, and when the reckoning was demanded, to be without money: if, as it often happened, his company were willing to defray his part, the affair ended, without any ill-consequences; but if they were refractory, and expected that the wine should be paid for by him that drank it, his method of composition was, to take them with him to his own apartment, assume the government of the house, and order the butler in an imperious manner to set the best wine in the cellar before his company, who often drank till they forgot the respect due to the house in which they were entertained, indulged themselves in the utmost extravagance of merriment, practised the most licentious frolics, and committed all the outrages of drunkenness.

Nor was this the only charge which Lord Tyrconnel brought against him. Having given him a collection of valuable books, stamped with his own arms, he had the mortification to see them in a short time exposed to sale upon the stalls, it being usual with Mr. Savage, when he wanted a small sum, to take his books to the pawnbroker.

Whoever was acquainted with Mr. Savage easily credited both these accusations; for having been obliged, from his first entrance into the world, to subsist upon expedients, affluence was not able to exalt him above them; and so much was he delighted with wine and conversation, and so long had he been accustomed to live by chance, that he would at any time go to the tavern without scruple, and trust for the reckoning to the liberality of his company, and frequently of company to whom he was very little known. This conduct indeed very seldom drew upon him those inconveniences that might be feared by any other person; for his conversation was so entertaining, and his address so pleasing, that few thought the pleasure which they received from him dearly purchased by paying for his wine. It was his peculiar happiness that he scarcely ever found a stranger whom he did not leave a friend; but it must likewise be added, that he had not often a friend long without obliging him to become a stranger.

Mr. Savage, on the other hand, declared that Lord Tyrconnel quarreled with him because he would not subtract from his own luxury and extravagance what he had promised to allow him, and that his resentment was only a plea for the violation of his promise. He asserted that he had done nothing that ought to exclude him from that subsistence which he thought not so much a favor as a debt, since it was offered him upon conditions which he had never broken; and that his only fault was, that he could not be supported with nothing.

He acknowledged that Lord Tyrconnel often exhorted him to regulate his method of life and not to spend all his nights in taverns and that he appeared desirous that he would pass those hours with him which he so freely bestowed upon others. This demand Mr. Savage considered as a censure of his conduct, which he could never patiently bear, and which, in the latter and cooler parts of his life, was so offensive to him that he declared it as his resolution "to spurn that friend who should presume to dictate to him"; and it is not likely that in his earlier years he received admonitions with more calmness.

He was likewise inclined to resent such expectations, as tending to infringe his liberty, of which he was very jealous, when it was necessary to the gratification of his passions; and declared that the request was still more unreasonable, as the company to which he was to have been confined was insupportably disagreeable. This assertion affords another instance of that inconsistency of his writings with his conversation which was so often to be observed. He forgot how lavishly he had, in his Dedication to *The Wanderer,* extolled the delicacy and penetration, the humanity and generosity, the candor and politeness of the man whom, when he no longer loved him, he declared to be a wretch without understanding, without good nature and without justice, of whose name he thought himself obliged to leave no trace in any future edition of his writings, and accordingly blotted it out of that copy of *The Wanderer* which was in his hands.

During his countinuance with the Lord Tyrconnel, he wrote [1730] *The Triumph of Health and Mirth,* on the recovery of Lady Tyrconnel from a languishing illness. This performance is remarkable, not only for the gaiety of the ideas and the melody of the numbers, but for the agreeable fiction upon which it is formed. Mirth, overwhelmed with sorrow for the sickness of her favorite, takes a flight in quest of her sister Health, whom she finds reclined upon the brow of a lofty mountain, amidst the fragrance of perpetual spring, with the breezes of the morning sporting about her. Being solicited by her sister Mirth, she readily promises her assistance, flies away in a cloud, and impregnates the waters of Bath with new virtues, by which the sickness of Belinda is relieved.

As the reputation of his abilities, the particular circumstances of his birth and life, the splendor of his appearance, and the distinction which was for some time paid him by Lord Tyrconnel, entitled him to familiarity with persons of higher rank than those to whose conversation he had been before admitted, he did not fail to gratify that curiosity, which induced him to take a nearer view of those whom their birth, their employments or their fortunes necessarily place at a distance from the greatest part of mankind, and to examine whether their merit was magnified or diminished by the medium through which it was contemplated; whether the splendor with which they dazzled their admirers was inherent in themselves, or only reflected on them by the objects that surrounded them; and whether great men were selected for high stations, or high stations made great men.

For this purpose he took all opportunities of conversing familiarly with those who were most conspicuous at that time for their power or their influence; he watched their looser moments, and examined their domestic behavior with that acuteness which nature had given him, and which the uncommon variety of his life had contributed to increase, and that inquisitiveness which must always be produced in a vigorous mind by an absolute freedom from all pressing or domestic engagements.

His discernment was quick, and therefore he soon found in every person and in every affair something that deserved attention; he was supported by others, without any care for himself, and was therefore at leisure to pursue his observations.

More circumstances to constitute a critic on human life could not easily concur; nor indeed could any man, who assumed from accidental advantages more praise than he could justly claim from his real merit, admit any acquaintance more dangerous than that of Savage; of whom likewise it must be confessed, that abilities really exalted above the common level or virtue refined from passion or

267

proof against corruption could not easily find an abler judge, or a warmer advocate.

What was the result of Mr. Savage's inquiry, though he was not much accustomed to conceal his discoveries, it may not be entirely safe to relate, because the persons whose characters he criticized are powerful, and power and resentment are seldom strangers; nor would it perhaps be wholly just, because what he asserted in conversation might, though true in general, be heightened by some momentary ardor of imagination, and, as it can be delivered only from memory, may be imperfectly represented; so that the picture, at first aggravated, and then unskilfully copied, may be justly suspected to retain no great resemblance of the original.

It may, however, be observed that he did not appear to have formed very elevated ideas of those to whom the administration of affairs, or the conduct of parties, has been entrusted—who have been considered as the advocates of the Crown or the guardians of the people and who have obtained the most implicit confidence and the loudest applauses. Of one particular person, who has been at one time so popular as to be generally esteemed, and at another so formidable as to be universally detested, he observed, that his acquisitions had been small, or that his capacity was narrow, and that the whole range of his mind was from obscenity to politics and from politics to obscenity.

But the opportunity of indulging his speculations on great characters was now at an end. He was banished from the table of Lord Tyrconnel and turned again adrift upon the world, without prospect of finding quickly any other harbor. As prudence was not one of the virtues by which he was distinguished, he had made no provision against a misfortune like this. And though it is not to be imagined but that the separation must for some time have been preceded by coldness, peevishness or neglect, though it was undoubtedly the consequence of accumulated provocations on both sides, yet everyone that knew Savage will readily believe that to him it was sudden as a stroke of thunder—that though he might have transiently suspected it, he had never suffered any thought so unpleasing to sink into his mind, but that he had driven it away by amusements, or dreams of future felicity and affluence, and had never taken any measures by which he might prevent a precipitation from plenty to indigence.

This quarrel and separation, and the difficulties to which Mr.

Savage was exposed by them, were soon known both to his friends and enemies; nor was it long before he perceived, from the behavior of both, how much is added to the luster of genius by the ornaments of wealth.

His condition did not appear to excite much compassion; for he had not always been careful to use the advantages he enjoyed with that moderation which ought to have been with more than usual caution preserved by him, who knew, if he had reflected, that he was only a dependent on the bounty of another, whom he could expect to support him no longer than he endeavored to preserve his favor by complying with his inclinations, and whom he nevertheless set at defiance, and was continually irritating by negligence or encroachments. . . .

His degradation, therefore, from the condition which he had enjoyed with such wanton thoughtlessness was considered by many as an occasion of triumph. Those who had before paid their court to him without success soon returned the contempt which they had suffered; and they who had received favors from him—for of such favors as he could bestow he was very liberal—did not always remember them. So much more certain are the effects of resentment than of gratitude: it is not only to many more pleasing to recollect those faults which place others below them than those virtues by which they are themselves comparatively depressed, but it is likewise more easy to neglect than to recompense; and though there are few who will practise a laborious virtue, there will never be wanting multitudes that will indulge in easy vice.

Savage, however, was very little disturbed at the marks of contempt which his ill-fortune brought upon him from those whom he never esteemed, and with whom he never considered himself as leveled by any calamities: and though it was not without some uneasiness that he saw some, whose friendship he valued, change their behavior, he yet observed their coldness without much emotion, considered them as the slaves of fortune and the worshippers of prosperity, and was more inclined to despise them than to lament himself.

It does not appear that, after this return of his wants, he found mankind equally favorable to him as at his first appearance in the world. His story, though in reality not less melancholy, was less affecting because it was no longer new; it therefore procured him no new friends, and those that had formerly relieved him thought they might now consign him to others. He was now likewise considered by many rather as criminal than as unhappy; for the friends of Lord Tyrconnel and of his mother were sufficiently industrious to publish his weaknesses, which were indeed very numerous; and nothing was forgotten that might make him either hateful or ridiculous.

It cannot but be imagined that such representations of his faults must make great numbers less sensible of his distress; many, who had only an opportunity to hear one part, made no scruple to propagate the account which they received; many assisted their circulation from malice or revenge; and perhaps many pretended to credit them that they might with a better grace withdraw their regard or withhold their assistance.

Savage, however, was not one of those who suffered himself to be injured without resistance, nor was less diligent in exposing the faults of Lord Tyrconnel, over whom he obtained at least this advantage, that he drove him first to the practice of outrage and violence; for he was so much provoked by the wit and virulence of Savage, that he came with a number of attendants, that did no honor to his courage, to beat him at a coffeehouse. But it happened that he had left the place a few minutes; and his Lordship had, without danger, the pleasure of boasting how he would have treated him. Mr. Savage went next day to repay his visit at his own house, but was prevailed on by his domestics to retire without insisting upon seeing him.

Lord Tyrconnel was accused by Mr. Savage of some actions which scarcely any provocations will be thought sufficient to justify, such as seizing what he had in his lodgings and other instances of wanton cruelty, by which he increased the distress of Savage without any advantage to himself.

These mutual accusations were retorted on both sides for many years with the utmost degree of virulence and rage, and time seemed rather to augment than diminish their resentment. That the anger of Mr. Savage should be kept alive is not strange, because he felt every day the consequences of the quarrel; but it might reasonably have been hoped that Lord Tyrconnel might have relented, and at length have forgot those provocations which, however they might have once inflamed him, had not in reality much hurt him.

The spirit of Mr. Savage indeed never suffered him to solicit a reconciliation; he returned reproach for reproach, and insult for insult; his superiority of wit supplied the disadvantages of his fortune, and enabled him to form a party and prejudice great numbers in his favor.

But though this might be some gratification of his vanity, it afforded very little relief to his necessities; and he was very frequently reduced to uncommon hardships, of which, however, he never made any mean or importunate complaints, being formed rather to bear misery with fortitude than enjoy prosperity with moderation.

He now thought himself again at liberty to expose the cruelty of his mother; and therefore, I believe, about this time published *The Bastard,* a poem remarkable for the vivacious sallies of thought in the beginning, where he makes a pompous enumeration of the imaginary advantages of base birth, and the pathetic sentiments at the end, where he recounts the real calamities which he suffered by the crime of his parents.

The vigor and spirit of the verses, the peculiar circumstances of the author, the novelty of the subject, and the notoriety of the story to which the allusions are made, procured this performance a very favorable reception; great numbers were immediately dispersed, and editions were multiplied with unusual rapidity.

One circumstance attended the publication which Savage used to relate with great satisfaction. His mother, to whom the poem was with "due reverence" inscribed, happened then to be at Bath, where she could not conveniently retire from censure or conceal herself from observation; and no sooner did the reputation of the poem begin to spread, than she heard it repeated in all places of concourse, nor could she enter the assembly rooms, or cross the walks, without being saluted with some lines from *The Bastard.*

This was perhaps the first time that ever she discovered a sense of shame, and on this occasion the power of wit was very conspicuous: the wretch who had, without scruple, proclaimed herself an adulteress, and who had first endeavored to starve her son, then to transport him, and afterward to hang him, was not able to bear the representation of her own conduct; but fled from reproach, though she felt no pain from guilt, and left Bath with the utmost haste to shelter herself among the crowds of London.

Thus Savage had the satisfaction of finding, that, though he could not reform his mother, he could punish her and that he did not always suffer alone.

The pleasure which he received from this increase of his poetical

271

reputation was sufficient for some time to overbalance the miseries of want, which this performance did not much alleviate; for it was sold for a very trivial sum to a bookseller [T. Worrall], who, though the success was so uncommon that five impressions were sold, of which many were undoubtedly very numerous, had not generosity sufficient to admit the unhappy writer to any part of the profit.

The sale of this poem was always mentioned by Mr. Savage with the utmost elevation of heart, and referred to by him as an incontestable proof of a general acknowledgment of his abilities. It was indeed the only production of which he could justly boast a general reception.

But though he did not lose the opportunity which success gave him of setting a high rate on his abilities, but paid due deference to the suffrages of mankind when they were given in his favor, he did not suffer his esteem of himself to depend upon others, nor found anything sacred in the voice of the people when they were inclined to censure him; he then readily showed the folly of expecting that the public should judge right, observed how slowly poetical merit had often forced its way into the world; he contented himself with the applause of men of judgment, and was somewhat disposed to exclude all those from the character of men of judgment who did not applaud him.

But he was at other times more favorable to mankind than to think them blind to the beauties of his works, and imputed the slowness of their sale to other causes: either they were published at a time when the town was empty, or when the attention of the public was engrossed by some struggle in the parliament, or some other object of general concern; or they were by the neglect of the publisher not diligently dispersed, or by his avarice not advertised with sufficient frequency. Address or industry or liberality was always wanting; and the blame was laid rather on any person than the author.

By arts like these, arts which every man practices in some degree, and to which too much of the little tranquillity of life is to be ascribed, Savage was always able to live at peace with himself. Had he indeed only made use of these expedients to alleviate the loss or want of fortune or reputation, or any other advantages which it is not in man's power to bestow upon himself, they might have been justly mentioned as instances of a philosophical mind and very properly proposed to the imitation of multitudes, who, for want of

272

diverting their imaginations with the same dexterity, languish under afflictions which might be easily removed.

It were doubtless to be wished that truth and reason were universally prevalent; that everything were esteemed according to its real value, and that men would secure themselves from being disappointed in their endeavors after happiness, by placing it only in virtue, which is always to be obtained; but if adventitious and foreign pleasures must be pursued, it would be perhaps of some benefit, since that pursuit must frequently be fruitless, if the practice of Savage could be taught, that folly might be an antidote to folly and one fallacy be obviated by another.

But the danger of this pleasing intoxication must not be concealed; nor indeed can anyone, after having observed the life of Savage, need to be cautioned against it. By imputing none of his miseries to himself, he continued to act upon the same principles, and to follow the same path; was never made wiser by his sufferings, nor preserved by one misfortune from falling into another. He proceeded throughout his life to tread the same steps on the same circle; always applauding his past conduct, or at least forgetting it, to amuse himself with phantoms of happiness which were dancing before him; and willingly turned his eyes from the light of reason, when it would have discovered the illusion and shown him what he never wished to see, his real state.

He is even accused, after having lulled his imagination with those ideal opiates, of having tried the same experiment upon his conscience; and, having accustomed himself to impute all deviations from the right to foreign causes, it is certain that he was upon every occasion too easily reconciled to himself; and that he appeared very little to regret those practices which had impaired his reputation. The reigning error of his life was, that he mistook the love for the practice of virtue, and was indeed not so much a good man, as the friend of goodness.

This at least must be allowed him, that he always preserved a strong sense of the dignity, the beauty, and the necessity of virtue; and that he never contributed deliberately to spread corruption amongst mankind. His actions, which were generally precipitate, were often blameable; but his writings, being the productions of study, uniformly tended to the exaltation of the mind and the propagation of morality and piety.

These writings may improve mankind when his failings shall be forgotten; and therefore he must be considered, upon the whole, as a benefactor to the world; nor can his personal example do any hurt, since, whoever hears of his faults, will hear of the miseries which they brought upon him, and which would deserve less pity, had not his condition been such as made his faults pardonable. He may be considered as a child exposed to all the temptations of indigence, at an age when resolution was not yet strengthened by conviction, nor virtue confirmed by habit; a circumstance which, in his *Bastard,* he laments in a very affecting manner

> ——*No Mother's care*
> *Shielded my infant innocence with prayer:*
> *No Father's guardian-hand my youth maintain'd,*
> *Call'd forth my virtues, or from vice restrain'd.*

The Bastard, however it might provoke or mortify his mother, could not be expected to melt her to compassion, so that he was still under the same want of the necessaries of life; and he therefore exerted all the interest which his wit or his birth or his misfortunes could procure, to obtain, upon the death of Eusden, the place of poet laureat, and prosecuted his application with so much diligence, that the King publicly declared it his intention to bestow it upon him; but such was the fate of Savage, that even the King, when he intended his advantage, was disappointed in his schemes; for the Lord Chamberlain, who has the disposal of the laurel, as one of the appendages of his office, either did not know the King's design or did not approve it or thought the nomination of the laureat an encroachment upon his rights, and therefore bestowed the laurel upon Colley Cibber.

Mr. Savage, thus disappointed, took a resolution of applying to the Queen that, having once given him life, she would enable him to support it, and therefore published a short poem on her birthday, to which he gave the odd title of *Volunteer Laureat.* . . .

Savage's life, unhappy as it may be already imagined, was yet embittered, in 1738, with new calamities. The death of the Queen [20th Nov. 1737] deprived him of all the prospects of preferment with which he so long entertained his imagination; and, as Sir Robert Walpole had before given him reason to believe that he never intended the performance of his promise, he was now abandoned again to fortune.

He was, however, at that time supported by a friend; and as it was not his custom to look out for distant calamities or to feel any other pain than that which forced itself upon his senses, he was not much afflicted at his loss, and perhaps comforted himself that his pension would be now continued without the annual tribute of a panegyric.

Another expectation contributed likewise to support him: he had taken a resolution to write a second tragedy upon the story of Sir Thomas Overbury, in which he preserved a few lines of his former play, but made a total alteration of the plan, added new incidents, and introduced new characters; so that it was a new tragedy, not a revival of the former.

Many of his friends blamed him for not making choice of another subject; but, in vindication of himself, he asserted that it was not easy to find a better; and that he thought it his interest to extinguish the memory of the first tragedy, which he could only do by writing one less defective upon the same story; by which he should entirely defeat the artifice of the booksellers, who, after the death of any author of reputation, are always industrious to swell his works by uniting his worst productions with his best.

In the execution of this scheme, however, he proceeded but slowly, and probably only employed himself upon it when he could find no other amusement; but he pleased himself with counting the profits, and perhaps imagined that the theatrical reputation which he was about to acquire would be equivalent to all that he had lost by the death of his patroness.

He did not, in confidence of his approaching riches, neglect the measures proper to secure the continuance of his pension, though some of his favorers thought him culpable for omitting to write on her death; but on her birthday next year [1st March, 1737–8] he gave a proof of the solidity of his judgment and the power of his genius. He knew that the track of elegy had been so long beaten that it was impossible to travel in it without treading in the footsteps of those who had gone before him; and that therefore it was necessary, that he might distinguish himself from the herd of encomiasts, to find out some new walk of funeral panegyric.

This difficult task he performed in such a manner that his poem may be justly ranked among the best pieces that the death of princes has produced. By transferring the mention of her death to her birthday he has formed a happy combination of topics, which any other man would have thought it very difficult to connect in one view, but which he has united in such a manner that the relation between them appears natural; and it may be justly said, that what no other man would have thought on, it now appears scarcely possible for any man to miss.

The beauty of this peculiar combination of images is so masterly that it is sufficient to set this poem above censure; and therefore it is not necessary to mention many other delicate touches which may be found in it, and which would deservedly be admired in any other performance.

To these proofs of his genius may be added, from the same poem, an instance of his prudence, an excellence for which he was not so often distinguished; he does not forget to remind the King, in the most delicate and artful manner, of continuing his pension.

With regard to the success of this address he was for some time in suspense, but was in no great degree solicitous about it, and continued his labor upon his new tragedy with great tranquillity, till the friend who had for a considerable time supported him, removing his family to another place, took occasion to dismiss him. It then became necessary to inquire more diligently what was determined in his affair, having reason to suspect that no great favor was intended him, because he had not received his pension at the usual time.

It is said that he did not take those methods of retrieving his interest which were most likely to succeed; and some of those who were employed in the Exchequer cautioned him against too much violence in his proceedings: but Mr. Savage, who seldom regulated his conduct by the advice of others, gave way to his passion and demanded of Sir Robert Walpole, at his levee, the reason of the distinction that was made between him and the other pensioners of the Queen, with a degree of roughness which perhaps determined him to withdraw what had been only delayed.

Whatever was the crime of which he was accused or suspected, and whatever influence was employed against him, he received soon after an account that took from him all hopes of regaining his pension; and he had now no prospect of subsistence but from his play, and he knew no way of living for the time required to finish it.

So peculiar were the misfortunes of this man, deprived of an estate and title by a particular law, exposed and abandoned by a mother, defrauded by a mother of a fortune which his father had allotted him, he entered the world without a friend; and though his abilities forced themselves into esteem and reputation, he was never able to obtain any real advantage, and whatever prospects arose were always intercepted as he began to approach them. The King's intentions in his favor were frustrated; his Dedication to the Prince, whose generosity on every other occasion was eminent, procured him no reward; Sir Robert Walpole, who valued himself upon keeping his promise to others, broke it to him without regret; and the bounty of the Queen was, after her death, withdrawn from him, and from him only.

Such were his misfortunes, which yet he bore not only with decency, but with cheerfulness; nor was his gaiety clouded even by his last disappointments, though he was in a short time reduced to the lowest degree of distress, and often wanted both lodging and food. At this time he gave another instance of the insurmountable obstinacy of his spirit: his clothes were worn out, and he received notice that at a coffeehouse some clothes and linen were left for him; the person who sent them did not, I believe, inform him to whom he was to be obliged, that he might spare the perplexity of acknowledging the benefit; but though the offer was so far generous, it was made with some neglect of ceremonies, which Mr. Savage so much resented that he refused the present, and declined to enter the house till the clothes that had been designed for him were taken away.

His distress was now publicly known, and his friends, therefore, thought it proper to concert some measures for his relief; and one of them [Pope] wrote a letter to him, in which he expressed his concern "for the miserable withdrawing of his pension," and gave him hopes that in a short time he should find himself supplied with a competence, "without any dependence on those little creatures which we are pleased to call the great."

The scheme proposed for this happy and independent subsistence was, that he should retire into Wales and receive an allowance of 50l. a year, to be raised by a subscription, on which he was to live privately in a cheap place, without aspiring any more to affluence, or having any further care of reputation.

This offer Mr. Savage gladly accepted, though with intentions very different from those of his friends; for they proposed that he should continue an exile from London forever, and spend all the remaining part of his life at Swansea; but he designed only to take the opportunity which their scheme offered him of retreating for a short time that he might prepare his play for the stage, and his other works for the press and then to return to London to exhibit his tragedy and live upon the profits of his own labor.

With regard to his works, he proposed very great improvements, which would have required much time or great application; and when he had finished them, he designed to do justice to his subscribers by publishing them according to his proposals.

As he was ready to entertain himself with future pleasures, he had planned out a scheme of life for the country, of which he had no knowledge but from pastorals and songs. He imagined that he should be transported to scenes of flowery felicity, like those which one poet has reflected to another; and had projected a perpetual round of innocent pleasures, of which he suspected no interruption from pride or ignorance or brutality.

With these expectations he was so enchanted, that when he was once gently reproached by a friend for submitting to live upon a subscription, and advised rather by a resolute exertion of his abilities to support himself, he could not bear to debar himself from the happiness which was to be found in the calm of a cottage, or lose the opportunity of listening without intermission to the melody of the nightingale, which he believed was to be heard from every bramble, and which he did not fail to mention as a very important part of the happiness of a country life.

While this scheme was ripening, his friends directed him to take a lodging in the liberties of the Fleet, that he might be secure from his creditors, and sent him every Monday a guinea, which he commonly spent before the next morning and trusted, after his usual manner, the remaining part of the week to the bounty of fortune.

He now began very sensibly to feel the miseries of dependence. Those by whom he was to be supported began to prescribe to him with an air of authority, which he knew not how decently to resent, nor patiently to bear; and he soon discovered, from the conduct of most of his subscribers, that he was yet in the hands of "little creatures."

Of the insolence that he was obliged to suffer he gave many instances, of which none appeared to raise his indignation to a greater height than the method which was taken of furnishing him with clothes. Instead of consulting him, and allowing him to send a tailor his orders for what they thought proper to allow him, they proposed to send for a tailor to take his measure, and then to consult how they should equip him.

This treatment was not very delicate, nor was it such as Savage's humanity would have suggested to him on a like occasion; but it had scarcely deserved mention had it not, by affecting him in an uncommon degree, shown the peculiarity of his character. Upon hearing the design that was formed, he came to the lodging of a friend with the most violent agonies of rage; and, being asked what it could be that gave him such disturbance, he replied with the utmost vehemence of indignation, "That they had sent for a tailor to measure him."

How the affair ended was never inquired, for fear of renewing his uneasiness. It is probable that, upon recollection, he submitted with a good grace to what he could not avoid, and that he discovered no resentment where he had no power.

He was, however, not humbled to implicit and universal compliance; for when the gentleman who had first informed him of the design to support him by a subscription attempted to procure a reconciliation with the Lord Tyrconnel, he could by no means be prevailed upon to comply with the measures that were proposed.

A letter was written for him to Sir William Leman, to prevail upon him to interpose his good offices with Lord Tyrconnel, in which he solicited Sir William's assistance "for a man who really needed it as much as any man could well do"; and informed him that he was retiring "for ever to a place where he should no more trouble his relations, friends or enemies"; he confessed that his passion had betrayed him to some conduct with regard to Lord Tyrconnel for which he could not but heartily ask his pardon; and as he imagined Lord Tyrconnel's passion might be yet so high that he would not "receive a letter from him," begged that Sir William would endeavor to soften him; and expressed his hopes that he would comply with his request, and that "so small a relation would not harden his heart against him."

That any man should presume to dictate a letter to him was not very agreeable to Mr. Savage; and therefore he was, before he had opened it, not much inclined to approve it. But when he read it, he found it contained sentiments entirely opposite to his own and, as he asserted, to the truth; and, therefore, instead of copying it, wrote his friend a letter full of masculine resentment and warm expostulations. He very justly observed, that the style was too supplicatory and

279

the representation too abject, and that he ought at least to have made him complain with "the dignity of a gentleman in distress." He declared that he would not write the paragraph in which he was to ask Lord Tyrconnel's pardon, for "he despised his pardon, and therefore could not heartily, and would not hypocritically, ask it." He remarked that his friend made a very unreasonable distinction between himself and him; for, says he, "when you mention men of high rank in your own character," they are "those little creatures whom we are pleased to call the great"; but when you address them "in mine," no servility is sufficiently humble. He then with great propriety explained the ill-consequences which might be expected from such a letter, which his relations would print in their own defence, and which would for ever be produced as a full answer to all that he should allege against them; for he always intended to publish a minute account of the treatment which he had received. It is to be remembered, to the honor of the gentleman by whom this letter was drawn up, that he yielded to Mr. Savage's reasons, and agreed that it ought to be suppressed.

After many alterations and delays a subscription was at length raised, which did not amount to 50*l.* a year, though twenty were paid by one gentleman: such was the generosity of mankind, that what had been done by a player without solicitation could not now be effected by application and interest; and Savage had a great number to court and to obey for a pension less than that which Mrs. Oldfield paid him without exacting any servilities.

Mr. Savage, however, was satisfied and willing to retire and was convinced that the allowance, though scanty, would be more than sufficient for him, being now determined to commence a rigid economist and to live according to the exact rules of frugality; for nothing was in his opinion more contemptible than a man who, when he knew his income, exceeded it; and yet he confessed that instances of such folly were too common, and lamented that some men were not to be trusted with their own money.

Full of these salutary resolutions, he left London in July 1739, having taken leave with great tenderness of his friends, and parted from the author of this narrative with tears in his eyes. He was furnished with fifteen guineas, and informed that they would be sufficient, not only for the expense of his journey, but for his support in Wales for some time; and that there remained but little more of the first collection. He promised a strict adherence to his maxims of parsimony, and went away in the stagecoach; nor did his friends expect to hear from him till he informed them of his arrival at Swansea.

But when they least expected, arrived a letter dated the fourteenth day after his departure, in which he sent them word that he was yet upon the road, and without money, and that he therefore could not proceed without a remittance. They then sent him the money that was in their hands, with which he was enabled to reach Bristol, from whence he was to go to Swansea by water.

At Bristol he found an embargo laid upon the shipping, so that he could not immediately obtain a passage; and being therefore obliged to stay there some time, he with his usual felicity ingratiated himself with many of the principal inhabitants, was invited to their houses, distinguished at their public feasts and treated with a regard that gratified his vanity, and therefore easily engaged his affection.

He began very early after his retirement to complain of the conduct of his friends in London and irritated many of them so much by his letters that they withdrew, however honorably, their contributions; and it is believed that little more was paid him than the 20*l.* a year which were allowed him by the gentleman who proposed the subscription.

After some stay at Bristol he retired [Sept. 1742] to Swansea, the place originally proposed for his residence, where he lived about a year, very much dissatisfied with the diminution of his salary; but contracted, as in other places, acquaintance with those who were most distinguished in that country, among whom he has celebrated Mr. Powell and Mrs. Jones, by some verses which he inserted in *The Gentleman's Magazine.*

Here he completed his tragedy, of which two acts were wanting when he left London; and was desirous of coming to town to bring it upon the stage. This design was very warmly opposed; and he was advised, by his chief benefactor [Pope], to put it into the hands of Mr. Thomson and Mr. Mallet * that it might be fitted for the stage, and to allow his friends to receive the profits, out of which an annual pension should be paid him.

This proposal he rejected with the utmost contempt. He was by no means convinced that the judgment of those to whom he was required to submit was superior to his own. He was now determined, as he expressed it, to be "no longer kept in leading-strings," and

* James Thomson and David Mallet, poets

had no elevated idea of "his bounty who proposed to pension him out of the profits of his own labors."

He attempted in Wales to promote a subscription for his works, and had once hopes of success; but in a short time afterward formed a resolution of leaving that part of the country, to which he thought it not reasonable to be confined for the gratification of those who, having promised him a liberal income, had no sooner banished him to a remote corner than they reduced his allowance to a salary scarcely equal to the necessities of life.

His resentment of this treatment, which, in his own opinion at least, he had not deserved, was such that he broke off all correspondence with most of his contributors and appeared to consider them as persecutors and oppressors; and in the latter part of his life declared that their conduct toward him since his departure from London "had been perfidiousness improving on perfidiousness and inhumanity on inhumanity."

It is not to be supposed that the necessities of Mr. Savage did not sometimes incite him to satirical exaggerations of the behavior of those by whom he thought himself reduced to them. But it must be granted that the diminution of his allowance was a great hardship, and that those who withdrew their subscription from a man who, upon the faith of their promise, had gone into a kind of banishment, and abandoned all those by whom he had been before relieved in his distresses, will find it no easy task to vindicate their conduct.

It may be alleged, and perhaps justly, that he was petulant and contemptuous—that he more frequently reproached his subscribers for not giving him more, than thanked them for what he received; but it is to be remembered that his conduct—and this is the worst charge that can be drawn up against him—did them no real injury; and that it therefore ought rather to have been pitied than resented—at least the resentment it might provoke ought to have been generous and manly; epithets which his conduct will hardly deserve that starves a man whom he has persuaded to put himself into his power.

It might have been reasonably demanded by Savage that they should, before they had taken away what they promised, have replaced him in his former state—that they should have taken no advantages from the situation to which the appearance of their kindness had reduced him—and that he should have been recalled to London before he was abandoned. He might justly represent that he ought to have been considered as a lion in the toils, and demand to be released before the dogs should be loosed upon him.

He endeavored, indeed, to release himself and, with an intent to return to London, went to Bristol, where a repetition of the kindness which he had formerly found, invited him to stay. He was not only caressed and treated, but had a collection made for him of about 30*l.*, with which it had been happy if he had immediately departed for London; but his negligence did not suffer him to consider that such proofs of kindness were not often to be expected, and that this ardor of benevolence was in a great degree the effect of novelty and might, probably, be every day less; and therefore he took no care to improve the happy time, but was encouraged by one favor to hope for another, till at length generosity was exhausted, and officiousness wearied.

Another part of his misconduct was the practice of prolonging his visits to unseasonable hours and disconcerting all the families into which he was admitted. This was an error in a place of commerce, which all the charms of his conversation could not compensate: for what trader would purchase such airy satisfaction by the loss of solid gain?—which must be the consequence of midnight merriment, as those hours which were gained at night were generally lost in the morning.

Thus Mr. Savage, after the curiosity of the inhabitants was gratified, found the number of his friends daily decreasing, perhaps without suspecting for what reason their conduct was altered; for he still continued to harass, with his nocturnal intrusions, those that yet countenanced him and admitted him to their houses.

But he did not spend all the time of his residence at Bristol in visits or at taverns, for he sometimes returned to his studies and began several considerable designs. When he felt an inclination to write, he always retired from the knowledge of his friends, and lay hid in an obscure part of the suburbs till he found himself again desirous of company, to which it is likely that intervals of absence made him more welcome.

He was always full of his design of returning to London to bring his tragedy upon the stage; but having neglected to depart with the money that was raised for him, he could not afterward procure a sum sufficient to defray the expenses of his journey; nor perhaps would a fresh supply have had any other effect than, by putting immediate pleasures into his power, to have driven the thoughts of his journey out of his mind.

While he was thus spending the day in contriving a scheme for the morrow, distress stole upon him by imperceptible degrees. His conduct had already wearied some of those who were at first enamored of his conversation; but he might, perhaps, still have devolved to others, whom he might have entertained with equal success, had not the decay of his clothes made it no longer consistent with their vanity to admit him to their tables, or to associate with him in public places. He now began to find every man from home at whose house he called, and was therefore no longer able to procure the necessaries of life, but wandered about the town, slighted and neglected, in quest of a dinner, which he did not always obtain.

To complete his misery, he was pursued by the officers for small debts which he had contracted, and was therefore obliged to withdraw from the small number of friends from whom he had still reason to hope for favors. His custom was to lie in bed the greatest part of the day, and to go out in the dark with the utmost privacy and, after having paid his visit, return again before morning to his lodging, which was in the garret of an obscure inn.

Being thus excluded on one hand, and confined on the other, he suffered the utmost extremities of poverty, and often fasted so long that he was seized with faintness and had lost his appetite, not being able to bear the smell of meat till the action of his stomach was restored by a cordial.

In this distress he received a remittance of 5*l*. from London, with which he provided himself a decent coat, and determined to go to London, but unhappily spent his money at a favorite tavern. Thus was he again confined to Bristol, where he was every day hunted by bailiffs. In this exigence he once more found a friend, who sheltered him in his house, though at the usual inconveniences with which his company was attended; for he could neither be persuaded to go to bed in the night, nor to rise in the day.

It is observable that in these various scenes of misery he was always disengaged and cheerful: he at some times pursued his studies, and at others continued or enlarged his epistolary correspondence; nor was he ever so far dejected as to endeavor to procure an increase of his allowance by any other methods than accusations and reproaches.

He had now no longer any hopes of assistance from his friends

284

at Bristol, who as merchants, and by consequence sufficiently studious of profit, cannot be supposed to have looked with much compassion upon negligence and extravagance, or to think any excellence equivalent to a fault of such consequence as neglect of economy. It is natural to imagine that many of those who would have relieved his real wants were discouraged from the exertion of their benevolence by observation of the use which was made of their favors, and conviction that relief would only be momentary, and that the same necessity would quickly return.

At last he quitted the house of his friend and returned to his lodging at the inn, still intending to set out in a few days for London; but on the 10th of January, 1742–3, having been at supper with two of his friends, he was at his return to his lodgings arrested for a debt of about 8*l.*, which he owed at a coffeehouse, and conducted to the house of a sheriff's officer. The account which he gives of this misfortune, in a letter to one of the gentlemen with whom he had supped, is too remarkable to be omitted.

"It was not a little unfortunate for me that I spent yesterday's evening with you, because the hour hindered me from entering on my new lodging; however, I have now got one, but such an one as I believe nobody would choose.

"I was arrested, at the suit of Mrs. Read, just as I was going upstairs to bed at Mr. Bowyer's, but taken in so private a manner, that I believe nobody at the White Lion is apprised of it: though I let the officers know the strength (or rather weakness) of my pocket, yet they treated me with the utmost civility; and even when they conducted me to confinement, it was in such a manner that I verily believe I could have escaped, which I would rather be ruined than have done, notwithstanding the whole amount of my finances was but threepence-halfpenny.

"In the first place I must insist that you will industriously conceal this from Mrs. S——s, because I would not have her good nature suffer that pain which, I know, she would be apt to feel on this occasion.

"Next, I conjure you, dear Sir, by all the ties of friendship, by no means to have one uneasy thought on my account, but to have the same pleasantry of countenance and unruffled serenity of mind which (God be praised!) I have in this, and have had in a much severer calamity. Furthermore, I charge you, if you value my friendship as truly as I do yours, not to utter, or even harbor, the least resentment against Mrs. Read. I believe she has ruined me, but I freely forgive her; and (though I will never more have any intimacy with her) I would, at a due distance, rather do her an act of good than ill-will. Lastly (pardon the expression), I absolutely command you not to offer me any pecuniary assistance, nor to attempt getting me any from any one of your friends. At another time, or on any other occasion, you may, dear friend, be well assured, I would rather write to you in the submissive style of a request, than that of a peremptory command.

"However, that my truly valuable friend may not think I am too proud to ask a favor, let me entreat you to let me have your boy to attend me for this day, not only for the sake of saving me the expense of porters, but for the delivery of some letters to people whose names I would not have known to strangers.

"The civil treatment I have thus far met from those whose prisoner I am makes me thankful to the Almighty, that though he has thought fit to visit me (on my birthnight) with affliction, yet (such is His great goodness!) my affliction is not without alleviating circumstances. I murmur not, but am all resignation to the Divine will. As to the world, I hope that I shall be endued by Heaven with that presence of mind, that serene dignity in misfortune, that constitutes the character of a true nobleman; a dignity far beyond that of coronets; a nobility arising from the just principles of philosophy, refined and exalted by those of Christianity."

He continued five days at the officer's, in hopes that he should be able to procure bail, and avoid the necessity of going to prison. The state in which he passed his time, and the treatment which he received, are very justly expressed by him in a letter which he wrote to a friend: "The whole day," says he, "has been employed in various people's filling my head with their foolish, chimerical systems, which has obliged me coolly (as far as nature will admit) to digest and accommodate myself to every different person's way of thinking; hurried from one wild system to another, till it has quite made a chaos of my imagination, and nothing done—promised—disappointed—ordered to send every hour from one part of the town to the other."

When his friends, who had hitherto caressed and applauded, found that to give bail and pay the debt was the same, they all refused to preserve him from a prison at the expense of 8*l.;* and

286

therefore, after having been for some time at the officer's house, "at an immense expense," as he observes in his letter, he was at length removed to Newgate.

This expense he was enabled to support by the generosity of Mr. Nash,* at Bath, who, upon receiving from him an account of his condition, immediately sent him five guineas, and promised to promote his subscription at Bath with all his interest.

By his removal to Newgate he obtained at least a freedom from suspense, and rest from the disturbing vicissitudes of hope and disappointment; he now found that his friends were only companions who were willing to share his gaiety, but not to partake of his misfortunes; and therefore he no longer expected any assistance from them.

It must, however, be observed of one gentleman that he offered to release him by paying the debt, but that Mr. Savage would not consent, I suppose, because he thought he had before been too burdensome to him.

He was offered by some of his friends that a collection should be made for his enlargement, but he "treated the proposal," and declared "he should again treat it, with disdain. As to writing any mendicant letters, he had too high a spirit, and determined only to write to some ministers of State to try to regain his pension."

He continued to complain of those that had sent him into the country, and objected to them that he had "lost the profits of his play, which had been finished three years"; and in another letter declares his resolution to publish a pamphlet, that the world might know how "he had been used."

This pamphlet was never written; for he in a very short time recovered his usual tranquillity and cheerfully applied himself to more inoffensive studies. He indeed steadily declared that he was promised a yearly allowance of 50l., and never received half the sum; but he seemed to resign himself to that as well as to other misfortunes, and lose the remembrance of it in his amusements and employments. . . .

He was treated by Mr. Dagge, the keeper of the prison, with great humanity; was supported by him at his own table without any certainty of recompense; had a room to himself to which he could at any time retire from all disturbance; was allowed to stand at the

* Beau Nash

door of the prison, and sometimes taken out into the fields; so that he suffered fewer hardships in prison than he had been accustomed to undergo in the greatest part of his life.

The keeper did not confine his benevolence to a gentle execution of his office, but made some overtures to the creditor for his release, though without effect; and continued, during the whole time of his imprisonment, to treat him with the utmost tenderness and civility.

Virtue is undoubtedly most laudable in that state which makes it most difficult, and therefore the humanity of a jailer certainly deserves this public attestation; and the man whose heart has not been hardened by such an employment, may be justly proposed as a pattern of benevolence. If an inscription was once engraved "to the honest tollgatherer," less honors ought not to be paid "to the tender jailer."

Mr. Savage very frequently received visits, and sometimes presents, from his acquaintances, but they did not amount to a subsistence, for the greater part of which he was indebted to the generosity of this keeper; but these favors, however they might endear to him the particular persons from whom he received them, were very far from impressing upon his mind any advantageous ideas of the people of Bristol, and therefore he thought he could not more properly employ himself in prison than in writing a poem called *London and Bristol delineated*.

When he had brought this poem to its present state, which, without considering the chasm, is not perfect, he wrote to London an account of his design, and informed his friend that he was determined to print it with his name, but enjoined him not to communicate his intention to his Bristol acquaintance. The gentleman, surprised at his resolution, endeavored to dissuade him from publishing it, at least from prefixing his name; and declared that he could not reconcile the injunction of secrecy with his resolution to own it at its first appearance. To this Mr. Savage returned an answer agreeable to his character in the following terms:

"I received yours this morning, and not without a little surprise at the contents. To answer a question with a question, you ask me concerning London and Bristol, Why will I add *delineated?* Why did Mr. Woolston * add the same word to his RELIGION OF NATURE? I suppose that it was his will and pleasure to add it in his case; and it is mine to do so in my own. You are pleased to tell me that you

* Thomas Woolston

understand not why secrecy is enjoined and yet I intend to set my name to it. My answer is, I have my private reasons, which I am not obliged to explain to anyone. You doubt my friend Mr. S—— would not approve of it. And what is it to me whether he does or not? Do you imagine that Mr. S—— is to dictate to me? If any man who calls himself my friend should assume such an air, I would spurn at his friendship with contempt. You say I seem to think so by not letting him know it. And suppose I do, what then? Perhaps I can give reasons for that disapprobation, very foreign from what you would imagine. You go on in saying, Suppose I should not put my name to it. My answer is, that I will not suppose any such thing, being determined to the contrary: neither, Sir, would I have you suppose that I applied to you for want of another press; nor would I have you imagine that I owe Mr. S—— obligations which I do not."

Such was his imprudence, and such his obstinate adherence to his own resolutions, however absurd! A prisoner! supported by charity! and, whatever insults he might have received during the latter part of his stay at Bristol, once caressed, esteemed and presented with a liberal collection, he could forget on a sudden his danger and his obligations to gratify the petulance of his wit or the eagerness of his resentment, and publish a satire, by which he might reasonably expect that he should alienate those who then supported him and provoke those whom he could neither resist nor escape.

This resolution, from the execution of which it is probable that only his death could have hindered him, is sufficient to show how much he disregarded all considerations that opposed his present passions, and how readily he hazarded all future advantages for any immediate gratifications. Whatever was his predominant inclination, neither hope nor fear hindered him from complying with it; nor had opposition any other effect than to heighten his ardor and irritate his vehemence.

This performance was however laid aside while he was employed in soliciting assistance from several great persons; and one interruption succeeding another hindered him from supplying the chasm, and perhaps from retouching the other parts, which he can hardly be imagined to have finished in his own opinion, for it is very unequal, and some of the lines are rather inserted to rhyme to others than to support or improve the sense; but the first and last parts are worked up with great spirit and elegance.

His time was spent in the prison for the most part in study or in receiving visits; but sometimes he descended to lower amusements and diverted himself in the kitchen with the conversation of the criminals; for it was not pleasing to him to be much without company; and though he was very capable of a judicious choice, he was often contented with the first that offered; for this he was sometimes reproved by his friends, who found him surrounded with felons; but the reproof was on that, as on other occasions, thrown away; he continued to gratify himself, and to set very little value on the opinion of others.

But here, as in every other scene of his life, he made use of such opportunities as occurred of benefiting those who were more miserable than himself, and was always ready to perform any office of humanity to his fellow prisoners.

He had now ceased from corresponding with any of his subscribers except one [Pope], who yet continued to remit him the 20*l.* a year which he had promised him, and by whom it was expected that he would have been in a very short time enlarged, because he had directed the keeper to inquire after the state of his debts.

However, he took care to enter his name according to the forms of the court, that the creditor might be obliged to make him some allowance if he was continued a prisoner, and when on that occasion he appeared in the hall, was treated with very unusual respect.

But the resentment of the city was afterward raised by some accounts that had been spread of the satire; and he was informed that some of the merchants intended to pay the allowance which the law required, and to detain him a prisoner at their own expense. This he treated as an empty menace, and perhaps might have hastened the publication, only to show how much he was superior to their insults, had not all his schemes been suddenly destroyed.

When he had been six months in prison he received from one of his friends [Pope], in whose kindness he had the greatest confidence, and on whose assistance he chiefly depended, a letter that contained a charge of very atrocious ingratitude, drawn up in such terms as sudden resentment dictated. Henley,* in one of his advertisements, had mentioned "Pope's treatment of Savage." This was supposed by Pope to be the consequence of a complaint made by Savage to Henley, and was therefore mentioned by him with much

* John Henley, ridiculed by Pope in the *Dunciad*

resentment. Mr. Savage returned a very solemn protestation of his innocence, but, however, appeared much disturbed at the accusation. Some days afterward he was seized with a pain in his back and side, which, as it was not violent, was not suspected to be dangerous; but growing daily more languid and dejected, on the 25th of July he confined himself to his room and a fever seized his spirits. The symptoms grew every day more formidable, but his condition did not enable him to procure any assistance. The last time that the keeper saw him was on July the 31st, 1743, when Savage, seeing him at his bedside, said with an uncommon earnestness, "I have something to say to you, Sir," but, after a pause, moved his hand in a melancholy manner, and finding himself unable to recollect what he was going to communicate, said, " 'Tis gone!" The keeper soon after left him, and the next morning he died. He was buried in the churchyard of St. Peter [at Bristol], at the espense of the keeper.

ALEXANDER POPE

1688–1744

* * *

THE PERSON OF POPE is well known not to have been formed by the nicest model. He has, in his account of the "Little Club," compared himself to a spider, and by another is described as protuberant behind and before. He is said to have been beautiful in his infancy; but he was of a constitution originally feeble and weak; and as bodies of a tender frame are easily distorted, his deformity was probably in part the effect of his application. His stature was so low, that, to bring him to a level with common tables, it was necessary to raise his seat. But his face was not displeasing and his eyes were animated and vivid.

By natural deformity, or accidental distortion, his vital functions were so much disordered, that his life was a "long disease." His most frequent assailant was the headache, which he used to relieve by inhaling the steam of coffee, which he very frequently required.

Most of what can be told concerning his petty peculiarities was communicated by a female domestic of the Earl of Oxford, who knew him perhaps after the middle of life. He was then so weak

291

as to stand in perpetual need of female attendance; extremely sensible of cold, so that he wore a kind of fur doublet under a shirt of a very coarse warm linen with fine sleeves. When he rose, he was invested in bodice made of stiff canvas, being scarce able to hold himself erect till they were laced, and he then put on a flannel waist-coat. One side was contracted. His legs were so slender, that he enlarged their bulk with three pair of stockings, which were drawn on and off by the maid; for he was not able to dress or undress himself and neither went to bed nor rose without help. His weakness made it very difficult for him to be clean.

His hair had fallen almost all away; and he used to dine sometimes with Lord Oxford, privately, in a velvet cap. His dress of ceremony was black, with a tiewig and a little sword.

The indulgence and accommodation which his sickness required had taught him all the unpleasing and unsocial qualities of a valetudinary man. He expected that everything should give way to his ease or humor, as a child whose parents will not hear her cry, has an unresisted dominion in the nursery.

> *C'est que l'enfant toujours est homme,*
> *C'est que l'homme est toujours enfant.*

When he wanted to sleep, he "nodded in company"; and once slumbered at his own table while the Prince of Wales was talking of poetry.

The reputation which his friendship gave procured him many invitations; but he was a very troublesome inmate. He brought no servant, and had so many wants that a numerous attendance was scarcely able to supply them. Wherever he was, he left no room for another, because he exacted the attention and employed the activity of the whole family. His errands were so frequent and frivolous that the footmen in time avoided and neglected him; and the Earl of Oxford discharged some of the servants for their resolute refusal of his messages. The maids, when they had neglected their business, alleged that they had been employed by Mr. Pope. One of his constant demands was of coffee in the night, and to the woman that waited on him in his chamber he was very burdensome: but he was careful to recompense her want of sleep; and Lord Oxford's servant declared, that in a house where her business was to answer his call she would not ask for wages.

He had another fault, easily incident to those who, suffering much pain, think themselves entitled to what pleasures they can snatch. He was too indulgent to his appetite; he loved meat highly seasoned and of strong taste; and, at the intervals of the table, amused himself with biscuits and dry conserves. If he sat down to a variety of dishes, he would oppress his stomach with repletion; and though he seemed angry when a dram was offered him, did not forbear to drink it. His friends, who knew the avenues to his heart, pampered him with presents of luxury, which he did not suffer to stand neglected. The death of great men is not always proportioned to the luster of their lives. Hannibal, says Juvenal,* did not perish by a javelin or a sword; the slaughters of Cannae were revenged by a ring. The death of Pope was imputed by some of his friends to a silver saucepan, in which it was his delight to heat potted lampreys. . . .

In familiar or convivial conversation it does not appear that he excelled. He may be said to have resembled Dryden as being not one that was distinguished by vivacity in company. It is remarkable that, so near his time, so much should be known of what he has written and so little of what he has said: traditional memory retains no sallies of raillery nor sentences of observation; nothing either pointed or solid, either wise or merry. One apothegm only stands upon record. When an objection raised against his inscription for Shakespeare was defended by the authority of Patrick,† he replied —*horresco referens*—that "he would allow the publisher of a Dictionary to know the meaning of a single word, but not of two words put together."

He was fretful and easily displeased, and allowed himself to be capriciously resentful. He would sometimes leave Lord Oxford silently, no one could tell why, and was to be courted back by more letters and messages than the footmen were willing to carry. The table was indeed infested by Lady Mary Wortley, who was the friend of Lady Oxford, and who, knowing his peevishness, could by no intreaties be restrained from contradicting him, till their disputes were sharpened to such asperity that one or the other quitted the house.

He sometimes condescended to be jocular with servants or inferiors; but by no merriment, either of others or his own, was he ever seen excited to laughter.

* Roman poet
† Samuel Patrick

Of his domestic character frugality was a part eminently remarkable. Having determined not to be dependent, he determined not to be in want, and therefore wisely and magnanimously rejected all temptations to expense unsuitable to his fortune. This general care must be universally approved; but it sometimes appeared in petty artifices of parsimony, such as the practice of writing his compositions on the back of letters, as may be seen in the remaining copy of the Iliad, by which perhaps in five years five shillings were saved; or in a niggardly reception of his friends and scantiness of entertainment, as, when he had two guests in his house, he would set at supper a single pint upon the table; and, having himself taken two small glasses, would retire and say, "Gentlemen, I leave you to your wine." Yet he tells his friends that "he has a heart for all, a house for all and, whatever they may think, a fortune for all."

He sometimes, however, made a splendid dinner, and is said to have wanted no part of the skill or elegance which such performances require. That this magnificence should be often displayed, that obstinate prudence with which he conducted his affairs would not permit; for his revenue, certain and casual, amounted only to about eight hundred pounds a year, of which however he declares himself able to assign one hundred to charity.

Of this fortune, which, as it arose from public approbation, was very honorably obtained, his imagination seems to have been too full: it would be hard to find a man, so well entitled to notice by his wit, that ever delighted so much in talking of his money. In his letters and in his poems, his garden and his grotto, his quincunx and his vines, or some hints of his opulence, are always to be found. The great topic of his ridicule is poverty; the crimes with which he reproaches his antagonists are their debts, their habitation in the Mint,* and their want of a dinner. He seems to be of an opinion not very uncommon in the world, that to want money is to want everything.

Next to the pleasure of contemplating his possessions seems to be that of enumerating the men of high rank with whom he was acquainted, and whose notice he loudly proclaims not to have been obtained by any practices of meanness or servility, a boast which was never denied to be true, and to which very few poets have ever aspired. Pope never set genius to sale; he never flattered those whom he did not love or praised those whom he did not esteem. Savage

* A place of asylum near Queens Prison, London

however remarked, that he began a little to relax his dignity when he wrote a distich for "his Highness's dog."

His admiration of the great seems to have increased in the advance of life. He passed over peers and statesmen to inscribe his *Iliad* to Congreve, with a magnanimity of which the praise had been complete, had his friend's virtue been equal to his wit. Why he was chosen for so great an honor it is not now possible to know; there is no trace in literary history of any particular intimacy between them. The name of Congreve appears in the letters among those of his other friends, but without any observable distinction or consequence.

To his latter works, however, he took care to annex names dignified with titles, but was not very happy in his choice; for, except Lord Bathurst, none of his noble friends were such as that a good man would wish to have his intimacy with them known to posterity: he can derive little honor from the notice of Cobham,* Burlington,† or Bolingbroke.‡

Of his social qualities, if an estimate be made from his Letters, an opinion too favorable cannot easily be formed; they exhibit a perpetual and unclouded effulgence of general benevolence and particular fondness. There is nothing but liberality, gratitude, constancy and tenderness. It has been so long said as to be commonly believed, that the true characters of men may be found in their letters, and that he who writes to his friend lays his heart open before him. But the truth is, that such were the simple friendships of the "Golden Age," and are now the friendships only of children. Very few can boast of hearts which they dare lay open to themselves, and of which, by whatever accident exposed, they do not shun a distinct and continued view; and, certainly, what we hide from ourselves we do not show to our friends. There is, indeed, no transaction which offers stronger temptations to fallacy and sophistication than epistolary intercourse. In the eagerness of conversation the first emotions of the mind often burst out before they are considered; in the tumult of business, interest and passion have their genuine effect; but a friendly letter is a calm and deliberate performance, in the cool of leisure, in the stillness of solitude, and surely no man sits down to depreciate by design his own character.

* Richard Temple, Viscount Cobham
† Richard Boyle, third Earl of Burlington
‡ Henry St. John, Viscount Bolingbroke, English statesman

Friendship has no tendency to secure veracity; for by whom can a man so much wish to be thought better than he is, as by him whose kindness he desires to gain or keep? Even in writing to the world there is less constraint; the author is not confronted with his reader and takes his chance of approbation among the different dispositions of mankind; but a letter is addressed to a single mind, of which the prejudices and partialities are known, and must therefore please, if not by favoring them, by forbearing to oppose them.

To charge those favorable representations which men give of their own minds with the guilt of hypocritical falsehood, would show more severity than knowledge. The writer commonly believes himself. Almost every man's thoughts, while they are general, are right; and most hearts are pure while temptation is away. It is easy to awaken generous sentiments in privacy; to despise death when there is no danger; to glow with benevolence when there is nothing to be given. While such ideas are formed they are felt, and self-love does not suspect the gleam of virtue to be the meteor of fancy.

If the Letters of Pope are considered merely as compositions, they seem to be premeditated and artificial. It is one thing to write, because there is something which the mind wishes to discharge; and another to solicit the imagination, because ceremony or vanity requires something to be written. Pope confesses his early letters to be vitiated with *affectation and ambition:* to know whether he disentangled himself from these perverters of epistolary integrity his book and his life must be set in comparison.

One of his favorite topics is contempt of his own poetry. For this, if it had been real, he would deserve no commendation; and in this he was certainly not sincere, for his high value of himself was sufficiently observed; and of what could he be proud but of his poetry? He writes, he says, when "he has just nothing else to do"; yet Swift complains that he was never at leisure for conversation, because he "had always some poetical scheme in his head." It was punctually required that his writing box should be set upon his bed before he rose; and Lord Oxford's domestic related, that in the dreadful winter of Forty [1740] she was called from her bed by him four times in one night to supply him with paper lest he should lose a thought.

He pretends insensibility to censure and criticism, though it was observed by all who knew him that every pamphlet disturbed his quiet, and that his extreme irritability laid him open to perpetual vexation; but he wished to despise his critics, and therefore hoped that he did despise them.

As he happened to live in two reigns when the Court paid little attention to poetry, he nursed in his mind a foolish disesteem of kings, and proclaims that "he never sees courts." Yet a little regard shown him by the Prince of Wales melted his obduracy; and he had not much to say when he was asked by his Royal Highness, "How he could love a prince while he disliked kings?"

He very frequently professes contempt of the world, and represents himself as looking on mankind, sometimes with gay indifference, as on emmets of a hillock, below his serious attention; and sometimes with gloomy indignation, as on monsters more worthy of hatred than of pity. These were dispositions apparently counterfeited. How could he despise those whom he lived by pleasing, and on whose approbation his esteem of himself was superstructed? Why should he hate those to whose favor he owed his honor and his ease? Of things that terminate in human life, the world is the proper judge; to despise its sentence, if it were possible, is not just; and if it were just, is not possible. Pope was far enough from this unreasonable temper; he was sufficiently *a fool to Fame,* and his fault was, that he pretended to neglect it. His levity and his sullenness were only in his Letters; he passed through common life, sometimes vexed and sometimes pleased, with the natural emotions of common men.

His scorn of the Great is repeated too often to be real; no man thinks much of that which he despises; and as falsehood is always in danger of inconsistency, he makes it his boast at another time that he lives among them.

It is evident that his own importance swells often in his mind. He is afraid of writing, lest the clerks of the post office should know his secrets; he has many enemies; he considers himself as surrounded by universal jealousy; "after many deaths and many dispersions, two or three of us," says he, "may still be brought together, not to plot, but to divert ourselves and the world too, if it pleases"; and they can live together, and "show what friends wits may be, in spite of all the fools in the world." All this while it was likely that the clerks did not know his hand; he certainly had no more enemies than a public character like his inevitably excites; and with what degree of friendship the wits might live, very few were so much fools as ever to inquire.

Some part of this pretended discontent he learned from Swift and expresses it, I think, most frequently in his correspondence with him. Swift's resentment was unreasonable, but it was sincere; Pope's was the mere mimicry of his friend, a fictitious part which he began to play before it became him. When he was only twenty-five years old, he related that "a glut of study and retirement had thrown him on the world," and that there was danger lest "a glut of the world should throw him back upon study and retirement." To this Swift answered with great propriety, that Pope had not yet either acted or suffered enough in the world to have become weary of it. And, indeed, it must be some very powerful reason that can drive back to solitude him who has once enjoyed the pleasures of society.

In the Letters both of Swift and Pope there appears such narrowness of mind as makes them insensible of any excellence that has not some affinity with their own, and confines their esteem and approbation to so small a number, that whoever should form his opinion of the age from their representation, would suppose them to have lived amidst ignorance and barbarity, unable to find among their contemporaries either virtue or intelligence, and persecuted by those that could not understand them.

When Pope murmurs at the world, when he professes contempt of fame, when he speaks of riches and poverty, of success and disappointment, with negligent indifference, he certainly does not express his habitual and settled sentiments, but either willfully disguises his own character or, what is more likely, invests himself with temporary qualities and sallies out in the colors of the present moment. His hopes and fears, his joys and sorrows, acted strongly upon his mind; and if he differed from others, it was not by carelessness; he was irritable and resentful; his malignity to Philips, whom he had first made ridiculous, and then hated for being angry, continued too long. Of his vain desire to make Bentley contemptible, I never heard any adequate reason. He was sometimes wanton in his attacks; and, before Chandos, Lady Wortley and Hill,* was mean in his retreat.

The virtues which seem to have had most of his affection were liberality and fidelity of friendship, in which it does not appear that he was other than he describes himself. His fortune did not suffer his charity to be splendid and conspicuous; but he assisted Dodsley † with a hundred pounds, that he might open a shop; and of the sub-

* Ambrose Philips, poet; Richard Bentley, scholar and critic; James Brydges, Duke of Chandos; Aaron Hill, poet
† Robert Dodsley, bookseller and publisher

scription of forty pounds a year that he raised for Savage, twenty were paid by himself. He was accused of loving money, but his love was eagerness to gain, not solicitude to keep it.

In the duties of friendship he was zealous and constant; his early maturity of mind commonly united him with men older than himself; and therefore, without attaining any considerable length of life, he saw many companions of his youth sink into the grave; but it does not appear that he lost a single friend by coldness or by injury; those who loved him once, continued their kindness. His ungrateful mention of Allen * in his will was the effect of his adherence to one whom he had known much longer, and whom he naturally loved with greater fondness. His violation of the trust reposed in him by Bolingbroke could have no motive inconsistent with the warmest affection; he either thought the action so near to indifferent that he forgot it, or so laudable that he expected his friend to approve it.

It was reported, with such confidence as almost to enforce belief, that in the papers intrusted to his executors was found a defamatory Life of Swift, which he had prepared as an instrument of vengeance, to be used if any provocation should be ever given. About this I inquired of the Earl of Marchmont, who assured me that no such piece was among his remains.

The religion in which he lived and died was that of the Church of Rome, to which in his correspondence with Racine † he professes himself a sincere adherent. That he was not scrupulously pious in some part of his life, is known by many idle and indecent applications of sentences taken from the Scriptures; a mode of merriment which a good man dreads for its profaneness, and a witty man disdains for its easiness and vulgarity. But to whatever levities he has been betrayed, it does not appear that his principles were ever corrupted, or that he ever lost his belief of Revelation. The positions which he transmitted from Bolingbroke he seems not to have understood, and was pleased with an interpretation that made them orthodox.

A man of such exalted superiority and so little moderation would naturally have all his delinquencies observed and aggravated: those who could not deny that he was excellent, would rejoice to find that he was not perfect.

Perhaps it may be imputed to the unwillingness with which the

* Ralph Allen
† Jean Baptiste Racine, French poet and dramatist

299

same man is allowed to possess many advantages, that his learning has been depreciated. He certainly was, in his early life, a man of great literary curiosity; and when he wrote his *Essay on Criticism* had, for his age, a very wide acquaintance with books. When he entered into the living world, it seems to have happened to him as to many others, that he was less attentive to dead masters; he studied in the academy of Paracelsus,* and made the universe his favorite volume. He gathered his notions fresh from reality, not from the copies of authors, but the originals of Nature. Yet there is no reason to believe that literature ever lost his esteem; he always professed to love reading; and Dobson, who spent some time at his house translating his *Essay on Man,* when I asked him what learning he found him to possess, answered, "More than I expected." His frequent references to history, his allusions to various kinds of knowledge and his images selected from art and nature, with his observations on the operations of the mind and the modes of life, show an intelligence perpetually on the wing, excursive, vigorous and diligent, eager to pursue knowledge, and attentive to retain it.

From this curiosity arose the desire of traveling, to which he alludes in his verses to Jervas,† and which, though he never found an opportunity to gratify it, did not leave him till his life declined.

Of his intellectual character, the constituent and fundamental principle was good sense, a prompt and intuitive perception of consonance and propriety. He saw immediately, of his own conceptions, what was to be chosen, and what to be rejected; and, in the works of others, what was to be shunned and what was to be copied.

But good sense alone is a sedate and quiescent quality, which manages its possessions well, but does not increase them; it collects few materials for its own operations and preserves safety, but never gains supremacy. Pope had likewise genius; a mind active, ambitious and adventurous, always investigating, always aspiring; in its widest searches still longing to go forward, in its highest flights still wishing to be higher; always imagining something greater than it knows, always endeavoring more than it can do.

To assist these powers, he is said to have had great strength and exactness of memory. That which he had heard or read was not easily lost; and he had before him not only what his own meditations

* Swiss alchemist and physician.
† Charles Jervas, painter

300

suggested, but what he had found in other writers, that might be accommodated to his present purpose.

These benefits of nature he improved by incessant and unwearied diligence; he had recourse to every source of intelligence and lost no opportunity of information; he consulted the living as well as the dead; he read his compositions to his friends and was never content with mediocrity when excellence could be attained. He considered poetry as the business of his life; and, however he might seem to lament his occupation, he followed it with constancy; to make verses was his first labor, and to mend them was his last.

From his attention to poetry he was never diverted. If conversation offered anything that could be improved, he committed it to paper; if a thought, or perhaps an expression more happy than was common, rose to his mind, he was careful to write it; an independent distich was preserved for an opportunity of insertion; and some little fragments have been found containing lines, or parts of lines, to be wrought upon at some other time.

He was one of those few whose labor is their pleasure: he was never elevated to negligence, nor wearied to impatience; he never passed a fault unamended by indifference, nor quitted it by despair. He labored his works first to gain reputation and afterward to keep it.

Of composition there are different methods. Some employ at once memory and invention and, with little intermediate use of the pen, form and polish large masses by continued meditation, and write their productions only when, in their own opinion, they have completed them. It is related of Vergil, that his custom was to pour out a great number of verses in the morning, and pass the day in retrenching exuberances and correcting inaccuracies. The method of Pope, as may be collected from his translation, was to write his first thoughts in his first words, and gradually to amplify, decorate, rectify and refine them.

With such faculties, and such dispositions, he excelled every other writer in poetical prudence; he wrote in such a manner as might expose him to few hazards. He used almost always the same fabric of verse; and, indeed, by those few essays which he made of any other, he did not enlarge his reputation. Of this uniformity the certain consequence was readiness and dexterity. By perpetual practice, language had, in his mind, a systematical arrangement; having always the same use for words, he had words so selected and combined as to be ready at his call. This increase of facility he confessed himself to have perceived in the progress of his translation.

But what was yet of more importance, his effusions were always voluntary and his subjects chosen by himself. His independence secured him from drudging at a task, and laboring upon a barren topic: he never exchanged praise for money, nor opened a shop of condolence or congratulation. His poems, therefore, were scarce ever temporary. He suffered coronations and royal marriages to pass without a song, and derived no opportunities from recent events, nor any popularity from the accidental disposition of his readers. He was never reduced to the necessity of soliciting the sun to shine upon a birthday, of calling the Graces and Virtues to a wedding, or of saying what multitudes have said before him. When he could produce nothing new, he was at liberty to be silent.

His publications were for the same reason never hasty. He is said to have sent nothing to the press till it had lain two years under his inspection: it is at least certain that he ventured nothing without nice examination. He suffered the tumult of imagination to subside, and the novelties of invention to grow familiar. He knew that the mind is always enamored of its own productions, and did not trust his first fondness. He consulted his friends, and listened with great willingness to criticism; and, what was of more importance, he consulted himself, and let nothing pass against his own judgment.

He professed to have learned his poetry from Dryden, whom, whenever an opportunity was presented, he praised through his whole life with unvaried liberality; and perhaps his character may receive some illustration, if he be compared with his master.

Integrity of understanding and nicety of discernment were not allotted in a less proportion to Dryden than to Pope. The rectitude of Dryden's mind was sufficiently shown by the dismission of his poetical prejudices, and the rejection of unnatural thoughts and rugged numbers. But Dryden never desired to apply all the judgment that he had. He wrote and professed to write merely for the people; and when he pleased others, he contented himself. He spent no time in struggles to rouse latent powers; he never attempted to make that better which was already good, nor often to mend what he must have known to be faulty. He wrote, as he tells us, with very little consideration; when occasion or necessity called upon him, he poured out what the present moment happened to supply, and, when once it had passed the press, ejected it from his mind; for when he had no pecuniary interest, he had no further solicitude.

Pope was not content to satisfy; he desired to excel, and therefore always endeavored to do his best: he did not court the candor, but dared the judgment of his reader and expecting no indulgence from others, he showed none to himself. He examined lines and words with minute and punctilious observation, and retouched every part with indefatigable diligence, till he had left nothing to be forgiven.

For this reason he kept his pieces very long in his hands, while he considered and reconsidered them. The only poems which can be supposed to have been written with such regard to the times as might hasten their publication were the two satires of *Thirty-eight;* of which Dodsley told me that they were brought to him by the author, that they might be fairly copied. "Almost every line," he said, "was then written twice over; I gave him a clean transcript, which he sent some time afterward to me for the press, with almost every line written twice over a second time."

His declaration that his care for his works ceased at their publication was not strictly true. His parental attention never abandoned them; what he found amiss in the first edition, he silently corrected in those that followed. He appears to have revised the *Iliad,* and freed it from some of its imperfections; and the *Essay on Criticism* received many improvements after its first appearance. It will seldom be found that he altered without adding clearness, elegance, or vigor. Pope had perhaps the judgment of Dryden; but Dryden certainly wanted the diligence of Pope.

In acquired knowledge, the superiority must be allowed to Dryden, whose education was more scholastic, and who before he became an author had been allowed more time for study, with better means of information. His mind has a larger range, and he collects his images and illustrations from a more extensive circumference of science. Dryden knew more of man in his general nature and Pope in his local manners. The notions of Dryden were formed by comprehensive speculation and those of Pope by minute attention. There is more dignity in the knowledge of Dryden and more certainty in that of Pope.

Poetry was not the sole praise of either; for both excelled likewise in prose; but Pope did not borrow his prose from his predecessor. The style of Dryden is capricious and varied; that of Pope is cautious and uniform. Dryden observes the motions of his own mind;

303

Pope constrains his mind to his own rules of composition. Dryden is sometimes vehement and rapid; Pope is always smooth, uniform and gentle. Dryden's page is a natural field, rising into inequalities and diversified by the varied exuberance of abundant vegetation; Pope's is a velvet lawn, shaven by the scythe and leveled by the roller.

Of genius, that power which constitutes a poet; that quality without which judgment is cold and knowledge is inert; that energy which collects, combines, amplifies and animates; the superiority must, with some hesitation, be allowed to Dryden. It is not to be inferred that of this poetical vigor Pope had only a little, because Dryden had more; for every other writer since Milton must give place to Pope; and even of Dryden it must be said, that, if he has brighter paragraphs, he has not better poems. Dryden's performances were always hasty, either excited by some external occasion, or extorted by domestic necessity; he composed without consideration and published without correction. What his mind could supply at call or gather in one excursion was all that he sought, and all that he gave. The dilatory caution of Pope enabled him to condense his sentiments, to multiply his images, and to accumulate all that study might produce or chance might supply. If the flights of Dryden therefore are higher, Pope continues longer on the wing. If of Dryden's fire the blaze is brighter, of Pope's the heat is more regular and constant. Dryden often surpasses expectation and Pope never falls below it. Dryden is read with frequent astonishment, and Pope with perpetual delight. . . .

The works of Pope are now to be distinctly examined, not so much with attention to slight faults or petty beauties, as to the general character and effect of each performance.

It seems natural for a young poet to initiate himself by pastorals, which, not professing to imitate real life, require no experience; and, exhibiting only the simple operation of unmingled passions, admit no subtle reasoning or deep inquiry. Pope's *Pastorals* are not, however, composed but with close thought; they have reference to the time of the day, the seasons of the year and the periods of human life. The last, that which turns the attention upon age and death, was the author's favorite. To tell of disappointment and misery, to thicken the darkness of futurity and perplex the labyrinth of uncertainty has been always a delicious employment of the poets. His preference was probably just. I wish, however, that his fondness had not overlooked a line in which the *Zephyrs* are made *to lament in silence*.

To charge these *Pastorals* with want of invention, is to require what was never intended. The imitations are so ambitiously frequent, that the writer evidently means rather to show his literature than his wit. It is surely sufficient for an author of sixteen, not only to be able to copy the poems of antiquity with judicious selection, but to have obtained sufficient power of language and skill in meter to exhibit a series of versification which had in English poetry no precedent, nor has since had an imitation.

The design of *Windsor Forest* is evidently derived from *Cooper's Hill,* with some attention to Waller's * poem on *The Park;* but Pope cannot be denied to excel his masters in variety and elegance, and the art of interchanging description, narrative and morality. The objection made by Dennis is the want of plan, of a regular subordination of parts terminating in the principal and original design. There is this want in most descriptive poems, because as the scenes, which they must exhibit successively, are all subsisting at the same time, the order in which they are shown must by necessity be arbitrary, and more is not to be expected from the last part than from the first. The attention, therefore, which cannot be detained by suspense, must be excited by diversity, such as his poem offers to its reader.

But the desire of diversity may be too much indulged; the parts of *Windsor Forest* which deserve least praise, are those which were added to enliven the stillness of the scene, the appearance of Father Thames and the transformation of Lodona. Addison had in his *Campaign* derided the rivers that "rise from their oozy beds" to tell stories of heroes; and it is therefore strange that Pope should adopt a fiction not only unnatural, but lately censured. The story of Lodona is told with sweetness; but a new metamorphosis is a ready and puerile expedient: nothing is easier than to tell how a flower was once a blooming virgin, or a rock an obdurate tyrant.

The *Temple of Fame* has, as Steele warmly declared, "a thousand beauties." Every part is splendid; there is great luxuriance of ornaments; the original vision of Chaucer was never denied to be much improved; the allegory is very skilfully continued, the imagery is properly selected and learnedly displayed: yet, with all this comprehension of excellence, as its scene is laid in remote ages and its

* Edmund Waller

sentiments, if the concluding paragraph be excepted, have little relation to general manners or common life, it never obtained much notice, but is turned silently over, and seldom quoted or mentioned with either praise or blame.

That the *Messiah* excels the *Pollio* is no great praise, if it be considered from what original the improvements are derived.

The *Verses on the Unfortunate Lady* have drawn much attention by the illaudable singularity of treating suicide with respect; and they must be allowed to be written in some parts with vigorous animation, and in others with gentle tenderness; nor has Pope produced any poem in which the sense predominates more over the diction. But the tale is not skilfully told; it is not easy to discover the character of either the Lady or her Guardian. History relates that she was about to disparage herself by a marriage with an inferior; Pope praises her for the dignity of ambition, and yet condemns the uncle to detestation for his pride; the ambitious love of a niece may be opposed by the interest, malice or envy of an uncle, but never by his pride. On such an occasion a poet may be allowed to be obscure, but inconsistency never can be right.

The *Ode for St. Cecilia's Day* was undertaken at the desire of Steele: in this the author is generally confessed to have miscarried, yet he has miscarried only as compared with Dryden; for he has far outgone other competitors. Dryden's plan is better chosen; history will always take stronger hold of the attention than fable: the passions excited by Dryden are the pleasures and pains of real life, the scene of Pope is laid in imaginary existence; Pope is read with calm acquiescence, Dryden with turbulent delight; Pope hangs upon the ear, and Dryden finds the passes of the mind.

Both the odes want the essential constituent of metrical compositions, the stated recurrence of settled numbers. It may be alleged, that Pindar is said by Horace * to have written *numeris lege solutis:* but as no such lax performances have been transmitted to us, the meaning of that expression cannot be fixed; and perhaps the like return might properly be made to a modern Pindarist, as Mr. Cobb †️ received from Bentley, who, when he found his criticisms upon a Greek Exercise, which Cobb had presented, refuted one after another by Pindar's authority, cried out at last, "Pindar was a bold fellow, but thou art an impudent one."

* Pindar, Greek poet; Horace, Roman poet
† Samuel Cobb

If Pope's ode be particularly inspected, it will be found that the first stanza consists of sounds well chosen indeed, but only sounds.

The second consists of hyperbolical commonplaces, easily to be found, and perhaps without much difficulty to be as well expressed.

In the third, however, there are numbers, images, harmony and vigor, not unworthy the antagonist of Dryden. Had all been like this —but every part cannot be the best.

The next stanzas place and detain us in the dark and dismal regions of mythology, where neither hope nor fear, neither joy nor sorrow, can be found: the poet, however, faithfully attends us; we have all that can be performed by elegance of diction or sweetness of versification; but what can form avail without better matter?

The last stanza recurs again to commonplaces. The conclusion is too evidently modeled by that of Dryden; and it may be remarked that both end with the same fault; the comparison of each is literal on one side, and metaphorical on the other.

Poets do not always express their own thoughts: Pope, with all this labor in the praise of music, was ignorant of its principles, and insensible of its effects.

One of his greatest, though of his earliest works, is the *Essay on Criticism,* which, if he had written nothing else, would have placed him among the first critics and the first poets, as it exhibits every mode of excellence that can embellish or dignify didactic composition—selection of matter, novelty of arrangement, justness of precept, splendor of illustration, and propriety of digression. I know not whether it be pleasing to consider that he produced this piece at twenty, and never afterwards excelled it: he that delights himself with observing that such powers may be soon attained, cannot but grieve to think that life was ever after at a stand.

To mention the particular beauties of the *Essay* would be unprofitably tedious; but I cannot forbear to observe, that the comparison of a student's progress in the sciences with the journey of a traveler in the Alps, is perhaps the best that English poetry can show. A simile, to be perfect, must both illustrate and ennoble the subject; must show it to the understanding in a clearer view, and display it to the fancy with greater dignity; but either of these qualities may be sufficient to recommend it. In didactic poetry, of which the great purpose is instruction, a simile may be praised which illustrates, though it does not ennoble; in heroics, that may be admitted which ennobles, though it does not illustrate. That it may be complete, it

307

is required to exhibit, independently of its references, a pleasing image; for a simile is said to be a short episode. To this antiquity was so attentive, that circumstances were sometimes added, which, having no parallels, served only to fill the imagination, and produced what Perrault * ludicrously called "comparisons with a long tail." In their similes the greatest writers have sometimes failed: the ship race, compared with the chariot race, is neither illustrated nor aggrandized; land and water make all the difference: when Apollo, running after Daphne, is likened to a greyhound chasing a hare, there is nothing gained; the ideas of pursuit and flight are too plain to be made plainer; and a god and the daughter of a god are not represented much to their advantage by a hare and dog. The simile of the Alps has no useless parts, yet affords a striking picture by itself; it makes the foregoing position better understood, and enables it to take faster hold on the attention; it assists the apprehension and elevates the fancy.

Let me likewise dwell a little on the celebrated paragraph in which it is directed that "the sound should seem an echo to the sense"; a precept which Pope is allowed to have observed beyond any other English poet.

This notion of representative meter, and the desire of discovering frequent adaptations of the sound to the sense, have produced, in my opinion, many wild conceits and imaginary beauties. All that can furnish this representation are the sounds of the words considered singly, and the time in which they are pronounced. Every language has some words framed to exhibit the noises which they express, as *thump, rattle, growl, hiss.* These, however, are but few; and the poet cannot make them more, nor can they be of any use but when sound is to be mentioned. The time of pronunciation was in the dactylic measures of the learned languages capable of considerable variety; but that variety could be accommodated only to motion of duration, and different degrees of motion were perhaps expressed by verses rapid or slow, without much attention of the writer, when the image had full possession of his fancy; but our language having little flexibility, our verses can differ very little in their cadence. The fancied resemblances, I fear, arise sometimes merely from the ambiguity of words; there is supposed to be some relation between a *soft* line and *soft* couch, or between *hard* syllables and *hard* fortune.

Motion, however, may be in some sort exemplified; and yet it

* Charles Perrault, French author of fairy tales

may be suspected that in such resemblances the mind often governs the ear, and the sounds are estimated by their meaning. One of their most successful attempts has been to describe the labor of Sisyphus:

> *With many a weary step, and many a groan,*
> *Up the high hill he heaves a huge round stone;*
> *The huge round stone, resulting with a bound,*
> *Thunders impetuous down, and smokes along the ground.*

Who does not perceive the stone to move slowly upward, and roll violently back? But set the same numbers to another sense:

> *While many a merry tale, and many a song,*
> *Cheer'd the rough road, we wish'd the rough road long;*
> *The rough road then, returning in a round,*
> *Mock'd our impatient steps, for all was fairy ground.*

We have now surely lost much of the delay, and much of the rapidity.

But, to show how little the greatest master of numbers can fix the principles of representative harmony, it will be sufficient to remark that the poet who tells us that

> *When Ajax strives some rock's vast weight to throw,*
> *The line too labors, and the words move slow;*
> *Not so when swift Camilla scours the plain,*
> *Flies o'er th' unbending corn, and skims along the main;*

when he had enjoyed for about thirty years the praise of Camilla's * lightness of foot, he tried another experiment upon *sound* and *time,* and produced this memorable triplet:

> *Waller was smooth; but Dryden taught to join*
> *The varying verse, the full resounding line,*
> *The long majestic march, and energy divine.*

Here are the swiftness of the rapid race, and the march of slow-paced majesty, exhibited by the same poet in the same sequence of syllables, except that the exact prosodist will find the line of *swiftness* by one time longer than that of *tardiness.*

Beauties of this kind are commonly fancied; and, when real, are technical and nugatory, not to be rejected, and not to be solicited.

To the praises which have been accumulated on *The Rape of the*

* Queen of the Volscians

Lock by readers of every class, from the critic to the waiting maid, it is difficult to make any addition. Of that which is universally allowed to be the most attractive of all ludicrous compositions, let it rather be now inquired from what sources the power of pleasing is derived.

Dr. Warburton,* who excelled in critical perspicacity, has remarked that the preternatural agents are very happily adapted to the purposes of the poem. The heathen deities can no longer gain attention: we should have turned away from a contest between Venus and Diana. The employment of allegorical persons always excites conviction of its own absurdity; they may produce effects, but cannot conduct actions: when the phantom is put in motion, it dissolves: thus *Discord* may raise a mutiny; but *Discord* cannot conduct a march, nor besiege a town. Pope brought in view a new race of beings, with powers and passions proportionate to their operation. The sylphs and gnomes act at the toilet and the tea table, what more terrific and more powerful phantoms perform on the stormy ocean or the field of battle; they give their proper help and do their proper mischief.

Pope is said, by an objector, not to have been the inventor of this petty nation; a charge which might with more justice have been brought against the author of the *Iliad,* who doubtless adopted the religious system of his country; for what is there but the names of his agents which Pope has not invented? Has he not assigned them characters and operations never heard of before? Has he not, at least, given them their first poetical existence? If this is not sufficient to denominate his work original, nothing original ever can be written.

In this work are exhibited, in a very high degree, the two most engaging powers of an author. New things are made familiar and familiar things are made new. A race of aerial people, never heard of before, is presented to us in a manner so clear and easy, that the reader seeks for no further information, but immediately mingles with his new acquaintance, adopts their interests and attends their pursuits, loves a sylph and detests a gnome.

That familiar things are made new, every paragraph will prove. The subject of the poem is an event below the common incidents of common life; nothing real is introduced that is not seen so often as to be no longer regarded; yet the whole detail of a female-day is here brought before us, invested with so much art of decoration,

* William Warburton, bishop and theologian

that, though nothing is disguised, everything is striking and we feel all the appetite of curiosity for that from which we have a thousand times turned fastidiously away.

The purpose of the poet is, as he tells us, to laugh at "the little unguarded follies of the female sex." It is therefore without justice that Dennis charges *The Rape of the Lock* with the want of a moral, and for that reason sets it below the *Lutrin,* which exposes the pride and discord of the clergy. Perhaps neither Pope nor Boileau * has made the world much better than he found it; but, if they had both succeeded, it were easy to tell who would have deserved most from public gratitude. The freaks and humors and spleen and vanity of women, as they embroil families in discord, and fill houses with disquiet, do more to obstruct the happiness of life in a year than the ambition of the clergy in many centuries. It has been well observed, that the misery of man proceeds not from any single crush of overwhelming evil, but from small vexations continually repeated.

It is remarked by Dennis likewise that the machinery is superfluous; that, by all the bustle of preternatural operation, the main event is neither hastened nor retarded. To this charge an efficacious answer is not easily made. The Sylphs cannot be said to help or to oppose, and it must be allowed to imply some want of art, that their power has not been sufficiently intermingled with the action. Other parts may likewise be charged with want of connection; the game at *ombre* might be spared; but if the Lady had lost her hair while she was intent upon her cards, it might have been inferred that those who are too fond of play will be in danger of neglecting more important interests. Those perhaps are faults; but what are such faults to so much excellence?

The *Epistle of Eloisa to Abelard* is one of the most happy productions of human wit; the subject is so judiciously chosen, that it would be difficult, in turning over the annals of the world, to find another which so many circumstances concur to recommend. We regularly interest ourselves most in the fortune of those who most deserve our notice. Abelard and Eloisa were conspicuous in their days for eminence of merit. The heart naturally loves truth. The adventures and misfortunes of this illustrious pair are known from undisputed history. Their fate does not leave the mind in hopeless dejection, for they both found quiet and consolation in retirement and piety. So new and so affecting is their story, that it supersedes

* French critic and poet

311

invention, and imagination ranges at full liberty without straggling into scenes of fable.

The story, thus skillfully adopted, has been diligently improved. Pope has left nothing behind him which seems more the effect of studious perseverance and laborious revisal. Here is particularly observable the *curiosa felicitas,* a fruitful soil and careful cultivation. Here is no crudeness of sense, nor asperity of language.

The sources from which sentiments which have so much vigor and efficacy have been drawn, are shown to be the mystic writers by the learned author of the *Essay on the Life and Writings of Pope;* a book which teaches how the brow of Criticism may be smoothed, and how she may be enabled, with all her severity, to attract and to delight.

The train of my disquisition has now conducted me to that poetical wonder, the translation of the *Iliad,* a performance which no age or nation can pretend to equal. To the Greeks translation was almost unknown; it was totally unknown to the inhabitants of Greece. They had no recourse to the Barbarians for poetical beauties, but sought for everything in Homer, where indeed there is but little which they might not find.

The Italians have been very diligent translators, but I can hear of no version, unless perhaps Anguillara's Ovid may be excepted, which is read with eagerness. The *Iliad* of Salvini every reader may discover to be punctiliously exact; but it seems to be the work of a linguist skillfully pedantic, and his countrymen, the proper judges of its power to please, reject it with disgust.

Their predecessors the Romans have left some specimens of translation behind them, and that employment must have had some credit in which Tully and Germanicus engaged; but unless we suppose, what is perhaps true, that the plays of Terence were versions of Menander, nothing translated seems ever to have risen to high reputation. The French, in the meridian hour of their learning, were very laudably industrious to enrich their own language with the wisdom of the ancients; but found themselves reduced, by whatever necessity, to turn the Greek and Roman poetry into prose. Whoever could read an author could translate him. From such rivals little can be feared.

The chief help of Pope in this arduous undertaking was drawn from the versions of Dryden. Vergil had borrowed much of his imagery from Homer, and part of the debt was now paid by his translator. Pope searched the pages of Dryden for happy combinations of heroic diction; but it will not be denied that he added much to what he found. He cultivated our language with so much diligence and art that he has left in his Homer a treasure of poetical elegances to posterity. His version may be said to have tuned the English tongue; for since its appearance no writer, however deficient in other powers, has wanted melody. Such a series of lines, so elaborately corrected and so sweetly modulated, took possession of the public ear; the vulgar was enamored of the poem and the learned wondered at the translation.

But in the most general applause discordant voices will always be heard. It has been objected by some, who wish to be numbered among the sons of learning, that Pope's version of Homer is not Homerical; that it exhibits no resemblance of the original and characteristic manner of the father of poetry, as it wants his awful simplicity, his artless grandeur, his unaffected majesty. This cannot be totally denied; but it must be remembered that *necessitas quod cogit defendit;* that may be lawfully done which cannot be forborne. Time and place will always enforce regard. In estimating this translation, consideration must be had of the nature of our language, the form of our meter, and above all of the change which two thousand years have made in the modes of life and the habits of thought. Vergil wrote in a language of the same general fabric with that of Homer, in verses of the same measure, and in an age nearer to Homer's time by eighteen hundred years, yet he found, even then, the state of the world so much altered, and the demand for elegance so much increased, that mere nature would be endured no longer; and perhaps, in the multitude of borrowed passages, very few can be shown which he has not embellished.

There is a time when nations emerging from barbarity, and falling into regular subordination, gain leisure to grow wise, and feel the shame of ignorance and the craving pain of unsatisfied curiosity. To this hunger of the mind plain sense is grateful; that which fills the void removes uneasiness, and to be free from pain for a while is pleasure; but repletion generates fastidiousness; a saturated intellect soon becomes luxurious, and knowledge finds no willing reception till it is recommended by artificial diction. Thus it will be found, in the progress of learning, that in all nations the first writers are simple,

313

and that every age improves in elegance. One refinement always makes way for another; and what was expedient to Vergil was necessary to Pope.

I suppose many readers of the English *Iliad,* when they have been touched with some unexpected beauty of the lighter kind, have tried to enjoy it in the original, where, alas! it was not to be found. Homer doubtless owes to his translator many Ovidian graces not exactly suitable to his character; but to have added can be no great crime, if nothing be taken away. Elegance is surely to be desired, if it be not gained at the expense of dignity. A hero would wish to be loved as well as to be reverenced.

To a thousand cavils one answer is sufficient: the purpose of a writer is to be read, and the criticism which would destroy the power of pleasing must be blown aside. Pope wrote for his own age and his own nation; he knew that it was necessary to color the images and point the sentiments of his author; he therefore made him graceful, but lost him some of his sublimity.

The copious notes with which the version is accompanied, and by which it is recommended to many readers, though they were undoubtedly written to swell the volumes, ought not to pass without praise: commentaries which attract the reader by the pleasure of perusal have not often appeared; the notes of others are read to clear difficulties, those of Pope to vary entertainment.

It has, however, been objected, with sufficient reason, that there is in the commentary too much of unseasonable levity and affected gaiety; that too many appeals are made to the ladies, and the ease which is so carefully preserved is sometimes the ease of a trifler. Every art has its terms, and every kind of instruction its proper style; the gravity of common critics may be tedious, but is less despicable than childish merriment.

Of the *Odyssey* nothing remains to be observed: the same general praise may be given to both translations, and a particular examination of either would require a large volume. The notes were written by Broome,* who endeavored, not unsuccessfully, to imitate his master.

Of *The Dunciad* the hint is confessedly taken from Dryden's *Mac Flecknoe;* but the plan is so enlarged and diversifed as justly to claim the praise of an original, and affords perhaps the best specimen that has yet appeared of personal satire ludicrously pompous.

* William Broome

That the design was moral, whatever the author might tell either his readers or himself, I am not convinced. The first motive was the desire of revenging the contempt with which Theobald * had treated his Shakespeare, and regaining the honor which he had lost, by crushing his opponent. Theobald was not of bulk enough to fill a poem, and therefore it was necessary to find other enemies with other names, at whose expense he might divert the public.

In this design there was petulance and malignity enough; but I cannot think it very criminal. An author places himself uncalled before the tribunal of criticism, and solicits fame at the hazard of disgrace. Dullness or deformity are not culpable in themselves, but may be very justly reproached when they pretend to the honor of wit or the influence of beauty. If bad writers were to pass without reprehension, what should restrain them? *impune diem consumpserit ingens Telephus;* and upon bad writers only will censure have much effect. The satire which brought Theobald and Moore † into contempt, dropped impotent from Bentley like the javelin of Priam.

All truth is valuable, and satirical criticism may be considered as useful when it rectifies error and improves judgment; he that refines the public taste is a public benefactor.

The beauties of this poem are well known; its chief fault is the grossness of its images. Pope and Swift had an unnatural delight in ideas physically impure, such as every other tongue utters with unwillingness, and of which every ear shrinks from the mention.

But even this fault, offensive as it is, may be forgiven for the excellence of other passages—such as the formation and dissolution of Moore, the account of the Traveler, the misfortune of the Florist, and the crowded thoughts and stately numbers which dignify the concluding paragraph.

The alterations which have been made in *The Dunciad,* not always for the better, require that it should be published, as in the present collection, with all its variations.

The *Essay on Man* was a work of great labor and long consideration, but certainly not the happiest of Pope's performances. The subject is perhaps not very proper for poetry, and the poet was not sufficiently master of his subject; metaphysical morality was to him a new study, he was proud of his acquisitions and, supposing himself

* In *Shakespeare Restored,* Lewis Theobald called attention to the errors in Pope's edition of Shakespeare.
† James Moore Smythe

315

master of great secrets, was in haste to teach what he had not learned. Thus he tells us, in the first epistle, that from the nature of the Supreme Being may be deduced an order of beings such as mankind, because Infinite Excellence can do only what is best. He finds out that these beings must be "somewhere," and that "all the question is whether man be in a wrong place." Surely if, according to the poet's Leibnitian reasoning,* we may infer that man ought to be, only because he is, we may allow that his place is the right place because he has it. Supreme Wisdom is not less infallible in disposing than in creating. But what is meant by *somewhere* and *place* and *wrong place,* it had been vain to ask Pope, who probably had never asked himself.

Having exalted himself into the chair of wisdom, he tells us much that every man knows and much that he does not know himself: that we see but little, and that the order of the universe is beyond our comprehension—an opinion not very uncommon; and that there is a chain of subordinate beings "from infinite to nothing," of which himself and his readers are equally ignorant. But he gives us one comfort which, without his help, he supposes unattainable, in the position "that though we are fools, yet God is wise."

This essay affords an egregious instance of the predominance of genius, the dazzling splendor of imagery and the seductive powers of eloquence. Never was penury of knowledge and vulgarity of sentiment so happily disguised. The reader feels his mind full, though he learns nothing; and when he meets it in its new array, no longer knows the talk of his mother and his nurse. When these wonder-working sounds sink into sense, and the doctrine of the *Essay,* disrobed of its ornaments, is left to the powers of its naked excellence, what shall we discover? That we are, in comparison with our Creator, very weak and ignorant—that we do not uphold the chain of existence—and that we could not make one another with more skill than we are made. We may learn yet more—that the arts of human life were copied from the instinctive operations of other animals— that if the world be made for man, it may be said that man was made for geese. To these profound principles of natural knowledge are added some moral instructions equally new: that self-interest, well understood, will produce social concord—that men are mutual gainers by mutual benefits—that evil is sometimes balanced by good —that human advantages are unstable and fallacious, of uncertain

* Based on the philosophy of Wilhelm Leibnitz

duration and doubtful effect—that our true honor is, not to have a great part, but to act it well—that virtue only is our own—and that happiness is always in our power.

Surely a man of no very comprehensive search may venture to say that he has heard all this before; but it was never till now recommended by such a blaze of embellishments, or such sweetness of melody. The vigorous contraction of some thoughts, the luxuriant amplification of others, the incidental illustrations and sometimes the dignity, sometimes the softness of the verses, enchain philosophy, suspend criticism and oppress judgment by overpowering pleasure. . . .

JONATHAN SWIFT

1667–1745

* * *

JONATHAN SWIFT WAS, according to an account said to be written by himself, the son of Jonathan Swift, an attorney, and was born at Dublin on St. Andrew's Day, 1667: according to his own report, as delivered by Pope to Spence, he was born at Leicester, the son of a clergyman, who was minister of a parish in Herefordshire. During his life the place of his birth was undetermined. He was contented to be called an Irishman by the Irish; but would occasionally call himself an Englishman. The question may, without much regret, be left in the obscurity in which he delighted to involve it.

Whatever was his birth, his education was Irish. He was sent at the age of six to the school at Kilkenny and in his fifteenth year (1682) was admitted into the University of Dublin.

In his academical studies he was either not diligent or not happy. It must disappoint every reader's expectation, that when at the usual time he claimed the Bachelorship of Arts, he was found by the examiners too conspicuously deficient for regular admission, and obtained his degree at last by *special favor;* a term used in that university to denote want of merit.

Of this disgrace it may be easily supposed that he was much ashamed, and shame had its proper effect in producing reformation. He resolved from that time to study eight hours a day, and contin-

317

ued his industry for seven years, with what improvement is sufficiently known. This part of his story well deserves to be remembered; it may afford useful admonition and powerful encouragement to men whose abilities have been made for a time useless by their passions or pleasures and who, having lost one part of life in idleness, are tempted to throw away the remainder in despair.

In this course of daily application he continued three years longer at Dublin; and in this time, if the observation of an old companion may be trusted, he drew the first sketch of his *Tale of a Tub*.

When he was about one-and-twenty (1688), being by the death of Godwin Swift, his uncle, who had supported him, left without subsistence, he went to consult his mother, who then lived at Leicester, about the future course of his life, and by her direction solicited the advice and patronage of Sir William Temple, who had married one of Mrs. Swift's relations, and whose father, Sir John Temple, Master of the Rolls in Ireland, had lived in great familiarity of friendship with Godwin Swift, by whom Jonathan had been to that time maintained.

Temple received with sufficient kindness the nephew of his father's friend, with whom he was, when they conversed together, so much pleased, that he detained him two years in his house. Here he became known to King William, who sometimes visited Temple when he was disabled by the gout and, being attended by Swift in the garden, showed him how to cut asparagus in the Dutch way.

King William's notions were all military; and he expressed his kindness to Swift by offering to make him a captain of horse.

When Temple removed to Moor Park, he took Swift with him; and when he was consulted by the Earl of Portland about the expedience of complying with a bill then depending for making parliaments triennial, against which King William was strongly prejudiced, after having in vain tried to show the Earl that the proposal involved nothing dangerous to royal power, he sent Swift for the same purpose to the King. Swift, who probably was proud of his employment and went with all the confidence of a young man, found his arguments and his art of displaying them made totally ineffectual by the predetermination of the King; and used to mention this disappointment as his first antidote against vanity.

Before he left Ireland he contracted a disorder, as he thought, by eating too much fruit. The original of diseases is commonly obscure. Almost every boy eats as much fruit as he can get, without any great inconvenience. The disease of Swift was giddiness with deafness,

318

which attacked him from time to time, began very early, pursued him through life, and at last sent him to the grave, deprived of reason.

Being much oppressed at Moor Park by this grievous malady, he was advised to try his native air and went to Ireland; but, finding no benefit, returned to Sir William, at whose house he continued his studies. . . . He thought exercise of great necessity, and used to run half a mile up and down a hill every two hours.

It is easy to imagine that the mode in which his first degree was conferred left him no great fondness for the University of Dublin, and therefore he resolved to become a Master of Arts at Oxford. In the testimonial which he produced, the words of disgrace were omitted; and he took his Master's degree (July 5, 1692) with such reception and regard as fully contented him.

While he lived with Temple, he used to pay his mother at Leicester a yearly visit. He traveled on foot, unless some violence of weather drove him into a wagon and at night he would go to a penny lodging, where he purchased clean sheets for sixpence. This practice Lord Orrery imputes to his innate love of grossness and vulgarity: some may ascribe it to his desire of surveying human life through all its varieties; and others, perhaps with equal probability, to a passion which seems to have been deep fixed in his heart—the love of a shilling.

In time he began to think that his attendance at Moor Park deserved some other recompence than the pleasure, however mingled with improvement, of Temple's conversation; and grew so impatient that (1694) he went away in discontent.

Temple, conscious of having given reason for complaint, is said to have made him Deputy Master of the Rolls in Ireland; which, according to his kinsman's account, was an office which he knew him not able to discharge. Swift therefore resolved to enter into the Church, in which he had at first no higher hopes than of the chaplainship to the Factory at Lisbon; but being recommended to Lord Capel [then Lord Lieutenant of Ireland], he obtained the prebend of Kilroot in Connor, of about a hundred pounds a year.

But the infirmities of Temple made a companion like Swift so necessary, that he invited him back, with a promise to procure him English preferment in exchange for the prebend, which he desired him to resign. With this request Swift complied, having perhaps equally repented their separation, and they lived on together with mutual satisfaction; and in the four years that passed between his return and Temple's death, it is probable that he wrote *The Tale of a Tub* and *The Battle of the Books*.

Swift began early to think, or to hope, that he was a poet and wrote Pindaric Odes to Temple, to the King and to the Athenian Society, a knot of obscure men, who published a periodical pamphlet of answers to questions sent, or supposed to be sent, by letters. I have been told that Dryden, having perused these verses, said, "Cousin Swift, you will never be a poet"; and that this denunciation was the motive of Swift's perpetual malevolence to Dryden.

In 1699 Temple died and left a legacy with his manuscripts to Swift, for whom he had obtained from King William a promise of the first prebend that should be vacant at Westminster or Canterbury.

That this promise might not be forgotten, Swift dedicated to the King the posthumous works with which he was intrusted; but neither the dedication nor tenderness for the man whom he once had treated with confidence and fondness revived in King William the remembrance of his promise. Swift awhile attended the Court, but soon found his solicitations hopeless.

He was then invited by the Earl of Berkeley to accompany him into Ireland as his private secretary; but after having done the business till their arrival at Dublin, he then found that one Bushe had persuaded the Earl that a clergyman was not a proper secretary and had obtained the office for himself. In a man like Swift such circumvention and inconstancy must have excited violent indignation.

But he had yet more to suffer. Lord Berkeley had the disposal of the deanery of Derry and Swift expected to obtain it, but by the secretary's influence, supposed to have been secured by a bribe, it was bestowed on somebody else; and Swift was dismissed with the livings of Laracor and Rathbeggan, in the diocese of Meath, which together did not equal half the value of the deanery.

At Laracor he increased the parochial duty by reading prayers on Wednesdays and Fridays and performed all the offices of his profession with great decency and exactness.

Soon after his settlement at Laracor he invited to Ireland the unfortunate Stella, a young woman whose name was Johnson, the daughter of the steward of Sir William Temple, who, in consideration of her father's virtues, left her 1000*l*. With her came Mrs. Dingley, whose whole fortune was 27*l*. a year for her life. With these ladies he passed his hours of relaxation and to them he opened his bosom; but they never resided in the same house, nor did he see either without a witness. They lived at the Parsonage when Swift was away, and when he returned, removed to a lodging or to the house of a neighboring clergyman.

Swift was not one of those minds which amaze the world with early pregnancy: his first work, except his few poetical Essays, was the *Dissensions in Athens and Rome,* published (1701) in his thirty-fourth year. After its appearance, paying a visit to some bishop, he heard mention made of the new pamphlet that Burnet * had written, replete with political knowledge. When he seemed to doubt Burnet's right to the work, he was told by the Bishop that he was "a young man"; and still persisting to doubt, that he was "a very positive young man."

Three years afterward (1704) was published *The Tale of a Tub:* of this book charity may be persuaded to think that it might be written by a man of a peculiar character, without ill-intention; but it is certainly of dangerous example. That Swift was its author, though it be universally believed, was never owned by himself, nor very well proved by any evidence; but no other claimant can be produced and he did not deny it when Archbishop Sharp and the Duchess of Somerset, by showing it to the Queen, debarred him from a bishopric.

When this wild work first raised the attention of the public, Sacheverell, meeting Smalridge,† tried to flatter him, seeming to think him the author; but Smalridge answered with indignation, "Not all that you and I have in the world, nor all that ever we shall have, should hire me to write *The Tale of a Tub."*

The digressions relating to Wotton ‡ and Bentley must be confessed to discover want of knowledge or want of integrity; he did not understand the two controversies or he willingly misrepresented them. But wit can stand its ground against truth only a little while. The honors due to learning have been justly distributed by the decision of posterity.

The Battle of the Books is so like the *Combat des Livres,* which the same question concerning the ancients and moderns had produced in France, that the improbability of such a coincidence of

* Gilbert Burnet, bishop and historian
† Henry Sacheverell, political preacher; George Smalridge, Bishop of Bristol
‡ William Wotton, English scholar

thoughts without communication is not, in my opinion, balanced by the anonymous protestation prefixed, in which all knowledge of the French book is peremptorily disowned.

For some time after Swift was probably employed in solitary study, gaining the qualifications requisite for future eminence. How often he visited England, and with what diligence he attended his parishes, I know not. It was not till about four years afterward that he became a professed author; and then one year (1708) produced *The Sentiments of a Church of England Man,* the ridicule of astrology, under the name of "Bickerstaff" the *Argument against Abolishing Christianity* and the defense of the *Sacramental Test.* . . .

Soon after began the busy and important part of Swift's life. He was employed (1710) by the primate of Ireland to solicit the Queen for a remission of the first fruits and twentieth parts to the Irish clergy. With this purpose he had recourse to Mr. Harley,* to whom he was mentioned as a man neglected and oppressed by the last ministry because he had refused to co-operate with some of their schemes. What he had refused has never been told; what he had suffered was, I suppose, the exclusion from a bishopric by the remonstrances of Sharp, whom he describes as "the harmless tool of others' hate," and whom he represents as afterward "suing for pardon."

Harley's designs and situation were such as made him glad of an auxiliary so well qualified for his service; he therefore soon admitted him to familiarity—whether ever to confidence some have made a doubt; but it would have been difficult to excite his zeal without persuading him that he was trusted, and not very easy to delude him by false persuasions.

He was certainly admitted to those meetings in which the first hints and original plan of action are supposed to have been formed, and was one of the sixteen ministers, or agents of the ministry, who met weekly at each other's houses, and were united by the name of "Brother."

Being not immediately considered as an obdurate Tory, he conversed indiscriminately with all the wits and was yet the friend of Steele, who, in *The Tatler,* which began in April 1709, confesses the advantage of his conversation and mentions something contributed by him to his paper. But he was now immerging into political controversy; for the year 1710 produced *The Examiner,* of which Swift

* Robert Harley (1st Earl of Oxford), English statesman

wrote thirty-three papers. In argument he may be allowed to have the advantage; for where a wide system of conduct and the whole of a public character is laid open to inquiry, the accuser, having the choice of facts, must be very unskillful if he does not prevail; but with regard to wit, I am afraid none of Swift's papers will be found equal to those by which Addison opposed him.

He wrote in the year 1711 a *Letter to the October Club,* a number of Tory gentlemen sent from the country to Parliament, who formed themselves into a club to the number of about a hundred and met to animate the zeal and raise the expectations of each other. They thought, with great reason, that the ministers were losing opportunities; that sufficient use was not made of the ardor of the nation; they called loudly for more changes and stronger efforts; and demanded the punishment of part, and the dismission of the rest, of those whom they considered as public robbers.

Their eagerness was not gratified by the Queen or by Harley. The Queen was probably slow because she was afraid, and Harley was slow because he was doubtful: he was a Tory only by necessity or for convenience; and, when he had power in his hands, had no settled purpose for which he should employ it; forced to gratify to a certain degree the Tories who supported him, but unwilling to make his reconcilement to the Whigs utterly desperate, he corresponded at once with the two expectants of the Crown and kept, as has been observed, the succession undetermined. Not knowing what to do, he did nothing; and, with the fate of a double dealer, at last he lost his power but kept his enemies.

Swift seems to have concurred in opinion with the October Club, but it was not in his power to quicken the tardiness of Harley, whom he stimulated as much as he could, but with little effect. He that knows not whither to go is in no haste to move. Harley, who was perhaps not quick by nature, became yet more slow by irresolution; and was content to hear that dilatoriness lamented as natural, which he applauded in himself as politic.

Without the Tories, however, nothing could be done; and as they were not to be gratified they must be appeased and the conduct of the minister, if it could not be vindicated, was to be plausibly excused. . . .

Swift now attained the zenith of his political importance: he published (1712) *The Conduct of the Allies,* ten days before the parliament assembled. The purpose was to persuade the nation to a peace

323

and never had any writer more success. The people, who had been amused with bonfires and triumphal processions and looked with idolatry on the General [Marlborough] and his friends, and who, as they thought, had made England the arbitress of nations, were confounded between shame and rage when they found that "mines had been exhausted and millions destroyed" to secure the Dutch or aggrandize the Emperor, without any advantage to ourselves; that we had been bribing our neighbors to fight their own quarrel and that amongst our enemies we might number our allies.

That is now no longer doubted, of which the nation was then first informed, that the war was unnecessarily protracted to fill the pockets of Marlborough; and that it would have been continued without end if he could have continued his annual plunder. But Swift, I suppose, did not yet know what he has since written, that a commission was drawn which would have appointed him General for life, had it not become ineffectual by the resolution of Lord Cowper, who refused the seal. . . .

Swift being now [1712–14] the declared favorite and supposed confidant of the Tory ministry, was treated by all that depended on the Court with the respect which dependents know how to pay. He soon began to feel part of the misery of greatness; he that could say that he knew him, considered himself as having fortune in his power. Commissions, solicitations, remonstrances, crowded about him; he was expected to do every man's business, to procure employment for one and to retain it for another. In assisting those who addressed him, he represents himself as sufficiently diligent; and desires to have others believe, what he probably believed himself, that by his interposition many Whigs of merit, and among them Addison and Congreve, were continued in their places. But every man of known influence has so many petitions which he cannot grant, that he must necessarily offend more than he gratifies, because the preference given to one affords all the rest reason for complaint. "When I give away a place," said Louis XIV, "I make a hundred discontented and one ungrateful."

Much has been said of the equality and independence which he preserved in his conversation with the ministers, of the frankness of his remonstrances and the familiarity of his friendship. In accounts of this kind a few single incidents are set against the general tenor of behavior. No man, however, can pay a more servile tribute to the great than by suffering his liberty in their presence to aggrandize him in his own esteem. Between different ranks of the community there is necessarily some distance: he who is called by his superior to pass the interval, may properly accept the invitation; but petulance and obtrusion are rarely produced by magnanimity, nor have often any nobler cause than the pride of importance and the malice of inferiority. He who knows himself necessary may set, while that necessity lasts, a high value upon himself; as, in a lower condition, a servant eminently skilful may be saucy; but he is saucy only because he is servile. Swift appears to have preserved the kindness of the great when they wanted him no longer; and therefore it must be allowed that the childish freedom, to which he seems enough inclined, was overpowered by his better qualities.

His disinterestedness has been likewise mentioned; a strain of heroism which would have been in his condition romantic and superfluous. Ecclesiastical benefices, when they become vacant, must be given away; and the friends of power may, if there be no inherent disqualification, reasonably expect them. Swift accepted (April 1713) the deanery of St. Patrick, the best preferment that his friends could venture to give him. That ministry was in a great degree supported by the clergy, who were not yet reconciled to the author of *The Tale of a Tub* and would not, without much discontent and indignation, have borne to see him installed in an English cathedral.

He refused, indeed, 50*l*. from Lord Oxford; but he accepted afterward a draft of 1000*l*. upon the Exchequer, which was intercepted by the Queen's death and which he resigned, as he says himself, *"multa gemens,* with many a groan."

In the midst of his power and his politics [1710–13] he kept a Journal of his visits, his walks, his interviews with ministers and quarrels with his servant and transmitted it to Mrs. Johnson and Mrs. Dingley, to whom he knew that whatever befell him was interesting and no accounts could be too minute. Whether these diurnal trifles were properly exposed to eyes which had never received any pleasure from the presence of the Dean, may be reasonably doubted; they have, however, some odd attraction; the reader, finding frequent mention of names which he has been used to consider as important, goes on in hope of information; and, as there is nothing to fatigue attention, if he is disappointed he can hardly complain. It is easy to perceive from every page that though ambition pressed Swift into a life of bustle, the wish for a life of ease was always returning.

He went [June 1713] to take possession of his deanery as soon as he had obtained it; but he was not suffered to stay in Ireland more than a fortnight before he was recalled to England, that he might reconcile Lord Oxford and Lord Bolingbroke, who began to look on one another with malevolence, which every day increased, and which Bolingbroke appeared to retain in his last years.

Swift contrived an interview, from which they both departed discontented: he procured a second, which only convinced him that the feud was irreconcileable; he told them his opinion, that all was lost. This denunciation was contradicted by Oxford; but Bolingbroke whispered that he was right.

Before this violent dissension had shattered the ministry, Swift had published, in the beginning of the year 1714, *The Public Spirit of the Whigs,* in answer to *The Crisis,* a pamphlet for which Steele was expelled from the House of Commons. Swift was now so far alienated from Steele as to think him no longer entitled to decency, and therefore treats him sometimes with contempt and sometimes with abhorrence.

In this pamphlet the Scotch were mentioned in terms so provoking to that irritable nation, that, resolving "not to be offended with impunity," the Scotch Lords in a body demanded an audience of the Queen and solicited reparation. A proclamation was issued, in which 300*l.* was offered for discovery of the author. From this storm he was, as he relates, "secured by a sleight"; of what kind, or by whose prudence, is not known; and such was the increase of his reputation that the Scottish "Nation applied again that he would be their friend."

He was become so formidable to the Whigs, that his familiarity with the ministers was clamored at in Parliament, particularly by two men afterward of great note, Aislabie and Walpole.*

But, by the disunion of his great friends, his importance and designs were now at an end; and seeing his services at last useless, he retired about June (1714) into Berkshire where, in the house of a friend, he wrote what was then suppressed, but has since appeared under the title of *Free Thoughts on the present State of Affairs.*

While he was waiting in his retirement for events which time or chance might bring to pass, the death of the Queen [1st Aug., 1714] broke down at once the whole system of Tory politics; and nothing remained but to withdraw from the implacability of triumphant Whiggism and shelter himself in unenvied obscurity.

* John Aislabie, politician; Robert Walpole, twice prime minister

The accounts of his reception in Ireland, given by Lord Orrery and Dr. Delany,* are so different, that the credit of the writers, both undoubtedly veracious, cannot be saved but by supposing, what I think is true, that they speak of different times. When Delany says that he was received with respect, he means for the first fortnight, when he came to take legal possession; and when Lord Orrery tells that he was pelted by the populace, he is to be understood of the time when, after the Queen's death, he became a settled resident.

The Archbishop of Dublin gave him at first some disturbance in the exercise of his jurisdiction; but it was soon discovered that between prudence and integrity he was seldom in the wrong; and that, when he was right, his spirit did not easily yield to opposition. . . .

Swift now, much against his will, commenced Irishman for life, and was to contrive how he might be best accommodated in a country where he considered himself as in a state of exile. It seems that his first recourse was to piety. The thoughts of death rushed upon him at this time with such incessant importunity, that they took possession of his mind when he first waked for many years together.

He opened his house by a public table two days a week, and found his entertainments gradually frequented by more and more visitants of learning among the men and of elegance among the women. Mrs. Johnson had left the country and lived in lodgings not far from the deanery. On his public days she regulated the table but appeared at it as a mere guest, like other ladies.

On other days he often dined, at a stated price, with Mr. Worrall, a clergyman of his cathedral, whose house was recommended by the peculiar neatness and pleasantry of his wife. To this frugal mode of living he was first disposed by care to pay some debts which he had contracted and he continued it for the pleasure of accumulating money. His avarice, however, was not suffered to obstruct the claims of his dignity; he was served in plate and used to say that he was the poorest gentleman in Ireland that ate upon plate and the richest that lived without a coach.

How he spent the rest of his time and how he employed his hours of study has been inquired with hopeless curiosity. For who can give an account of another's studies? Swift was not likely to admit any to his privacies or to impart a minute account of his business or his leisure.

Soon after (1716), in his forty-ninth year, he was privately mar-

* Dr. Patrick Delany, Irish preacher

ried to Mrs. Johnson, by Dr. Ashe, Bishop of Clogher, as Dr. Madden told me, in the garden. The marriage made no change in their mode of life; they lived in different houses, as before; nor did she ever lodge in the deanery but when Swift was seized with a fit of giddiness. "It would be difficult," says Lord Orrery, "to prove that they were ever afterward together without a third person."

The Dean of St. Patrick's lived in a private manner, known and regarded only by his friends, till, about the year 1720, he, by a pamphlet, recommended to the Irish the use, and consequently the improvement, of their manufacture. For a man to use the productions of his own labor is surely a natural right, and to like best what he makes himself is a natural passion. But to excite this passion and enforce this right appeared so criminal to those who had an interest in the English trade, that the printer was imprisoned; and, as Hawkesworth justly observes, the attention of the public being by this outrageous resentment turned upon the proposal, the author was by consequence made popular.

In 1723 died [at Celbridge, near Dublin] Mrs. [Esther] Van Homrigh, a woman made unhappy by her admiration of wit, and ignominiously distinguished by the name of Vanessa, whose conduct has been already sufficiently discussed and whose history is too well known to be minutely repeated. She was a young woman fond of literature, whom Decanus the Dean, called Cadenus by transposition of the letters, took pleasure in directing and instructing; till, from being proud of his praise, she grew fond of his person. Swift was then about forty-seven, at an age when vanity is strongly excited by the amorous attention of a young woman. If it be said that Swift should have checked a passion which he never meant to gratify, recourse must be had to that extenuation which he so much despised, "men are but men": perhaps, however, he did not at first know his own mind and, as he represents himself, was undetermined. For his admission of her courtship and his indulgence of her hopes after his marriage to Stella, no other honest plea can be found, than that he delayed a disagreeable discovery from time to time, dreading the immediate bursts of distress and watching for a favorable moment. She thought herself neglected and died of disappointment; having ordered by her will the poem to be published, in which Cadenus had proclaimed her excellence and confessed his love. The effect of the publication upon the Dean and Stella is thus related by Delany:

"I have good reason to believe that they both were greatly shocked and distressed (though it may be differently) upon this occasion. The Dean made a tour to the south of Ireland, for about two months, at this time, to dissipate his thoughts and give place to obloquy; and Stella retired (upon the earnest invitation of the owner) to the house of a cheerful, generous, good-natured friend of the Dean's, whom she also much loved and honored. There my informer often saw her; and, I have reason to believe, used his utmost endeavors to relieve, support and amuse her, in this sad situation.

"One little incident he told me of, on that occasion, I think I shall never forget. As her friend was an hospitable, open-hearted man, well-beloved and largely acquainted, it happened one day that some gentlemen dropped in to dinner, who were strangers to Stella's situation; and as the poem of *Cadenus and Vanessa* was then the general topic of conversation, one of them said, 'Surely that Vanessa must be an extraordinary woman, that could inspire the Dean to write so finely upon her.' Mrs. Johnson smiled and answered, 'that she thought that point not quite so clear; for it was well-known the Dean could write finely upon a broomstick.' "

The great acquisition of esteem and influence was made by the *Drapier's Letters* in 1724. One Wood, of Wolverhampton in Staffordshire, a man enterprising and rapacious, had, as is said by a present to the Duchess of Munster, obtained a patent, empowering him to coin one hundred and eighty thousand pounds of halfpence and farthings for the kingdom of Ireland, in which there was a very inconvenient and embarrassing scarcity of copper coin; so that it was impossible to run in debt upon the credit of a piece of money; for the cook or keeper of an alehouse could not refuse to supply a man that had silver in his hand and the buyer would not leave his money without change.

The project was therefore plausible. The scarcity, which was already great, Wood took care to make greater, by agents who gathered up the old halfpence; and was about to turn his brass into gold, by pouring the treasures of his new mint upon Ireland, when Swift, finding that the metal was debased to an enormous degree, wrote Letters, under the name of "M. B. Drapier," to show the folly of receiving and the mischief that must ensue by giving gold and silver for coin worth perhaps not a third part of its nominal value.

The nation was alarmed; the new coin was universally refused; but the governors of Ireland considered resistance to the King's patent as highly criminal; and one Whitshed, then Chief Justice, who had tried the printer of the former pamphlet and sent out the jury nine times, till by clamor and menaces they were frightened into a special verdict, now presented the *Drapier,* but could not prevail on the grand jury to find the bill.

Lord Carteret and the Privy Council published [1724] a proclamation, offering 300*l.* for discovering the author of the Fourth Letter. Swift had concealed himself from his printers and trusted only his butler, who transcribed the paper. The man, immediately after the appearance of the proclamation, strolled from the house and stayed out all night and part of the next day. There was reason enough to fear that he had betrayed his master for the reward; but he came home and the Dean ordered him to put off his livery and leave the house; "for," says he, "I know that my life is in your power and I will not bear, out of fear, either your insolence or negligence." The man excused his fault with great submission and begged that he might be confined in the house while it was in his power to endanger his master; but the Dean resolutely turned him out, without taking farther notice of him, till the term of information had expired and then received him again. Soon afterward he ordered him and the rest of the servants into his presence, without telling his intentions, and bade them take notice that their fellow-servant was no longer Robert the butler, but that his integrity had made him Mr. Blakeley, verger of St. Patrick's; an officer whose income was between thirty and forty pounds a year: yet he still continued for some years to serve his old master as his butler.

Swift was known from this time by the appellation of *The Dean.* He was honored by the populace as the champion, patron and instructor of Ireland; and gained such power as, considered both in its extent and duration, scarcely any man has ever enjoyed without greater wealth or higher station.

He was from this important year the oracle of the traders and the idol of the rabble and by consequence was feared and courted by all to whom the kindness of the traders or the populace were necessary. The *Drapier* was a sign; the *Drapier* was a health; and which way soever the eye or the ear was turned, some tokens were found of the nation's gratitude to the *Drapier.*

The benefit was indeed great: he had rescued Ireland from a very oppressive and predatory invasion; and the popularity which he had gained he was diligent to keep, by appearing forward and zealous on every occasion where the public interest was supposed to be involved. Nor did he much scruple to boast his influence; for when, upon some attempts to regulate the coin, Archbishop Boulter, then one of the justices, accused him of exasperating the people, he exculpated himself by saying, "If I had lifted up my finger, they would have torn you to pieces."

But the pleasure of popularity was soon interrupted by domestic misery. Mrs. Johnson, whose conversation was to him the great softener of the ills of life, began in the year of the *Drapier's* triumph to decline; and two years afterward [1726] was so wasted with sickness, that her recovery was considered as hopeless.

Swift was then [1726] in England and had been invited by Lord Bolingbroke to pass the winter with him in France; but this call of calamity hastened him to Ireland, where perhaps his presence contributed to restore her to imperfect and tottering health.

He was now so much at ease that (1727) he returned to England, where he collected three volumes of *Miscellanies* in conjunction with Pope, who prefixed a querulous and apologetical Preface.

This important year [1727] sent likewise into the world *Gulliver's Travels,* a production so new and strange that it filled the reader with a mingled emotion of merriment and amazement. It was received with such avidity that the price of the first edition was raised before the second could be made; it was read by the high and the low, the learned and illiterate. Criticism was for a while lost in wonder; no rules of judgment were applied to a book written in open defiance of truth and regularity. But when distinctions came to be made, the part which gave the least pleasure was that which describes the Flying Island and that which gave most disgust must be the history of the Houyhnhnms.

While Swift was enjoying the reputation of his new work, the news of the King's death [June 1727] arrived; and he kissed the hands of the new King and Queen [George II and Queen Caroline] three days after their accession.

By the Queen, when she was Princess, he had been treated with some distinction, and was well received by her in her exaltation; but whether she gave hopes which she never took care to satisfy, or he formed expectations which she never meant to raise, the event was that he always afterward thought on her with malevolence and particularly charged her with breaking her promise of some medals which she engaged to send him.

I know not whether she had not in her turn some reason for com-

331

plaint. A letter was sent her, not so much entreating as requiring her patronage of Mrs. Barber, an ingenious Irishwoman, who was then begging subscriptions for her poems. To this letter was subscribed the name of Swift and it has all the appearances of his diction and sentiments; but it was not written in his hand and had some little improprieties. When he was charged with this letter, he laid hold of the inaccuracies and urged the improbability of the accusation, but never denied it: he shuffles between cowardice and veracity and talks big when he says nothing.

He seemed desirous enough of recommencing courtier and endeavored to gain the kindness of Mrs. Howard,* remembering what Mrs. Masham † had performed in former times; but his flatteries were, like those of other wits, unsuccessful; the lady either wanted power or had no ambition of poetical immortality.

He was seized not long afterward by a fit of giddiness and again heard of the sickness and danger of Mrs. Johnson. He then left [Sept. 1727] the house of Pope, as it seems, with very little ceremony, finding "that two sick friends cannot live together" and did not write to him till he found himself at Chester.

He returned to a home of sorrow: poor Stella was sinking into the grave and, after a languishing decay of about two months, died in her forty-fourth year, on January 28, 1727–8. How much he wished her life his papers show; nor can it be doubted that he dreaded the death of her whom he loved most, aggravated by the consciousness that himself had hastened it.

Beauty and the power of pleasing, the greatest external advantages that woman can desire or possess, were fatal to the unfortunate Stella. The man whom she had the misfortune to love was, as Delany observes, fond of singularity and desirous to make a mode of happiness for himself, different from the general course of things and order of Providence. From the time of her arrival in Ireland he seems resolved to keep her in his power, and therefore hindered a match sufficiently advantageous by accumulating unreasonable demands and prescribing conditions that could not be performed. While she was at her own disposal he did not consider his possession as secure; resentment, ambition or caprice might separate them; he was therefore resolved to make "assurance doubly sure" and to appropriate her by a private marriage, to which he had annexed the expectation

* Henrietta Howard, favorite of George II
† Lady Abigail Masham, confidante of Queen Anne

of all the pleasures of perfect friendship without the uneasiness of conjugal restraint. But with this state poor Stella was not satisfied; she never was treated as a wife and to the world she had the appearance of a mistress. She lived sullenly on, in hope that in time he would own and receive her; but the time did not come till the change of his manners and depravation of his mind made her tell him, when he offered to acknowledge her, that "it was too late." She then gave up herself to sorrowful resentment and died under the tyranny of him by whom she was in the highest degree loved and honored.

What were her claims to this eccentric tenderness, by which the laws of nature were violated to retain her, curiosity will inquire; but how shall it be gratified? Swift was a lover; his testimony may be suspected. Delany and the Irish saw with Swift's eyes and therefore add little confirmation. That she was virtuous, beautiful and elegant, in a very high degree, such admiration from such a lover makes it very probable; but she had not much literature, for she could not spell her own language; and of her wit, so loudly vaunted, the smart sayings which Swift himself has collected afford no splendid specimen.

The reader of Swift's *Letter to a Lady on her Marriage* may be allowed to doubt whether his opinion of female excellence ought implicitly to be admitted; for if his general thoughts on women were such as he exhibits, a very little sense in a lady would enrapture and a very little virtue would astonish him. Stella's supremacy therefore was perhaps only local; she was great because her associates were little.

In some remarks lately published on the Life of Swift, his marriage is mentioned as fabulous or doubtful; but, alas! poor Stella, as Dr. Madden told me, related her melancholy story to Dr. Sheridan when he attended her as a clergyman to prepare her for death; and Delany mentions it not with doubt but only with regret. Swift never mentioned her without a sigh.

The rest of his life [1728–45] was spent in Ireland—in a country to which not even power almost despotic, nor flattery almost idolatrous, could reconcile him. He sometimes wished to visit England but always found some reason to delay. He tells Pope, in the decline of life, that he hopes once more to see him; "but if not," says he, "we must part as all human beings have parted."

After the death of Stella his benevolence was contracted and his severity exasperated; he drove his acquaintance from his table and wondered why he was deserted. But he continued his attention to the public and wrote from time to time such directions, admonitions or censures as the exigency of affairs, in his opinion, made proper; and nothing fell from his pen in vain.

In a short poem on the Presbyterians, whom he always regarded with detestation, he bestowed [1733–4] one stricture upon Bettesworth, a lawyer eminent for his insolence to the clergy which, from very considerable reputation, brought him into immediate and universal contempt. Bettesworth, enraged at his disgrace and loss, went to Swift and demanded whether he was the author of that poem? "Mr. Bettesworth," answered he, "I was in my youth acquainted with great lawyers, who, knowing my disposition to satire, advised me that if any scoundrel or blockhead whom I had lampooned should ask, 'Are you the author of this paper?' I should tell him that I was not the author; and therefore I tell you, Mr. Bettesworth, that I am not the author of these lines."

Bettesworth was so little satisfied with this account that he publicly professed his resolution of a violent and corporal revenge; but the inhabitants of St. Patrick's district embodied themselves in the Dean's defense. Bettesworth declared in Parliament that Swift had deprived him of 1200*l.* a year.

Swift was popular awhile by another mode of beneficence. He set aside some hundreds to be lent in small sums to the poor, from 5*s.*, I think, to 5*l.* He took no interest and only required that, at repayment, a small fee should be given to the accountant: but he required that the day of promised payment should be exactly kept. A severe and punctilious temper is ill-qualified for transactions with the poor; the day was often broken and the loan was not repaid. This might have been easily foreseen; but for this Swift had made no provision of patience or pity. He ordered his debtors to be sued. A severe creditor has no popular character; what then was likely to be said of him who employs the catchpoll under the appearance of charity? The clamor against him was loud and the resentment of the populace outrageous; he was therefore forced to drop his scheme and own the folly of expecting punctuality from the poor.

His asperity continually increasing condemned him to solitude; and his resentment of solitude sharpened his asperity. He was not, however, totally deserted; some men of learning and some women of elegance often visited him; and he wrote from time to time either verse or prose; of his verses he willingly gave copies and is supposed to have felt no discontent when he saw them printed. His favorite maxim was "Vive la bagatelle": he thought trifles a necessary part of life and perhaps found them necessary to himself. It seems impossible to him to be idle and his disorders made it difficult or dangerous to be long seriously studious or laboriously diligent. The love of ease is always gaining upon age and he had one temptation to petty amusements peculiar to himself: whatever he did he was sure to hear applauded; and such was his predominance over all that approached, that all their applauses were probably sincere. He that is much flattered soon learns to flatter himself: we are commonly taught our duty by fear or shame and how can they act upon the man who hears nothing but his own praises?

As his years increased, his fits of giddiness and deafness grew more frequent and his deafness made conversation difficult: they grew likewise more severe, till in 1736, as he was writing a poem called *The Legion Club,* he was seized with a fit so painful and so long continued that he never after thought it proper to attempt any work of thought or labor.

He was always careful of his money and was therefore no liberal entertainer; but was less frugal of his wine than of his meat. When his friends of either sex came to him in expectation of a dinner, his custom was to give every one a shilling that they might please themselves with their provision. At last his avarice grew too powerful for his kindness; he would refuse a bottle of wine and in Ireland no man visits where he cannot drink.

Having thus excluded conversation and desisted from study, he had neither business nor amusement; for, having by some ridiculous resolution or mad vow determined never to wear spectacles, he could make little use of books in his later years: his ideas therefore, being neither renovated by discourse nor increased by reading, wore gradually away and left his mind vacant to the vexations of the hour, till at last his anger was heightened into madness. . . .

He grew more violent; and his mental powers declined, till (1741) it was found necessary that legal guardians should be appointed of his person and fortune. He now lost distinction. His madness was compounded of rage and fatuity. The last face that he knew was that of Mrs. Whiteway; and her he ceased to know in a little time. His meat was brought him cut into mouthfuls; but he would never touch it while the servant stayed and at last, after it had stood per-

335

haps an hour, would eat it walking; for he continued his old habit, and was on his feet ten hours a day.

Next year (1742) he had an inflammation in his left eye, which swelled it to the size of an egg, with boils in other parts; he was kept long waking with the pain and was not easily restrained by five attendants from tearing out his eye.

The tumor at last subsided; and a short interval of reason ensuing, in which he knew his physician and his family, gave hopes of his recovery; but in a few days he sunk into lethargic stupidity, motionless, heedless and speechless. But it is said, that, after a year of total silence, when his housekeeper, on the 30th of November, told him that the usual bonfires and illuminations were preparing to celebrate his birthday, he answered, "It is all folly; they had better let it alone."

It is remembered, that he afterward spoke now and then or gave some intimation of a meaning; but at last sunk into a perfect silence, which continued till about the end of October 1745, when, in his seventy-eighth year, he expired without a struggle.

When Swift is considered as an author, it is just to estimate his powers by their effects. In the reign of Queen Anne he turned the stream of popularity against the Whigs and must be confessed to have dictated for a time the political opinions of the English nation. In the succeeding reign he delivered Ireland from plunder and oppression; and showed that wit, confederated with truth, had such force as authority was unable to resist. He said truly of himself, that Ireland "was his debtor." It was from the time when he first began to patronize the Irish that they may date their riches and prosperity. He taught them first to know their own interest, their weight and their strength and gave them spirit to assert that equality with their fellow-subjects to which they have ever since been making vigorous advances, and to claim those rights which they have at last established. Nor can they be charged with ingratitude to their benefactor; for they reverenced him as a guardian and obeyed him as a dictator.

In his works he has given very different specimens both of sentiments and expression. His *Tale of a Tub* has little resemblance to his other pieces. It exhibits a vehemence and rapidity of mind, a copiousness of images and vivacity of diction, such as he afterward never possessed or never exerted. It is of a mode so distinct and peculiar, that it must be considered by itself; what is true of that, is not true of anything else which he has written.

In his other works is found an equable tenor of easy language, which rather trickles than flows. His delight was in simplicity. That he has in his works no metaphor, as has been said, is not true; but his few metaphors seem to be received rather by necessity than choice. He studied purity; and though perhaps all his strictures are not exact, yet it is not often that solecisms can be found; and whoever depends on his authority may generally conclude himself safe. His sentences are never too much dilated or contracted; and it will not be easy to find any embarrassment in the complication of his clauses, any inconsequence in his connections or abruptness in his transitions.

His style was well suited to his thoughts, which are never subtilized by nice disquisitions, decorated by sparkling conceits, elevated by ambitious sentences or variegated by far-sought learning. He pays no court to the passions; he excites neither surprise nor admiration; he always understands himself and his readers always understand him: the peruser of Swift wants little previous knowledge; it will be sufficient that he is acquainted with common words and common things; he is neither required to mount elevations nor to explore profundities; his passage is always on a level, along solid ground, without asperities, without obstruction.

This easy and safe conveyance of meaning it was Swift's desire to attain, and for having attained he deserves praise, though perhaps not the highest praise. For purposes merely didactic, when something is to be told that was not known before, it is the best mode; but against that inattention by which known truths are suffered to lie neglected, it makes no provision; it instructs but does not persuade.

By his political education he was associated with the Whigs; but he deserted them when they deserted their principles, yet without running into the contrary extreme; he continued throughout his life to retain the disposition which he assigns to the "Church-of-England Man," of thinking commonly with the Whigs of the State and with the Tories of the Church.

He was a churchman rationally zealous; he desired the prosperity and maintained the honor of the clergy; of the dissenters he did not wish to infringe the toleration but he opposed their encroachments.

To his duty as dean he was very attentive. He managed the revenues of his church with exact economy; and it is said by Delany that more money was, under his direction, laid out in repairs than had ever been in the same time since its first erection. Of his choir he was eminently careful; and, though he neither loved nor understood music, took care that all the singers were well qualified, admitting none without the testimony of skillful judges.

In his church he restored the practice of weekly communion and distributed the sacramental elements in the most solemn and devout manner with his own hand. He came to church every morning, preached commonly in his turn and attended the evening anthem, that it might not be negligently performed.

He read the service "rather with a strong, nervous voice than in a graceful manner; his voice was sharp and high-toned, rather than harmonious."

He entered upon the clerical state with hope to excel in preaching; but complained that, from the time of his political controversies, "he could only preach pamphlets." This censure of himself, if judgment be made from those sermons which have been printed, was unreasonably severe.

The suspicions of his irreligion proceeded in a great measure from his dread of hypocrisy; instead of wishing to seem better, he delighted in seeming worse than he was. He went in London to early prayers, lest he should be seen at church; he read prayers to his servants every morning with such dexterous secrecy, that Dr. Delany was six months in his house before he knew it. He was not only careful to hide the good which he did, but willingly incurred the suspicion of evil which he did not. He forgot what himself had formerly asserted that hypocrisy is less mischievous than open impiety. Dr. Delany, with all his zeal for his honor, has justly condemned this part of his character.

The person of Swift had not many recommendations. He had a kind of muddy complexion, which, though he washed himself with Oriental scrupulosity, did not look clear. He had a countenance sour and severe, which he seldom softened by any appearance of gaiety. He stubbornly resisted any tendency to laughter.

To his domestics he was naturally rough; and a man of a rigorous temper, with that vigilance of minute attention which his works discover, must have been a master that few could bear. That he was disposed to do his servants good, on important occasions, is no great mitigation; benefaction can be but rare and tyrannic peevish-

338

ness is perpetual. He did not spare the servants of others. Once, when he dined alone with the Earl of Orrery, he said of one that waited in the room, "That man has, since we sat to the table, committed fifteen faults." What the faults were, Lord Orrery, from whom I heard the story, had not been attentive enough to discover. My number may perhaps not be exact.

In his economy he practised a peculiar and offensive parsimony without disguise or apology. The practice of saving being once necessary became habitual and grew first ridiculous and at last detestable. But his avarice, though it might exclude pleasure, was never suffered to encroach upon his virtue. He was frugal by inclination but liberal by principle; and if the purpose to which he destined his little accumulations be remembered, with his distribution of occasional charity, it will perhaps appear that he only liked one mode of expense better than another and saved merely that he might have something to give. He did not grow rich by injuring his successors but left both Laracor and the Deanery more valuable than he found them. With all this talk of his covetousness and generosity, it should be remembered that he was never rich. The revenue of his Deanery was not much more than seven hundred a year.

His beneficence was not graced with tenderness or civility; he relieved without pity and assisted without kindness; so that those who were fed by him could hardly love him.

He made a rule to himself to give but one piece at a time and therefore always stored his pocket with coins of different value.

Whatever he did, he seemed willing to do in a manner peculiar to himself, without sufficiently considering that singularity, as it implies a contempt of the general practice, is a kind of defiance which justly provokes the hostility of ridicule; he, therefore, who indulges peculiar habits is worse than others, if he be not better.

Of his humor, a story told by Pope may afford a specimen.

"Dr. Swift has an odd, blunt way, that is mistaken, by strangers, for ill-nature. 'Tis so odd, that there's no describing it but by facts. I'll tell you one that just comes into my head. One evening, Gay and I went to see him: you know how intimately we were all acquainted. On our coming in, 'Hey-day, gentlemen (says the Doctor), what's the meaning of this visit? How come you to leave all the great Lords, that you are so fond of, to come hither to see a poor Dean?' 'Because we would rather see you than any of them.' 'Ay, any one that did not know you so well as I do, might believe you.

But since you are come, I must get some supper for you, I suppose.' 'No, Doctor, we have supped already.' 'Supped already? that's impossible! why, 'tis not eight o'clock yet.' 'Indeed, we have.' 'That's very strange; but, if you had not supped, I must have got something for you. Let me see, what should I have had? A couple of lobsters; ay, that would have done very well; two shillings—tarts a shilling: but you will drink a glass of wine with me, though you supped so much before your usual time only to spare my pocket?' 'No, we had rather talk with you than drink with you.' 'But if you had supped with me, as in all reason you ought to have done, you must have drank with me.—A bottle of wine, two shillings—two and two is four, and one is five: just two-and-sixpence apiece. There, Pope, there's half a crown for you and there's another for you, Sir; for I won't save anything by you, I am determined.' This was all said and done with his usual seriousness on such occasions; and, in spite of everything we could say to the contrary, he actually obliged us to take the money."

In the intercourse of familiar life, he indulged his disposition to petulance and sarcasm and thought himself injured if the licentiousness of his raillery, the freedom of his censures or the petulance of his frolics was resented or repressed. He predominated over his companions with very high ascendency, and probably would bear none over whom he could not predominate. To give him advice was, in the style of his friend Delany, "to venture to speak to him." This customary superiority soon grew too delicate for truth; and Swift, with all his penetration, allowed himself to be delighted with low flattery.

On all common occasions, he habitually affects a style of arrogance, and dictates rather than persuades. This authoritative and magisterial language he expected to be received as his peculiar mode of jocularity: but he apparently flattered his own arrogance by an assumed imperiousness, in which he was ironical only to the resentful and to the submissive sufficiently serious.

He told stories with great felicity and delighted in doing what he knew himself to do well; he was therefore captivated by the respectful silence of a steady listener and told the same tales too often.

He did not, however, claim the right of talking alone; for it was his rule, when he had spoken a minute, to give room by a pause for any other speaker. Of time, on all occasions, he was an exact computer and knew the minutes required to every common operation.

It may be justly supposed that there was in his conversation, what appears so frequently in his letters, an affectation of familarity with the great, an ambition of momentary equality sought and enjoyed by the neglect of those ceremonies which custom has established as the barriers between one order of society and another. This transgression of regularity was by himself and his admirers termed greatness of soul. But a great mind disdains to hold anything by courtesy and therefore never usurps what a lawful claimant may take away. He that encroaches on another's dignity, puts himself in his power; he is either repelled with helpless indignity or endured by clemency and condescension.

Of Swift's general habits of thinking, if his letters can be supposed to afford any evidence, he was not a man to be either loved or envied. He seems to have wasted life in discontent, by the rage of neglected pride and the languishment of unsatisfied desire. He is querulous and fastidious, arrogant and malignant; he scarcely speaks of himself but with indignant lamentations or of others but with insolent superiority when he is gay, and with angry contempt when he is gloomy. From the letters that pass between him and Pope, it might be inferred that they, with Arbuthnot and Gay, had engrossed all the understanding and virtue of mankind; that their merits filled the world or that there was no hope of more. They show the age involved in darkness and shade the picture with sullen emulation.

When [1714] the Queen's death drove him into Ireland, he might be allowed to regret for a time the interception of his views, the extinction of his hopes, and his ejection from gay scenes, important employment and splendid friendships; but when time had enabled reason to prevail over vexation, the complaints, which at first were natural, became ridiculous because they were useless. But querulousness was now grown habitual and he cried out when he probably had ceased to feel. His reiterated wailings persuaded Bolingbroke that he was really willing to quit his deanery for an English parish; and Bolingbroke procured an exchange, which was rejected; and Swift still retained the pleasure of complaining.

The greatest difficulty that occurs in analyzing his character is to discover by what depravity of intellect he took delight in revolving ideas from which almost every other mind shrinks with disgust. The ideas of pleasure, even when criminal, may solicit the imagination; but what have disease, deformity and filth, upon which the thoughts can be allured to dwell? Delany is willing to think that Swift's mind was not much tainted with this gross corruption before his [first] long visit to Pope. He does not consider how he degrades his hero by making him at fifty-nine the pupil of turpitude and liable to the malignant influence of an ascendant mind. But the truth is, that Gulliver had described his Yahoos before the visit; and he that had formed those images had nothing filthy to learn.

I have here given the character of Swift as he exhibits himself to my perception; but now let another be heard who knew him better. Dr. Delany, after long acquaintance, describes him to Lord Orrery in these terms:

"My Lord, when you consider Swift's singular, peculiar and most variegated vein of wit, always rightly intended (although not always so rightly directed), delightful in many instances and salutary even where it is most offensive; when you consider his strict truth, his fortitude in resisting oppression and arbitrary power; his fidelity in friendship, his sincere love and zeal for religion, his uprightness in making right resolutions and his steadiness in adhering to them; his care of his church, its choir, its economy and its income; his attention to all those that preached in his cathedral, in order to their amendment in pronunciation and style; as also his remarkable attention to the interest of his successors, preferably to his own present emoluments; his invincible patriotism, even to a country which he did not love; his very various, well-devised, well-judged and extensive charities, throughout his life and his whole fortune (to say nothing of his wife's) conveyed to the same Christian purposes at his death; charities from which he could enjoy no honor, advantage or satisfaction of any kind in this world; when you consider his ironical and humorous, as well as his serious schemes, for the promotion of true religion and virtue, his success in soliciting for the first fruits and twentieths, to the unspeakable benefit of the Established Church of Ireland; and his felicity (to rate it no higher) in giving occasion to the building of fifty new churches in London:

"All this considered, the character of his life will appear like that of his writings; they will both bear to be reconsidered and re-examined with the utmost attention, and always discover new beauties and excellences upon every examination.

"They will bear to be considered as the sun, in which the brightness will hide the blemishes; and whenever petulant ignorance, pride, malignity or envy interposes to cloud or sully his fame, I will take upon me to pronounce that the eclipse will not last long.

"To conclude—No man ever deserved better of his country than Swift did of his. A steady, persevering, inflexible friend; a wise, a watchful and a faithful counselor, under many severe trials and bitter persecutions, to the manifest hazard both of his liberty and fortune.

"He lived a blessing, he died a benefactor and his name will ever live an honor to Ireland.". . .

JAMES THOMSON

1700–1748

JAMES THOMSON, THE SON of [the Rev. Thomas Thomson] a minister well esteemed for his piety and diligence, was born September 11, 1700, at Ednam, in the shire of Roxburgh, of which his father was pastor. His mother, whose name was Trotter, inherited as co-heiress a portion of a small estate. The revenue of a parish in Scotland is seldom large; and it was probably in commiseration of the difficulty with which Mr. Thomson supported his family, having nine children, that Mr. Riccaltoun, a neighboring minister, discovering in James uncommon promises of future excellence, undertook to superintend his education and provide him books.

He was taught the common rudiments of learning at the school of Jedburgh, a place which he delights to recollect in his poem of *Autumn;* but was not considered by his master as superior to common boys, though in those early days he amused his patron and his friends with poetical compositions; with which, however, he so little pleased himself, that on every New Year's day he threw into the fire all the productions of the foregoing year.

From the school he was removed to Edinburgh, where he had not resided two years when his father died and left all his children to the care of their mother, who raised upon her little estate what money a mortgage could afford and, removing with her family to Edinburgh, lived to see her son rising into eminence.

The design of Thomson's friends was to breed him a minister. He

343

lived at Edinburgh, as at school, without distinction or expectation till, at the usual time, he performed a probationary exercise by explaining a psalm. His diction was so poetically splendid that Mr. Hamilton, the Professor of Divinity, reproved him for speaking language unintelligible to a popular audience, and he censured one of his expressions as indecent, if not profane.

This rebuke is reported to have repressed his thoughts of an ecclesiastical character and he probably cultivated with new diligence his blossoms of poetry, which, however, were in some danger of a blast; for, submitting his productions to some who thought themselves qualified to criticize, he heard of nothing but faults; but, finding other judges more favorable, he did not suffer himself to sink into despondence.

He easily discovered that the only stage on which a poet could appear, with any hope of advantage, was London; a place too wide for the operation of petty competition and private malignity, where merit might soon become conspicuous and would find friends as soon as it became reputable to befriend it. A lady, who was acquainted with his mother, advised him to the journey and promised some countenance or assistance, which at last he never received; however, he justified his adventure by her encouragement and came [1725] to seek in London patronage and fame.

At his arrival he found his way to Mr. Mallet, then tutor to the sons of the Duke of Montrose. He had recommendations to several persons of consequence, which he had tied up carefully in his handkerchief; but as he passed along the street, with the gaping curiosity of a newcomer, his attention was upon everything rather than his pocket and his magazine of credentials was stolen from him.

His first want was a pair of shoes. For the supply of all his necessities his whole fund was his *Winter,* which for a time could find no purchaser; till, at last [1726] Mr. Millan was persuaded to buy it at a low price; and this low price he had for some time reason to regret; but, by accident, Mr. Whatley,* a man not wholly unknown among authors, happening to turn his eye upon it, was so delighted that he ran from place to place celebrating its excellence. Thomson obtained likewise the notice of Aaron Hill, whom, being friendless and indigent and glad of kindness, he courted with every expression of servile adulation.

* Thomas Whatley, politician and literary student

LIVES OF THE POETS

Winter was dedicated to Sir Spencer Compton,* but attracted no regard from him to the author; till Aaron Hill awakened his attention by some verses addressed to Thomson and published in one of the newspapers, which censured the great for their neglect of ingenious men. Thomson then received a present of twenty guineas, of which he gives this account to Mr. Hill:

"I hinted to you in my last that on Saturday morning I was with Sir Spencer Compton. A certain gentleman, without my desire, spoke to him concerning me: his answer was that I had never come near him. Then the gentleman put the question if he desired that I should wait on him? He returned, he did. On this the gentleman gave me an introductory letter to him. He received me in what they commonly call a civil manner, asked me some commonplace questions and made me a present of twenty guineas. I am very ready to own that the present was larger than my performance deserved and shall ascribe it to his generosity or any other cause, rather than the merit of the address."

The poem which, being of a new kind, few would venture at first to like, by degrees gained upon the public; and one edition was very speedily succeeded by another. . . .

Thomson, having been some time entertained in the family of the Lord Binning, was desirous of testifying his gratitude by making him the patron of his *Summer;* but the same kindness which had first disposed Lord Binning to encourage him, determined him to refuse the Dedication, which was by his advice addressed to Mr. Dodington,† a man who had more power to advance the reputation and fortune of a poet.

Spring was published next year [June 1728] with a Dedication to the Countess of Hertford, whose practice it was to invite every summer some poet into the country, to hear her verses and assist her studies. This honor was one summer conferred on Thomson, who took more delight in carousing with Lord Hertford and his friends than assisting her Ladyship's poetical operations and therefore never received another summons.

Autumn, the season to which the *Spring* and *Summer* are preparatory, still remained unsung, and was delayed till he published (May 1730) his works collected.

* Speaker of the House of Commons
† Bubb Dodington, politician

345

He produced in 1729 the tragedy of *Sophonisba,* which raised such expectation, that every rehearsal was dignified with a splendid audience collected to anticipate the delight that was preparing for the public. It was observed, however, that nobody was much affected and that the company rose as from a moral lecture. . . .

Thomson, in his travels on the Continent, found or fancied so many evils arising from the tyranny of other governments, that he resolved to write a very long poem, in five parts, upon Liberty. . . .

Upon this great poem two years were spent and the author congratulated himself upon it as his noblest work; but an author and his reader are not always of a mind. Liberty called in vain upon her votaries to read her praises and reward her encomiast: her praises were condemned to harbor spiders and to gather dust: none of Thomson's performances were so little regarded.

The judgment of the public was not erroneous; the recurrence of the same images must tire in time; an enumeration of examples to prove a position which nobody denied, as it was from the beginning superfluous, must quickly grow disgusting.

. . . He produced (1738) the tragedy of *Agamemnon,* which was much shortened in the representation. It had the fate which most commonly attends mythological stories and was only endured but not favored. It struggled with such difficulty through the first night, that Thomson, coming late to his friends with whom he was to sup, excused his delay by telling them how the sweat of his distress had so disordered his wig, that he could not come till he had been refitted by a barber.

He so interested himself in his own drama that, if I remember right, as he sat in the upper gallery, he accompanied the players by audible recitation, till a friendly hint frighted him to silence. Pope countenanced *Agamemnon* by coming to it the first night and was welcomed to the theater by a general clap; he had much regard for Thomson, and once expressed it in a poetical Epistle sent to Italy, of which, however, he abated the value by transplanting some of the lines into his *Epistle to Arbuthnot.*

About this time [1737] the Act was passed for licensing plays, of which the first operation was the prohibition of *Gustavus Vasa,* a tragedy of Mr. Brooke * whom the public recompensed by a very liberal subscription; the next was the refusal of *Edward and Eleo-*

* Henry Brooke, Irish poet

nora, offered by Thomson. It is hard to discover why either play should have been obstructed. Thomson likewise endeavored to repair his loss by a subscription, of which I cannot now tell the success.

When the public murmured at the unkind treatment of Thomson, one of the ministerial writers remarked that "he had taken a *Liberty* which was not agreeable to *Britannia* in any *Season.*"

He was soon after employed in conjunction with Mr. Mallet, to write the masque of *Alfred,* which was acted before the Prince at Cliveden House.

His next work (1745) was *Tancred and Sigismunda,* the most successful of all his tragedies, for it still keeps its turn upon the stage. It may be doubted whether he was, either by the bent of nature or habits of study, much qualified for tragedy. It does not appear that he had much sense of the pathetic and his diffusive and descriptive style produced declamation rather than dialogue. . . .

The last piece that he lived to publish [1748] was the *Castle of Indolence,* which was many years under his hand but was at last finished with great accuracy. The first canto opens a scene of lazy luxury that fills the imagination. . . .

As a writer, he is entitled to one praise of the highest kind: his mode of thinking and of expressing his thoughts is original. His blank verse is no more the blank verse of Milton, or of any other poet, than the rhymes of Prior are the rhymes of Cowley. His numbers, his pauses, his diction are of his own growth, without transcription, without imitation. He thinks in a peculiar train and he thinks always as a man of genius; he looks round on Nature and on life with the eye which Nature bestows only on a poet; the eye that distinguishes, in everything presented to its view, whatever there is on which imagination can delight to be detained and with a mind that at once comprehends the vast and attends to the minute. The reader of *The Seasons* wonders that he never saw before what Thomson shows him and that he never yet has felt what Thomson impresses.

His is one of the works in which blank verse seems properly used. Thomson's wide expansion of general views and his enumeration of circumstantial varieties would have been obstructed and embarrassed by the frequent intersections of the sense, which are the necessary effects of rhyme.

His descriptions of extended scenes and general effects bring before us the whole magnificence of Nature, whether pleasing or dreadful. The gaiety of Spring, the splendor of Summer, the tranquillity of Autumn and the horror of Winter take in their turns possession of the mind. The poet leads us through the appearances of things as they are successively varied by the vicissitudes of the year and imparts to us so much of his own enthusiasm, that our thoughts expand with his imagery and kindle with his sentiments. Nor is the naturalist without his part in the entertainment; for he is assisted to recollect and to combine, to arrange his discoveries and to amplify the sphere of his contemplation.

The great defect of *The Seasons* is want of method; but for this I know not that there was any remedy. Of many appearances subsisting all at once, no rule can be given why one should be mentioned before another; yet the memory wants the help of order and the curiosity is not excited by suspense or expectation.

His diction is in the highest degree florid and luxuriant, such as may be said to be to his images and thoughts "both their luster and their shade"; such as invest them with splendor, through which perhaps they are not always easily discerned. It is too exuberant and sometimes may be charged with filling the ear more than the mind.

These poems, with which I was acquainted at their first appearance, I have since found altered and enlarged by subsequent revisals, as the author supposed his judgment to grow more exact, and as books or conversation extended his knowledge and opened his prospects. They are, I think, improved in general; yet I know not whether they have not lost part of what Temple calls their "race"; a word which, applied to wines in its primitive sense, means the flavor of the soil.

Liberty, when it first appeared, I tried to read and soon desisted. I have never tried again and therefore will not hazard either praise or censure.

The highest praise which he has received ought not to be suppressed: it is said by Lord Lyttelton, in the Prologue to his posthumous play,* that his works contained

No line which, dying, he could wish to blot.

* *Coriolanus*

THOMAS GRAY

1716–1771

THOMAS GRAY, THE SON of Mr. Philip Gray, a scrivener of London, was born in Cornhill, November 26, 1716. His grammatical education he received at Eton under the care of Mr. Antrobus, his mother's brother, then assistant to Dr. George; and when he left school, in 1734, entered a pensioner at Peterhouse in Cambridge.

The transition from the school to the college is, to most young scholars, the time from which they date their years of manhood, liberty and happiness; but Gray seems to have been very little delighted with academical gratifications; he liked at Cambridge neither the mode of life nor the fashion of study and lived sullenly on to the time when his attendance on lectures was no longer required. As he intended to profess the Common Law, he took no degree.

When he had been at Cambridge about five years, Mr. Horace Walpole, whose friendship he had gained at Eton, invited him to travel with him as his companion. They wandered through France into Italy; and Gray's letters contain a very pleasing account of many parts of their journey. But unequal friendships are easily dissolved: at Florence they quarreled and parted; and Mr. Walpole is now content to have it told that it was by his fault. If we look, however, without prejudice on the world, we shall find that men whose consciousness of their own merit sets them above the compliances of servility are apt enough in their association with superiors to watch their own dignity with troublesome and punctilious jealousy, and in the fervor of independence to exact that attention which they refuse to pay. Part they did, whatever was the quarrel and the rest of their travels was doubtless more unpleasant to them both. Gray continued his journey in a manner suitable to his own little fortune, with only an occasional servant.

He returned to England in September 1741 and in about two months afterward buried his father, who had, by an injudicious waste of money upon a new house, so much lessened his fortune, that Gray thought himself too poor to study the law. He therefore retired to Cambridge, where he soon after became Bachelor of Civil Law; and where, without liking the place or its inhabitants or professing to like them, he passed, except a short residence in London, the rest of his life.

About this time [1742] he was deprived of Mr. West,* the son of a chancellor of Ireland, a friend on whom he appears to have set a high value, and who deserved his esteem by the powers which he shows in his letters and in the *Ode to May* which Mr. Mason † has preserved, as well as by the sincerity with which, when Gray sent him part of *Agrippina,* a tragedy that he had just begun, he gave an opinion which probably intercepted the progress of the work and which the judgment of every reader will confirm. It was certainly no loss to the English stage that *Agrippina* was never finished.

In this year (1742) Gray seems first to have applied himself seriously to poetry; for in this year were produced the *Ode to Spring,* his *Prospect of Eton* and his *Ode to Adversity.* He began likewise a Latin poem, *De principiis cogitandi.*

It may be collected from the narrative of Mr. Mason, that his first ambition was to have excelled in Latin poetry: perhaps it were reasonable to wish that he had prosecuted his design; for though there is at present some embarrassment in his phrase and some harshness in his lyric numbers, his copiousness of language is such as very few possess; and his lines, even when imperfect, discover a writer whom practice would quickly have made skillful.

He now lived on at Peterhouse, very little solicitous what others did or thought, and cultivated his mind and enlarged his views without any other purpose than of improving and amusing himself; when Mr. Mason being elected Fellow of Pembroke Hall, brought him a companion who was afterward to be his editor, and whose fondness and fidelity has kindled in him a zeal of admiration which cannot be reasonably expected from the neutrality of a stranger, and the coldness of a critic.

In this retirement he wrote (1747) an ode on the *Death of Mr. Walpole's Cat;* and the year afterward attempted a poem of more importance, on *Government and Education,* of which the fragments which remain have many excellent lines.

His next production (1751) was his far-famed *Elegy in the Churchyard,* which, finding its way into a magazine, first, I believe, made him known to the public.

* Richard West
† William Mason, poet, author of a life of Gray

An invitation from Lady Cobham about this time gave occasion to an odd composition called *A Long Story,* which adds little to Gray's character.

Several of his pieces were published (1753), with designs by Mr. Bentley * and, that they might in some form or other make a book, only one side of each leaf was printed. I believe the poems and the plates recommended each other so well, that the whole impression was soon bought. This year he lost his mother.

Some time afterward (1756) some young men of the college, whose chambers were near his, diverted themselves with disturbing him by frequent and troublesome noises and, as is said, by pranks yet more offensive and contemptuous. This insolence, having endured it a while, he represented to the governors of the society, among whom perhaps he had no friends and, finding his complaint little regarded, removed himself to Pembroke Hall.

In 1757 he published *The Progress of Poetry* and *The Bard,* two compositions at which the readers of poetry were at first content to gaze in mute amazement. Some that tried them confessed their inability to understand them, though Warburton said that they were understood as well as the works of Milton and Shakespeare, which it is the fashion to admire. Garrick † wrote a few lines in their praise. Some hardy champions undertook to rescue them from neglect and in a short time many were content to be shown beauties which they could not see.

Gray's reputation was now so high, that, after the death of Cibber [1757], he had the honor of refusing the laurel, which was then bestowed on Mr. Whitehead.‡

His curiosity, not long after, drew him away [1759] from Cambridge to a lodging near the Museum, where he resided near three years, reading and transcribing; and, so far as can be discovered, very little affected by two odes on *Oblivion* and *Obscurity,* in which his lyric performances were ridiculed with much contempt and much ingenuity.

When [1762] the Professor of Modern History at Cambridge died, he was, as he says, "cockered and spirited up" till he asked it of Lord Bute, who sent him a civil refusal; and the place was given to Mr. Brocket, the tutor of Sir James Lowther.

* Richard Bentley
† David Garrick, English actor
‡ William Whitehead

351

His constitution was weak, and believing that his health was promoted by exercise and change of place, he undertook (1765) a journey into Scotland, of which his account, so far as it extends, is very curious and elegant: for, as his comprehension was ample, his curiosity extended to all the works of art, all the appearances of nature and all the monuments of past events. He naturally contracted a friendship with Dr. Beattie,* whom he found a poet, a philosopher and a good man. The Marischal College at Aberdeen offered him the degree of Doctor of Laws, which, having omitted to take it at Cambridge, he thought it decent to refuse.

What he had formerly solicited in vain was at last given him without solicitation. The Professorship of History became again vacant and he received (1768) an offer of it from the Duke of Grafton. He accepted, and retained it to his death; always designing lectures but never reading them; uneasy at his neglect of duty and appeasing his uneasiness with designs of reformation and with a resolution which he believed himself to have made of resigning the office, if he found himself unable to discharge it.

Ill health made another journey necessary and he visited (1769) Westmoreland and Cumberland. He that reads his epistolary narration wishes that to travel, and to tell his travels, had been more of his employment; but it is by studying at home that we must obtain the ability of traveling with intelligence and improvement.

His travels and his studies were now near their end. The gout, of which he had sustained many weak attacks, fell upon his stomach and, yielding to no medicines, produced strong convulsions, which (July 30, 1771) terminated in death. . . .

Gray's poetry is now to be considered and I hope not to be looked on as an enemy to his name, if I confess that I contemplate it with less pleasure than his life.

His ode on *Spring* has something poetical, both in the language and the thought; but the language is too luxuriant and the thoughts have nothing new. There has of late arisen a practice of giving to adjectives derived from substantives, the termination of participles; such as the *cultured* plain, the *daisied* bank; but I was sorry to see, in the lines of a scholar like Gray, the *honied* Spring. The morality is natural but too stale; the conclusion is pretty.

The poem *On the Cat* was doubtless by its author considered as

* James Beattie

a trifle, but it is not a happy trifle. In the first stanza "the azure flowers *that* blow" show how resolutely a rhyme is sometimes made when it cannot easily be found. Selima, the Cat, is called a nymph, with some violence both to language and sense; but there is good use made of it when it is done; for of the two lines,

> *What female heart can gold despise?*
> *What cat's averse to fish?*

the first relates merely to the nymph and the second only to the cat. The sixth stanza contains a melancholy truth, that "a favorite has no friend"; but the last ends in a pointed sentence of no relation to the purpose: if *what glistered* had been *gold,* the cat would not have gone into the water; and if she had, would not less have been drowned.

The *Prospect of Eton College* suggests nothing to Gray which every beholder does not equally think and feel. His supplication to Father Thames, to tell him who drives the hoop or tosses the ball, is useless and puerile. Father Thames has no better means of knowing than himself. His epithet "buxom health" is not elegant; he seems not to understand the word. Gray thought his language more poetical as it was more remote from common use: finding in Dryden "honey redolent of Spring," an expression that reaches the utmost limits of our language, Gray drove it a little more beyond common apprehension by making "gales" to be "redolent of joy and youth."

Of the *Hymn to Adversity,* the hint was at first taken from *O Diva, gratum quae regis Antium;* but Gray has excelled his original by the variety of his sentiments, and by their moral application. Of this piece, at once poetical and rational, I will not by slight objections violate the dignity.

My process has now brought me to the *wonderful* "Wonder of Wonders," the two Sister Odes; by which, though either vulgar ignorance or common sense at first universally rejected them, many have been since persuaded to think themselves delighted. I am one of those that are willing to be pleased and therefore would gladly find the meaning of the first stanza of the *Progress of Poetry*.

Gray seems in his rapture to confound the images of "spreading sound and running water." A "stream of music" may be allowed; but where does "music," however "smooth and strong," after having visited the "verdant vales, roll down the steep amain," so as that "rocks and nodding groves rebellow to the roar"? If this be said

353

of music, it is nonsense; if it be said of water, it is nothing to the purpose.

The second stanza, exhibiting Mars's car and Jove's eagle, is unworthy of further notice. Criticism disdains to chase a schoolboy to his commonplaces.

To the third it may likewise be objected that it is drawn from mythology, though such as may be more easily assimilated to real life. Idalia's "velvet-green" has something of cant. An epithet or metaphor drawn from nature ennobles art: an epithet or metaphor drawn from art degrades nature. Gray is too fond of words arbitrarily compounded. "Many-twinkling" was formerly censured as not analogical; we may say "many-spotted," but scarcely "many-spotting." This stanza, however, has something pleasing.

Of the second ternary of stanzas, the first endeavors to tell something, and would have told it had it not been crossed by Hyperion: the second describes well enough the universal prevalence of poetry; but I am afraid that the conclusion will not rise from the premises. The caverns of the North and the plains of Chili are not the residences of "glory and generous shame." But that poetry and virtue go always together is an opinion so pleasing, that I can forgive him who resolves to think it true.

The third stanza sounds big with "Delphi," and "Aegean," and "Ilissus" and "Meander" and "hallowed fountains" and "solemn sound"; but in all Gray's odes there is a kind of cumbrous splendor which we wish away. His position is at last false: in the time of Dante and Petrarch, from whom we derive our first school of poetry, Italy was overrun by "tyrant power" and "coward vice"; nor was our state much better when we first borrowed the Italian arts.

Of the third ternary, the first gives a mythological birth of Shakespeare. What is said of that mighty genius is true; but it is not said happily: the real effects of this poetical power are put out of sight by the pomp of machinery. Where truth is sufficient to fill the mind, fiction is worse than useless; the counterfeit debases the genuine.

His account of Milton's blindness, if we suppose it caused by study in the formation of his poem—a supposition surely allowable—is poetically true and happily imagined. But the *car* of Dryden, with his *two coursers,* has nothing in it peculiar; it is a car in which any other rider may be placed.

The Bard appears at the first view to be, as Algarotti * and others have remarked, an imitation of the prophecy of Nereus.† Algarotti thinks it superior to its original, and if preference depends only on the imagery and animation of the two poems, his judgment is right. There is in *The Bard* more force, more thought and more variety. But to copy is less than to invent and the copy has been unhappily produced at a wrong time. The fiction of Horace was to the Romans credible; but its revival disgusts us with apparent and unconquerable falsehood. *Incredulus odi.*

To select a singular event and swell it to a giant's bulk by fabulous appendages of specters and predictions, has little difficulty; for he that forsakes the probable may always find the marvelous. And it has little use: we are affected only as we believe; we are improved only as we find something to be imitated or declined. I do not see that *The Bard* promotes any truth, moral or political.

His stanzas are too long, especially his epodes; the ode is finished before the ear has learned its measure, and consequently before it can receive pleasure from their consonance and recurrence.

Of the first stanza the abrupt beginning has been celebrated; but technical beauties can give praise only to the inventor. It is in the power of any man to rush abruptly upon his subject that has read the ballad of *Johnny Armstrong:*

Is there ever a man in all Scotland.

The initial resemblances or alliterations "ruin, ruthless, helm or hauberk," are below the grandeur of a poem that endeavors at sublimity.

In the second stanza the Bard is well described; but in the third we have the puerilities of obsolete mythology. When we are told that "Cadwallo hush'd the stormy main" and that "Modred made huge Plinlimmon bow his cloud-topp'd head," attention recoils from the repetition of a tale that, even when it was first heard, was heard with scorn.

The *weaving* of the *winding sheet* he borrowed, as he owns, from the Northern bards; but their texture, however, was very properly the work of female powers, as the act of spinning the thread of life in another mythology. Theft is always dangerous; Gray has made weavers of slaughtered bards, by a fiction outrageous and incon-

* Francesco Algarotti, Italian critic
† Father of the water nymphs

355

gruous. They are then called upon to "weave the warp, and weave the woof," perhaps with no great propriety; for it is by crossing the *woof* with the *warp* that men *weave* the *web* or piece; and the first line was dearly bought by the admission of its wretched correspondent, "Give ample room and verge enough." He has, however, no other line as bad.

The third stanza of the second ternary is commended, I think, beyond its merit. The personification is indistinct. *Thirst* and *hunger* are not alike; and their features, to make the imagery perfect, should have been discriminated. We are told in the same stanza how "towers are fed." But I will no longer look for particular faults; yet let it be observed that the ode might have been concluded with an action of better example; but suicide is always to be had without expense of thought.

These odes are marked by glittering accumulations of ungraceful ornaments; they strike, rather than please; the images are magnified by affectation; the language is labored into harshness. The mind of the writer seems to work with unnatural violence. "Double, double, toil and trouble." He has a kind of strutting dignity and is tall by walking on tiptoe. His art and his struggle are too visible and there is too little appearance of ease and nature.

To say that he has no beauties, would be unjust: a man like him, of great learning and great industry, could not but produce something valuable. When he pleases least, it can only be said that a good design was ill-directed.

His translations of Northern and Welsh poetry deserve praise; the imagery is preserved, perhaps often improved; but the language is unlike the language of other poets.

In the character of his *Elegy* I rejoice to concur with the common reader; for by the common sense of readers uncorrupted with literary prejudices, after all the refinements of subtilty and the dogmatism of learning, must be finally decided all claim to poetical honors. The *Churchyard* abounds with images which find a mirror in every mind and with sentiments to which every bosom returns an echo. The four stanzas beginning "Yet even these bones" are to me original: I have never seen the notions in any other place; yet he that reads them here, persuades himself that he has always felt them. Had Gray written often thus, it had been vain to blame, and useless to praise him.

Harriet Beecher Stowe

TELLS

WHAT SORT OF

WOMAN

SHE IS

February 16, 1853

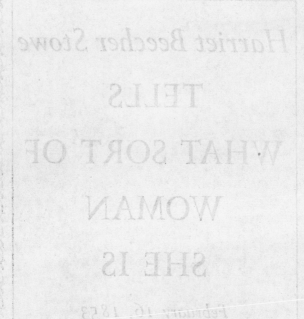

Harriet Beecher Stowe

TELLS

WHAT SORT OF

WOMAN

SHE IS

February 16, 1853

HOME COURSE APPRECIATION

"So THIS IS THE LITTLE LADY who made this big war?" According to Stowe and Beecher family legend, Mr. Lincoln was gentle when, in 1862, this "little bit of a woman" was introduced to him in the White House. And no one can seriously doubt that Lincoln was right in supposing *Uncle Tom's Cabin* had played an important part in furthering the cause of Abolition, even if he was more than a little jocular in crediting Mrs. Stowe with bringing on the Civil War.

The Beechers were accustomed to stirring at the center of great events. Lyman Beecher, Harriet's father, was a famous Connecticut divine and the founder of the Temperance movement as an active force in American moral and political life. Henry Ward Beecher, Harriet's brother, was the most eminent American preacher of his day, a day in which a great preacher was a national figure. Like the military and political heroes of our secularized times, a Henry Ward Beecher was revered; and like the great actors of the present day, the nineteenth-century preacher found his audience prepared to be deeply moved. Add to such influence the appeal of the modern evangelist, and one gets some notion of the powers which Harriet's father and brother exercised.

Then, when we say that Harriet Beecher, the wife of Calvin Ellis Stowe, a poor college professor, outdid her father and brother in the degree to which she moved men's hearts toward great events, and when we observe that *Uncle Tom's Cabin* is probably second in importance only to *Pilgrim's Progress* among fictional works of faith and evangelism, we are prepared to read this modest little letter in the right light.

The letter was addressed to another great woman of the period, Mrs. Eliza Lee Cabot Follen, one of the wealthy Boston ladies who were working for the abolition of slavery. Mrs. Follen, who was living in London at just this time, was the author of a volume of poems for children, called *The Well-Spent Hour.* This is the book to which Mrs. Stowe refers in her first paragraph.

The great tract, *Uncle Tom's Cabin,* appeared serially in an Abolitionist weekly newspaper during 1851 and made no great stir there. But its publication in two volumes in 1852 swiftly electrified the world. Its effect in America was to intensify immeasurably the bitterness of factional feeling between North and South. And in the rest of the world it became a document of liberation, not only for slaves, but for all those who might take its subtitle, "Life Among the Lowly," as having application to them.

BIOGRAPHICAL DETAILS

THE "THIN AND DRY" LITTLE WOMAN who was to write, as she tells us, with her heart's blood, was born on June 14, 1811, at Litchfield, Connecticut, in the midst of an old-style Calvinistic Congregationalism so intense that Harriet did not learn until she was six or seven years old that other people celebrated a feast called Christmas.

Harriet Beecher Stowe at the age of forty-two.

She went to Miss Pierce's Seminary for Young Ladies in Litchfield; and when she was fifteen, she joined the faculty of the Hartford Female Seminary, which her older sister had founded, and taught Vergil. Harriet's observations of life in the little New England villages, augmented by her husband's recollections, became the material for the series of books she was to publish after her success with her anti-slavery novels, *Uncle Tom's Cabin* and *Dred: A Tale of The Great Dismal Swamp*. This series was to make a real contribution to the literature of regional life in America.

In 1832 she moved to Cincinnati with her father, who had been elected president of the Lane Theological Seminary, and there Harriet, with her sister, founded another school. The habit of instruction was strong in the Beechers. One of the professors at the theological seminary was Calvin Stowe, and his wife became Harriet's close friend.

Cincinnati was just across the river from slave-holding Kentucky, and in 1832 it was already an important center for Abolitionist agitation. Lane Seminary, in fact, and Lyman Beecher's career as its president were ruined by a dramatic fight over the question of fraternization between the white students and Negroes of the town. In 1835 most of the student body and some of the teachers left Dr. Beecher's seminary and went to Oberlin College where women and Negroes were admitted on an equal basis with white males.

After the first Mrs. Stowe died of cholera (the plague which was the bane of the nineteenth-century city), Professor Stowe, in 1836, married Harriet, then a twenty-five-year-old spinster. The seven children to which Mrs. Stowe's letter refers were all born in Cincinnati, and it was cholera again that killed her baby in 1849.

Calvin Stowe was appointed to the faculty of Bowdoin College in Brunswick, Maine, and in 1850 the family left Ohio. But it was the events and conditions she had observed in Cincinnati and across the Ohio in Kentucky that moved Harriet toward the writing of her great tract.

RECOGNITION ABROAD

A month after writing to Mrs. Follen, Harriet went, as promised, to visit the Scottish churches. However, she had little opportunity, this daughter of the New England conscience and of the Beecher passion for exhortation, to see very much of "old, old England." What was meant to be the visit of a clergyman's wife, a clergyman's wife who was also the author of a popular novel, to a congregation in Glasgow, turned into a kind of Roman triumph. Mrs. Stowe was seized upon by England's leading moral and political reformers. She had, in the end, such a reception as no American had ever had in Europe, not even Benjamin Franklin, and such as no other American was to have until Lindbergh dazzled the world with his audacity. Yet his bold gallantry is hardly to be compared with that of this "little bit of a woman—somewhat more than forty, about as thin and dry as a pinch of snuff," whose personal fight with slavery had such violent and long-lasting consequences.

Andover, February 16, 1853.

MY DEAR MADAM,—I hasten to reply to your letter, to me the more interesting that I have long been acquainted with you, and during all the nursery part of my life made daily use of your poems for children.

I used to think sometimes in those days that I would write to you and tell you how much I was obliged to you for the pleasure which they gave us all.

So you want to know something about what sort of a woman I am! Well, if this is any object, you shall have statistics free of charge. To begin, then, I am a little bit of a woman, somewhat more than forty, about as thin and dry as a pinch of snuff; never very much to look at in my best days, and looking like a used-up article now.

I was married when I was twenty-five years old to a man rich in Greek and Hebrew, Latin and Arabic and, alas! rich in nothing else. When I went to housekeeping, my entire stock of china for parlor and kitchen was bought for eleven dollars. That lasted very well for two years, till my brother was married and brought his bride to visit me. I then found, on review, that I had neither plates nor teacups to set a table for my father's family; wherefore I thought it best to reinforce the establishment by getting me a tea set that cost ten dollars more and this, I believe, formed my whole stock in trade for some years.

But then I was abundantly enriched with wealth of another sort.

I had two little, curly-headed twin daughters to begin with, and my stock in this line has gradually increased, till I have been the mother of seven children, the most beautiful and the most loved of whom lies buried near my Cincinnati residence. It was at his dying bed and at his grave that I learned what a poor slave mother may feel when her child is torn away from her. In those depths of sorrow which seemed to me immeasurable, it was my only prayer to God that such anguish might not be suffered in vain. There were circumstances about his death of such peculiar bitterness, of what seemed almost cruel suffering, that I felt that I could never be consoled for it, unless this crushing of my own heart might enable me to work out some great good to others. . . .

I allude to this here because I have often felt that much that is in that book ("Uncle Tom") had its root in the awful scenes and bitter sorrows of that summer. It has left now, I trust, no trace on my mind, except a deep compassion for the sorrowful, especially for mothers who are separated from their children.

During long years of struggling with poverty and sickness, and a hot, debilitating climate, my children grew up around me. The nursery and the kitchen were my principal fields of labor. Some of my friends, pitying my trials, copied and sent a number of little sketches from my pen to certain liberally paying "Annuals" with my name. With the first money that I earned in this way I bought a feather bed! for as I had married into poverty and without a dowry, and as my husband had only a large library of books and a great deal of learning, the bed and pillows were thought the most profitable investment. After this I thought that I had discovered the philosopher's stone. So when a new carpet or mattress was going to be needed or when, at the close of the year, it began to be evident that my family accounts, like poor Dora's, "wouldn't add up," then I used to say to my faithful friend and factotum, Anna, who shared all my joys and sorrows, "Now, if you will keep the babies and attend to the things in the house for one day, I'll write a piece, and then we shall be out of the scrape." So I became an author, very modest at first, I do assure you, and remonstrating very seriously with the friends who had thought it best to put my name to the pieces by way of getting up a reputation; and if you ever see a woodcut of me, with an immoderately long nose, on the cover of all the U. S. Almanacs, I wish you to take notice that I have been forced into it contrary to my natural modesty by the imperative solicitations of my dear five thousand friends and the public generally. One thing I must say with regard to my life at the West, which you will understand better than many English women could.

I lived two miles from the city of Cincinnati, in the country, and domestic service, not always, you know, to be found in the city, is next to an impossibility to obtain in the country, even by those who are willing to give the highest wages; so what was to be expected for poor me, who had very little of this world's goods to offer?

Had it not been for my inseparable friend Anna, a noble-hearted English girl, who landed on our shores in destitution and sorrow, and clave to me as Ruth to Naomi, I had never lived through all the trials which this uncertainty and want of domestic service imposed on both: you may imagine, therefore, how glad I was when, our seminary property being divided out into small lots which were rented at a low price, a number of poor families settled in our vicinity, from whom we could occasionally obtain domestic service. About a dozen families of liberated slaves were among the number, and they became my favorite resort in cases of emergency. If anybody wishes to have a black face look handsome, let them be left, as I have been, in feeble health in oppressive hot weather, with a sick baby in arms, and two or three other little ones in the nursery, and not a servant in the whole house to do a single turn. Then, if they could see my good old Aunt Frankie coming with her honest, bluff, black face, her long, strong arms, her chest as big and stout as a barrel, and her hilarious, hearty laugh, perfectly delighted to take one's washing and do it at a fair price, they would appreciate the beauty of black people.

My cook, poor Eliza Buck—how she would stare to think of her name going to England!—was a regular epitome of slave life in herself: fat, gentle, easy, loving and lovable, always calling my very modest house and dooryard "The Place," as if it had been a plantation with seven hundred hands on it. She had lived through the whole sad story of a Virginia-raised slave's life. In her youth she must have been a very handsome mulatto girl. Her voice was sweet and her manners refined and agreeable. She was raised in a good family as a nurse and seamstress. When the family became embarrassed, she was suddenly sold on to a plantation in Louisiana. She has often told me how, without any warning, she was suddenly forced into a carriage, and saw her little mistress screaming and stretching her arms from the window toward her as she was driven away. She has told me of scenes on the Louisiana plantation, and she has often been out at night by stealth ministering to poor slaves who had been mangled and lacerated by the lash. Hence she was sold into Kentucky, and her last master was the father of all her children. On this point she ever maintained a delicacy and reserve that always appeared to me remarkable. She always called him her husband; and it was not till after she had lived with me some years that I discovered the real nature of the connection. I shall never forget how sorry I felt for her, nor my feelings at her humble apology, "You know, Mrs. Stowe, slave women cannot help themselves." She had two very pretty quadroon daughters, with her beautiful hair and eyes, interesting children, whom I had instructed in the family school with my children. Time would fail to tell you all that I learned incidentally of the slave system in the history of various slaves who came into my family, and of the underground railroad which, I may say, ran through our house. But the letter is already too long.

You ask with regard to the remuneration which I have received for my work here in America. Having been poor all my life and expecting to be poor the rest of it, the idea of making money by a book which I wrote just because I could not help it, never occurred to me. It was therefore an agreeable surprise to receive ten thousand dollars as the first fruits of three months' sale. I presume as much more is now due. Mr. Bosworth in England, the firm of Clarke & Co. and Mr. Bentley have all offered me an interest in the sales of their editions in London. I am very glad of it, both on account of the value of what they offer, and the value of the example they set in this matter, wherein I think that justice has been too little regarded.

I have been invited to visit Scotland, and shall probably spend the summer there and in England.

I have very much at heart a design to erect in some of the Northern States a normal school, for the education of colored teachers in the United States and in Canada. I have very much wished that some permanent memorial of good to the colored race might be created out of the proceeds of a work which promises to have so unprecedented a sale. My own share of the profits will be less than that of the publishers', either English or American; but I am willing to give largely for this purpose, and I have no doubt that the publishers, both American and English, will unite with me; for nothing

366

tends more immediately to the emancipation of the slave than the education and elevation of the free.

I am now writing a work which will contain, perhaps, an equal amount of matter with "Uncle Tom's Cabin." It will contain all the facts and documents on which that story was founded, and an immense body of facts, reports of trials, legal documents and testimony of people now living South, which will more than confirm every statement in "Uncle Tom's Cabin."

I must confess that till I began the examination of facts in order to write this book, much as I thought I knew before, I had not begun to measure the depth of the abyss. The law records of courts and judicial proceedings are so incredible as to fill me with amazement whenever I think of them. It seems to me that the book cannot but be felt, and, coming upon the sensibility awaked by the other, do something.

I suffer exquisitely in writing these things. It may be truly said that I write with my heart's blood. Many times in writing "Uncle Tom's Cabin" I thought my health would fail utterly; but I prayed earnestly that God would help me till I got through, and still I am pressed beyond measure and above strength.

This horror, this nightmare abomination! can it be in my country! It lies like lead on my heart, it shadows my life with sorrow; the more so that I feel, as for my own brothers, for the South, and am pained by every horror I am obliged to write, as one who is forced by some awful oath to disclose in court some family disgrace. Many times I have thought that I must die, and yet I pray God that I may live to see something done. I shall in all probability be in London in May; shall I see you?

It seems to me so odd and dream-like that so many persons desire to see me, and now I cannot help thinking that they will think, when they do, that God hath chosen "the weak things of this world."

If I live till spring I shall hope to see Shakespeare's grave, and Milton's mulberry tree, and the good land of my fathers—old, old England! May that day come!

Yours affectionately,
H. B. Stowe.

ETHICS

DEMONSTRATED IN
GEOMETRICAL ORDER

by

Baruch Spinoza

TRANSLATED BY
W. H. White

A CONDENSATION

HOME COURSE APPRECIATION

O N A QUIET, TREE-LINED STREET of The Hague in Holland a
museum has been made of a house which dates back to the
seventeenth century, when it was tenanted by a portrait
painter and his family. It is not because of the painter, however, that
the three-story brick structure has attracted international interest.
It is because in the single garret room, reached by a built-in ladder,
Baruch Spinoza lived, wrote and died.

Baruch (or Benedictus) Spinoza was born in 1632 in Amsterdam,
the son of well-to-do Portuguese crypto-Jews who had fled to Holland
to escape religious persecution. By the time he was twenty he was
already a brilliant scholar who was expected to become a rabbi.
When Spinoza's father died in 1654 the young man was embroiled
by the greed of his half-sister in a lawsuit over the estate. Having
won the suit, he gave the inheritance to the sister. Thereafter he lived
without family ties. Money did not interest him and he spent what
little he had on books, Latin, Hebrew and Greek classics and treatises
on science. To support himself he worked as a sort of tutor to various
people and as a lens grinder. There is no doubt that his death from
consumption at the age of forty-four was hastened by the glass dust
that filled his confined quarters. All his leisure he gave to the studies
which caused him to clash with the Synagogue authorities who, when
they could not silence him with bribes, excommunicated him in 1656.

Though Spinoza accumulated in his lifetime little in the way of
material goods, he had spiritual goods in abundance—the friendship and respect of some of the really great minds of his time, the
love and admiration of neighbors who knew his gentle, almost saintly
ways, and above all, his superb intellectual abilities. There is some
justice in the remark that the modern thinker sees the world through
lenses ground by Baruch Spinoza. "If Napoleon had been as intel-

371

The house in The Hague where Baruch Spinoza lived, wrote and died.

ligent as Spinoza," said Anatole France, "he would have lived in a garret and written four books."

SPINOZA'S CONCEPT OF GOD

THE BASIS OF SPINOZA'S THOUGHT is his concept of God, distinct in that it is entirely grounded in reason. He rejected revelation, mystery or mere subjective faith. In his *Ethics,* which contains an entire system of philosophy, Spinoza proceeded in mathematical fashion. In fact, because he considered the geometrical method the most precise and logical, he wrote the entire work "in the form of geometry." He began with definitions and axioms and passed on to propositions and demonstrations in the manner of Euclid.

First, he reasoned, there could be no beginning of existence; for if existence itself had had a beginning, it would mean that before existence there had been nothing. In other words, nothingness would have given rise to something, to the beginning of the whole universe. But, said Spinoza, this is logically absurd. Therefore, the stream of existence, the universe as a whole, must be thought of as existing without any beginning. There must always have been something.

By the same reasoning, the stream of existence can have no end. It is quite as impossible to turn something *into* nothing as it is to make something *out of* nothing. One something can only be extracted from another something; and to change something is, by the definition of the word "change," always to end with something. Therefore, when we speak of a substance being "destroyed," we do not mean that its basic content has been annihilated; we mean only that its form has been altered beyond further recognition under its former name. When, for example, we burn a piece of paper, we do not destroy any of the atoms that make up that paper. Instead, we release them in the form of new physical and chemical combinations. In science we call this principle the conservation of energy.

The totality of existence, then, must be without beginning or end. It could have had nothing before it and can have nothing after it and nothing outside it. Therefore, concluded Spinoza, when we speak of God, in a rational sense, we must identify Him and the totality of existence. Anything less would make God only a part of the totality, hence finite rather than infinite. In that case, there would be something greater than God, namely, the totality: God plus the rest of existence. Spinoza demonstrated that this would be so, even if God had created the universe, since the carpenter plus the bench is

373

greater than the carpenter alone, even though the carpenter himself made the bench.

GOD AND EXISTENCE ARE ONE

As Spinoza saw it, traditional theology fell into grave error when it stated that God, the greatest being, without beginning and without end, was one thing, and the universe, or stream of existence, was another. If that were so, reasoned Spinoza, God would not be infinite. For infinity necessarily includes everything. If an outside creator were needed to account for existence, something outside the creator would be needed to account for the creator, and so on. Therefore, he concluded, God and the totality of existence are one.

Hence, God is literally in everything. "All things are in Him, and so depend on Him that without Him they can neither be, nor be conceived." We can begin to understand the infinity or illimitability of God by thinking of an arithmetical series with no beginning and no end. There is no highest number, since every number, however great, can be added to. And, there is no smallest number, since negative numbers, -1, -2, and so on, also are infinitely continuous.

THE DIFFERENT ASPECTS OF GOD

SPINOZA CALLED THE BASIC ELEMENT of existence *substance*. To the transitory things—thoughts, plants, animals and so forth—he gave the name *modes*. Modes are modifications or diversifications of substance. He named the essential characteristics of substance *attributes*. God, for example, has infinite attributes and we can perceive the two principle ones: matter and mind. God is, therefore, both tangible and intangible. He is the all.

But would this not mean, it was asked of the philosopher, that if God were in everything, there would be more of God in an elephant than in a mouse? Not at all, replied Spinoza, for God is in the elephant and mouse not as *quantity* of matter, but as *indestructibility* of basic element. The elephant and the mouse, like everything else, can be "destroyed" only as individual modes or form. Their substance is eternal, as expressed by the law of conservation of energy. Simply because the elephant is larger than the mouse, it does not follow that its substance is more eternal than that of the mouse. To imagine so, would be like imagining that a large circle is more *circular* than a small one.

Spinoza's pantheistic and impersonal God was not to be ap-

374

proached through prayer or ceremony, but through reason—what he called *amor intellectualis dei,* the intellectual love of God. He maintained that his logical conception of God was actually that of the Hebrew writers of the Scriptures, who, however, had expressed themselves figuratively. Over the years, their poetic language had come to be accepted in a literal sense that actually distorted the original meaning. Spinoza thus became the founder of what is called the "higher criticism" of the Bible.

Spinoza knew that his unorthodox idea of God would excite great opposition and controversy, and might even cause him to be punished by the state. For this reason he feared to publish the *Ethics* during his lifetime and left instructions that it should be printed only after his death. He had been attacked as an atheist and enemy of religion on the basis of his other published works and only the friendship of the powerful leader Jan de Witt protected him from severe persecution.

A patron of the sciences, Jan de Witt, was a close friend of Spinoza's.

375

Yet the German poet Novalis was to refer to him as "the God-intoxicated man," and in our own day Albert Einstein, on being asked whether he, as a scientist, believed in God, replied: "My God is the God of Spinoza."

NECESSITY AND FREE WILL

In Part One of the *Ethics* Spinoza sets down as Axiom 3: "From a given determinate cause an effect necessarily follows; and, on the other hand, if no determinate cause be given, it is impossible that an effect can follow." This axiom might be called the law of universal causation, the principle underlying all other principles in the rational understanding of anything that exists. Wherever there is a cause in operation, some effect necessarily follows; and, what is more important, anything that exists must be the result of a definite cause. If this were not so, a cause would operate and produce no effect whatsoever, or something could come into existence without having been caused in some definite manner. In other words, it would be a case of something turned into nothing, or something made out of nothing.

Some of the implications of this statement might be put in this way: the universe in which we live is rational in the sense that everything that happens can be understood in terms of cause and effect relations. Hence it is an *understandable* system, a universe of laws that the mind of man can discover. Knowledge of laws and causes leads to the power to predict and utilize them, and therefore it is difficult to set any prior limits to what man may do and understand.

When we speak of laws of the universe, of nature or of existence, we must remember, says Spinoza, that it is the same as speaking of God. The will of God, he observes, is the law of nature. To know the universe man must learn its laws; to know God man must understand His will. That is what is meant by the intellectual love of God.

The axiom that whatever individually exists or happens must be the product of a definite cause, and the related principle that the same cause under the same conditions will produce the same effect, is known as causal necessity or determinism. It must be emphasized that Spinoza's determinism is very different from fatalism, which is the view that certain things are going to happen no matter what we do. Determinism asserts that whatever happens is the result of specific causes; and that if the causes were different the results would also have to be different.

It is this determinism that dictates Spinoza's view of the "free will." Free from what? he asks. Since nothing is free from causation, no one can rationally expect the human will to be so. If by "free will" is meant a will free from specific causation, Spinoza replies that such a will is as impossible as a square circle. There can be a will free from ignorance, prejudice, hatred and many other conditions; there can be none free from causation.

When an individual "makes up his mind," as we say, "of his own free will," what actually takes place? According to Spinoza, the individual plucks his decision out of no void; he makes it as the result of being influenced by multiple factors—his upbringing, his education, his associations, as well as his biological inheritance. It is often difficult to say exactly what dictated a particular decision or choice, for there are many aspects of human motivation about which we still know little. But causal factors of some kind there must be; otherwise the effect—here the making up of one's mind—could never take place.

ETHICS AND HAPPINESS

IN THE BASIC CONCEPTS OF GOD as the totality of existence, and of existence as a logically understandable system of cause-effect relations and natural laws, Spinoza finds the key to human happiness. Here again, his approach is objective. What everyone wants from life, he finds, is continuous and genuine happiness—an in no way unnatural desire. The whole purpose of ethics, then, is to throw light on the nature of genuine happiness and to point the way through which it may be attained.

Most men act, the philosopher observed, as though they believed that happiness consists in having money, sensual pleasures and fame. But, he contends, such pleasures are always relative. For example many a "poor man" today enjoys material comforts which would have been regarded as treasures by the wealthiest people of the Middle Ages. Still he considers himself poor because he compares his possessions with those of men richer than himself. He feels that he can be happy only when he has as much as they.

Attacking such notions as folly, Spinoza points out that money, fame and pleasure are very largely beyond the control of the individual. He can so easily be deprived of them by external forces that it is almost impossible to count on them. Money and material treasures can be stolen, or destroyed by natural catastrophe or social

A reluctant outcast of the community.

disaster. Fame, depending entirely on other people, commits the individual to forces beyond his control and puts his chances for happiness too much in the hands of others. And sensual pleasure, by its very nature, cannot be continuous; the life that is just a "round of pleasures" ends in boredom and physical deterioration.

Is there anything within the individual's own control that can yield continuous happiness? For Spinoza the answer is the rational understanding of life and the world. Such understanding becomes a part of the individual's character. It does not come or go in accordance with the caprice of other people or the vagaries of outside forces. It remains his as long as he lives, serving to transform a nightmare of indefinable gloom into a thing of beauty.

PAST, PRESENT AND FUTURE

The individual who develops the understanding described by Spinoza will, in considering the past, realize that everything that has actually happened has come about through the operation of definite causes. The results could not have been different since the causes were what they were. The specific causes were in turn the result of general laws which could not have been different because the laws flow from the very nature of the universe, the totality of existence, which, finally, could not be different, since it is the all. For the past to have been different, the universe would have had to be different and that is impossible.

Yet much human unhappiness results from brooding over the past. Without realizing it individuals convince themselves that the past might have happened differently. It *might* have, they imagine, but it *didn't;* hence they are unhappy. They ignore the fact that every act a person performs is as inevitably the result of preceding causes as the sum four is of the addition of two and two. If men understood this, they would accept the past and cease to brood about it, in the same way that they accept the facts of additions and do not worry about them.

But does this mean that the present and the future must be like the past? Not at all, declared Spinoza. The lesson is clear. If you want the present and future to be different from the past, study the past, find out the causes that made it what it was and then bring different causes to bear. This is possible only because the whole of existence is a system of causes, effects and laws. In the recognition of that idea, Spinoza tells us, lies the key to all human progress, and to the meaning of God.

379

PART ONE

Of God

DEFINITIONS

I BY CAUSE OF ITSELF, I understand that, whose essence involves existence; or that, whose nature cannot be conceived unless existing.

2 That thing is called finite in its own kind which can be limited by another thing of the same nature. For example, a body is called finite, because we always conceive another which is greater. Similarly, a thought is limited by another thought; but a body is not limited by a thought, nor a thought by a body.

3 By substance, I understand that which is in itself and is conceived through itself; in other words, that, the conception of which does not need the conception of another thing from which it must be formed.

4 By attribute, I understand that which the intellect perceives of substance, as if constituting its essence.

5 By mode, I understand the modifications of substance, or that which is in another thing through which also it is conceived.

6 By God, I understand Being absolutely infinite, that is to say, substance consisting of infinite attributes, each one of which expresses eternal and infinite essence.

Explanation I say absolutely infinite but not infinite in its own kind; for of whatever is infinite only in its own kind, we can deny infinite attributes; but to the essence of that which is absolutely infinite pertains whatever expresses essence and involves no negation.

7 That thing is called free which exists from the necessity of its

381

own nature alone, and is determined to action by itself alone. That thing, on the other hand, is called necessary, or rather compelled, which by another is determined to existence and action in a fixed and prescribed manner.

8   By eternity, I understand existence itself, so far as it is conceived necessarily to follow from the definition alone of an eternal thing.

Explanation   For such an existence is conceived as eternal truth; and also as the essence of the thing. It cannot therefore be explained by duration or time, even if the duration be conceived without beginning or end.

AXIOMS

1   Everything which is, is either in itself or in another.

2   That which cannot be conceived through another must be conceived through itself.

3   From a given determinate cause an effect necessarily follows; and, on the other hand, if no determinate cause be given, it is impossible that an effect can follow.

4   The knowledge of an effect depends upon and involves the knowledge of the cause.

5   Those things which have nothing mutually in common with one another cannot through one another be mutually understood, that is to say, the conception of the one does not involve the conception of the other.

6   A true idea must agree with that of which it is the idea.

7   The essence of that thing which can be conceived as not existing does not involve existence.

PROPOSITION 1   *Substance is by its nature prior to its modifications.*
Demonstration   This is evident from DEFS. 3 and 5.

PROPOSITION 2   *Two substances having different attributes have nothing in common with one another.*
Demonstration   This is also evident from DEF. 3. For each substance must be in itself and must be conceived through itself, that is to say, the conception of one does not involve the conception of the other. Q.E.D.

PROPOSITION 3 *If two things have nothing in common with one another, one cannot be the cause of the other.*

Demonstration If they have nothing mutually in common with one another, they cannot (AX. 5) through one another be mutually understood, and therefore (AX. 4) one cannot be the cause of the other. Q.E.D.

PROPOSITION 4 *Two or more distinct things are distinguished from one another, either by the difference of the attributes of the substances, or by the difference of their modifications.*

Demonstration Everything which is, is either in itself or in another (AX. 1), that is to say (DEFS. 3 and 5), outside the intellect there is nothing but substances and their modifications. There is nothing therefore outside the intellect by which a number of things can be distinguished one from another, but substances or (which is the same thing by DEF. 4) their attributes and their modifications. Q.E.D.

PROPOSITION 5 *In nature there cannot be two or more substances* of the same nature or attribute.

Demonstration If there were two or more distinct substances, they must be distinguished one from the other by difference of attributes or difference of modifications (PROP. 4). If they are distinguished only by difference of attributes, it will be granted that there is but one substance of the same attribute. But if they are distinguished by difference of modifications, since substance is prior by nature to its modifications (PROP. 1), the modifications therefore being placed on one side, and the substance being considered in itself, or, in other words (DEF. 3 and AX. 6), truly considered, it cannot be conceived as distinguished from another substance, that is to say (PROP. 4), there cannot be two or more substances, but only one possessing the same nature or attribute. Q.E.D.

PROPOSITION 6 *One substance cannot be produced by another substance.*

Demonstration There cannot in nature be two substances of the same attribute (PROP. 5), that is to say (PROP. 2), two which have anything in common with one another. And therefore (PROP. 3) one cannot be the cause of the other, that is to say, one cannot be produced by the other. Q.E.D.

Corollary Hence it follows that there is nothing by which substance can be produced, for in nature there is nothing but substances and their modifications (as is evident from AX. 1 and DEFS. 3 and 5). But substance cannot be produced by substance (PROP. 6). Therefore absolutely there is nothing by which substance can be produced. Q.E.D.

Another Demonstration This corollary is demonstrated more easily by the *reductio ad absurdum*. For if there were anything by which substance could be produced, the knowledge of substance would be dependent upon the knowledge of its cause (AX. 4), and therefore (DEF. 3) it would not be substance.

PROPOSITION 7 *It pertains to the nature of substance to exist.*

Demonstration There is nothing by which substance can be produced (COROL., PROP. 6). It will therefore be the cause of itself, that is to say (DEF. 1), its essence necessarily involves existence, or in other words it pertains to its nature to exist. Q.E.D.

PROPOSITION 8 *Every substance is necessarily infinite.*

Demonstration Substance which has only one attribute cannot exist except as one substance (PROP. 5), and to the nature of this one substance it pertains to exist (PROP. 7). It must therefore from its nature exist as finite or infinite. But it cannot exist as finite substance, for (DEF. 2) it must (if finite) be limited by another substance of the same nature, which also must necessarily exist (PROP. 7), and therefore there would be two substances of the same attribute, which is absurd (PROP. 5). It exists therefore as infinite substance. Q.E.D.

Note 1 Since finiteness is in truth partly negation, and infinitude absolute affirmation of existence of some kind, it follows from PROP. 7 alone that all substance must be infinite.

Note 2 I fully expect that those who judge things confusedly, and who have not been accustomed to cognize things through their first causes, will find it difficult to comprehend the demonstration of PROPOSITION 7, since they do not distinguish between the modifications of substances and substances themselves, and are ignorant of the manner in which things are produced. Hence it comes to pass that they erroneously ascribe to substances a beginning like that which they see belongs to natural things; for those who are ignorant of the true causes of things confound everything, and without any mental repugnance represent trees speaking like men, or imagine that men are made out of stones as well as begotten from seed, and that all forms can be changed the one into the other. So also those who confound human nature with the divine, readily attribute to God human emotions, especially so long as they are ignorant of the manner in which emotions are produced in the mind. But if men would attend to the nature of substance, they could not entertain a single doubt of the truth of PROPOSITION 7; indeed this proposition would be considered by all to be axiomatic, and reckoned among common notions. For by "substance" would be understood that which is in itself and is conceived through itself, or, in other words, that, the knowledge of which does not need the knowledge of another thing. But by "modifications" would be understood those things which are in another thing—those things, the conception of which is formed from the conception of the thing in which they are. Hence we can have true ideas of non-existent modifications, since although they may not actually exist outside the intellect, their essence nevertheless is so comprehended in something else, that they may be conceived through it. But the truth of substances is not outside the intellect unless in the substances themselves, because they are conceived through themselves. If anyone, therefore, were to say that he possessed a clear and distinct, that is to say, a true idea of substance, and that he nevertheless doubted whether such a substance exists, he would forsooth be in the same position as if he were to say that he had a true idea and nevertheless doubted whether or not it was false (as is evident to anyone who pays a little attention). Similarly if anyone were to affirm that substance is created, he would affirm at the same time that a false idea had become true, and this is a greater absurdity than can be conceived. It is therefore necessary to admit that the existence of substance, like its essence, is an eternal truth. Hence a demonstration (which I have thought worth while to append) by a different method is possible, showing that there are not two substances possessing the same nature. But in order to prove this methodically it is to be noted: *1*. That the true definition of any one thing neither involves nor expresses anything except the nature of the thing defined. From which it follows, *2*. That a definition does not involve or express any certain number of individuals, since it expresses nothing but the nature of the thing defined. For example, the definition of a triangle expresses nothing but the simple nature of a triangle, and not any certain number of triangles. *3*. It is to be observed that of every existing thing there is

385

some certain cause by reason of which it exists. *4.* Finally, it is to be observed that this cause, by reason of which a thing exists, must either be contained in the nature itself and definition of the existing thing (simply because it pertains to the nature of the thing to exist), or it must exist outside the thing. This being granted, it follows that if a certain number of individuals exist in nature, there must necessarily be a cause why those individuals, and neither more nor fewer, exist. If, for example, there are twenty men in existence (whom, for the sake of greater clearness, I suppose existing at the same time, and that no others existed before them), it will not be sufficient, in order that we may give a reason why twenty men exist, to give a cause for human nature generally; but it will be necessary, in addition, to give a reason why neither more nor fewer than twenty exist, since, as we have already observed under the third head, there must necessarily be a cause why each exists. But this cause (as we have shown under the second and third heads) cannot be contained in human nature itself, since the true definition of a man does not involve the number twenty, and therefore (by the fourth head) the cause why these twenty men exist, and consequently the cause why each exists, must necessarily lie outside each one; and therefore we must conclude generally that everything of such a nature that there can exist several individuals of it must necessarily have an external cause of their existence.

Since now it pertains to the nature of substance to exist (as we have shown in this *Note*), its definition must involve necessary existence, and consequently from its definition alone its existence must be concluded. But from its definition (as we have already shown under the second and third heads) the existence of more substances than one cannot be deduced. It follows, therefore, from this definition necessarily that there cannot be two substances possessing the same nature.

PROPOSITION 9 *The more reality or being a thing possesses, the more attributes belong to it.*

Demonstration This is evident from DEF. 4.

PROPOSITION 10 *Each attribute of a substance must be conceived through itself.*

Demonstration For an attribute is that which the intellect perceives of substance, as if constituting its essence (DEF. 4), and therefore (DEF. 3) it must be conceived through itself. Q.E.D.

386

Note From this it is apparent that although two attributes may be conceived as really distinct—that is to say, one without the assistance of the other—we cannot thence conclude that they constitute two beings or two different substances; for this is the nature of substance, that each of its attributes is conceived through itself, since all the attributes which substance possesses were always at the same time in itself, nor could one be produced by another; but each expresses the reality or being of substance. It is very far from being absurd, therefore, to ascribe to one substance a number of attributes, since nothing in nature is clearer than that each being must be conceived under some one attribute, and the more reality or being it has, the more attributes it possesses expressing necessity or eternity and infinity. Nothing consequently is clearer than that Being absolutely infinite is necessarily defined, as we have shown (DEF. 6), as Being which consists of infinite attributes, each one of which expresses a certain essence, eternal and infinite. But if anyone now asks by what sign, therefore, we may distinguish between substances, let him read the following propositions, which show that in nature only one substance exists, and that it is absolutely infinite. For this reason that sign would be sought for in vain.

PROPOSITION 11 *God, or substance consisting of infinite attributes, each one of which expresses eternal and infinite essence, necessarily exists.*

Demonstration If this be denied, conceive, if it be possible, that God does not exist. Then it follows (AX. 7) that His essence does not involve existence. But this (PROP. 7) is absurd. Therefore God necessarily exists. Q.E.D.

Another proof For the existence or non-existence of everything there must be a reason or cause. For example, if a triangle exists, there must be a reason or cause why it exists; and if it does not exist, there must be a reason or cause which hinders its existence or which negates it. But this reason or cause must either be contained in the nature of the thing or lie outside it. For example, the nature of the thing itself shows the reason why a square circle does not exist, the reason being that a square circle involves a contradiction. And the reason, on the other hand, why substance exists follows from its nature alone, which involves existence (see PROP. 7). But the reason why a circle or triangle exists or does not exist is not drawn from their nature, but from the order of corporeal nature generally; for from that it must follow, either that a triangle necessarily exists, or that it is impossible for it to exist. But this is self-evident. Therefore it follows that if there be no cause nor reason which hinders a thing from existing, it exists necessarily. If, therefore, there be no reason nor cause which hinders God from existing, or which negates His existence, we must conclude absolutely that He necessarily exists. But if there be such a reason or cause, it must be either in the nature itself of God or must lie outside it, that is to say, in another substance of another nature. For if the reason lay in a substance of the same nature, the existence of God would be by this very fact admitted. But substance possessing another nature could have nothing in common with God (PROP. 2), and therefore could not give Him existence nor negate it. Since, therefore, the reason or cause which could negate the divine existence cannot be outside the divine nature, it will necessarily, supposing that the divine nature does not exist, be in His nature itself, which would therefore involve a contradiction. But to affirm this of the Being absolutely infinite and consummately perfect is absurd. Therefore neither in God nor outside God is there any cause or reason which can negate His existence, and therefore God necessarily exists. Q.E.D.

Another proof Inability to exist is impotence, and, on the other hand, ability to exist is power, as is self-evident. If, therefore, there is nothing which necessarily exists excepting things finite, it follows that things finite are more powerful than the absolutely infinite Being, and this (as is self-evident) is absurd; therefore either nothing exists or Being absolutely infinite also necessarily exists. But we ourselves exist, either in ourselves or in something else which necessarily exists (AX. 1 and PROP. 7). Therefore the Being absolutely infinite, that is to say (DEF. 6), God, necessarily exists. Q.E.D.

Note In this last demonstration I wished to prove the existence of God *a posteriori,* in order that the demonstration might be the more easily understood, and not because the existence of God does not follow *a priori* from the same grounds. For since ability to exist is power, it follows that the more reality belongs to the nature of anything, the greater is the power for existence it derives from itself; and it also follows, therefore, that the Being absolutely infinite, or God, has from Himself an absolutely infinite power of existence, and that He therefore necessarily exists. Many persons, nevertheless, will perhaps not be able easily to see the force of this demonstration, because they have been accustomed to contemplate those things

388

alone which flow from external causes, and they see also that those things which are quickly produced from these causes, that is to say, which easily exist, easily perish, while, on the other hand, they adjudge those things to be of a more difficult origin, that is to say, their existence is not so easy, to which they conceive more properties pertain. In order that these prejudices may be removed, I do not need here to show in what respect this saying, "What is quickly made quickly perishes," is true, nor to inquire whether, looking at the whole of nature, all things are or are not equally easy. But this only it will be sufficient for me to observe, that I do not speak of things which are produced by external causes, but that I speak of substances alone which (PROP. 6) can be produced by no external cause. For whatever perfection or reality those things may have which are produced by external causes, whether they consist of many parts or of few, they owe it all to the virtue of an external cause, and therefore their existence springs from the perfection of an external cause alone and not from their own. On the other hand, whatever perfection substance has is due to no external cause. Therefore its existence must follow from its nature alone, and is therefore nothing else than its essence. Perfection consequently does not prevent the existence of a thing, but establishes it; imperfection, on the other hand, prevents existence, and so of no existence can we be more sure than of the existence of the Being absolutely infinite or perfect, that is to say, God. For since His essence shuts out all imperfection and involves absolute perfection, for this very reason all cause of doubt concerning its existence is taken away, and the highest certainty concerning it is given—a truth which I trust will be evident to anyone who bestows only moderate attention.

PROPOSITION 12 *No attribute of substance can be truly conceived from which it follows that substance can be divided.*

Demonstration For the parts into which substance thus conceived would be divided will or will not retain the nature of substance. If they retain it, then (PROP. 8) each part will be infinite, and (PROP. 6) the cause of itself, and will consist of an attribute differing from that of any other part (PROP. 5), so that from one substance more substances could be formed, which (PROP. 6) is absurd. Moreover the parts (PROP. 2) would have nothing in common with their whole, and the whole (DEF. 4 and PROP. 10) could be, and could be conceived without its parts, which no one will doubt to be an absurd-

389

ity. But if the second case be supposed, namely, that the parts will not retain the nature of substance, then, since the whole substance might be divided into equal parts, it would lose the nature of substance and cease to be, which (PROP. 7) is absurd.

PROPOSITION 13   *Substance absolutely infinite is indivisible.*

Demonstration   For if it were divisible, the parts into which it would be divided will or will not retain the nature of substance absolutely infinite. If they retain it, there will be a plurality of substances possessing the same nature, which (PROP. 5) is absurd. If the second case be supposed, then (as above), substance absolutely infinite can cease to be, which (PROP. 11) is also absurd.

Corollary   Hence it follows that no substance, and consequently no bodily substance in so far as it is substance, is divisible.

Note   That substance is indivisible is more easily to be understood from this consideration alone, that the nature of substance cannot be conceived unless as infinite, and that by a part of substance nothing else can be understood than finite substance, which (PROP. 8) involves a manifest contradiction.

PROPOSITION 14   *Besides God, no substance can be nor can be conceived.*

Demonstration   Since God is Being absolutely infinite, of whom no attribute can be denied which expresses the essence of substance (DEF. 6), and since He necessarily exists (PROP. 11), it follows that if there were any substance besides God, it would have to be explained by some attribute of God, and thus two substances would exist possessing the same attribute, which (PROP. 5) is absurd; and therefore there cannot be any substance excepting God, and consequently none other can be conceived. For if any other could be conceived, it would necessarily be conceived as existing, and this (by the first part of this demonstration) is absurd. Therefore besides God no substance can be, nor can be conceived. Q.E.D.

Corollary 1   Hence it follows with the greatest clearness, firstly, that God is one, that is to say (DEF. 6), in nature there is but one substance, and it is absolutely infinite, as (*Note,* PROP. 10) we have already intimated.

Corollary 2   It follows, secondly, that the thing extended and the thing thinking are either attributes of God or (AX. 1) modifications of the attributes of God.

PROPOSITION 15   *Whatever is, is in God, and nothing can either be or be conceived without God.*

Demonstration   Besides God there is no substance, nor can any be conceived (PROP. 14), that is to say (DEF. 3), nothing which is in itself and is conceived through itself. But modes (DEF. 5) can neither be nor be conceived without substance; therefore in the divine nature only can they be, and through it alone can they be conceived. But besides substances and modes nothing is assumed (AX. 1). Therefore nothing can be or be conceived without God. Q.E.D.

Note   There are those who imagine God to be like a man, composed of body and soul and subject to passions; but it is clear enough from what has already been demonstrated how far off men who believe this are from the true knowledge of God. But these I dismiss, for all men who have in any way looked into the divine nature deny that God is corporeal. That He cannot be so they conclusively prove by showing that by "body" we understand a certain quantity possessing length, breadth, and depth, limited by some fixed form; and that to attribute these to God, a being absolutely infinite, is the greatest absurdity. But yet at the same time, from other arguments by which they endeavor to confirm their proof, they clearly show that they remove altogether from the divine nature substance itself corporeal or extended, affirming that it was created by God. By what divine power, however, it could have been created they are altogether ignorant, so that it is clear they do not understand what they themselves say. But I have demonstrated, at least in my own opinion, with sufficient clearness (see *Corol.,* PROP. 6 and *Note 2,* PROP. 8), that no substance can be produced or created by another. Moreover (PROP. 14), we have shown that besides God no substance can be nor can be conceived; and hence we have concluded that extended substance is one of the infinite attributes of God. But for the sake of a fuller explanation, I will refute my adversaries' arguments, which, taken altogether, come to this. First, that corporeal substance, in so far as it is substance, consists, as they suppose, of parts, and therefore they deny that it can be infinite, and consequently that it can pertain to God. This they illustrate by many examples, one or two of which I will adduce. If corporeal substance, they say, be infinite, let us conceive it to be divided into two parts; each part, therefore, will be either finite or infinite. If each part be finite, then the infinite is composed of two finite parts, which is absurd. If each part be infinite, there is then an infinite twice as great as another infinite, which is also absurd. Again, if infinite quantity be measured by equal parts of a foot each, it must contain an infinite number of such parts, and similarly if it be measured by equal parts of an inch each; and therefore one infinite number will be twelve times greater than another infinite number. Lastly, if from one point of any infinite quantity it be imagined that two lines, AB, AC, which at first are at a certain and determinate distance from one another, be infinitely extended, it is plain that the distance between B and C will be continually increased, and at length from being determinate will be indeterminable. Since therefore these absurdities follow, as they think, from supposing quantity to be infinite, they conclude that corporeal substance must be finite, and consequently cannot pertain to the essence of God. A second argument is assumed from the absolute perfection of God. For God, they say, since He is a being absolutely perfect, cannot suffer; but corporeal substance, since it is divisible, can suffer: it follows, therefore, that it does not pertain to God's essence. These are the arguments which I find in authors, by which they endeavor to show that corporeal substance is unworthy of the divine nature, and cannot pertain to it. But anyone who will properly attend will discover that I have already answered these arguments, since the sole foundation of them is the supposition that bodily substance consists of parts, a supposition which (PROP. 12 and *Corol.,* PROP. 13) I have shown to be absurd. Moreover, if anyone will rightly consider the matter, he will see that all these absurdities (supposing that they are all absurdities, a point which I will now take for granted), from which these authors attempt to draw the conclusion that substance extended is finite, do not by any means follow from the supposition that quantity is infinite, but from the supposition that infinite quantity is measurable, and that it is made up of finite parts. Therefore, from the absurdities to which this leads nothing can be concluded, excepting that infinite quantity is not measurable, and that it cannot be composed of finite parts. But this is what we have already demonstrated (PROP. 12, etc.), and therefore the shaft which is aimed at us turns against those who cast it. If, therefore, from these absurdities anyone should attempt to conclude that substance extended must be finite, he would, forsooth, be in the position of the man who supposes a circle to have the properties of a square, and then concludes that it has no center, such that all the lines drawn from it to the circumference are equal. For corporeal substance, which cannot be conceived except as infinite, one and indivisible (PROPS. 8, 5, and 12), is conceived by those against whom I argue to be composed of finite parts, and to be multiplex and divisible, in order that they may prove it finite. Just in the same way others, after they have imagined a line to consist of points, know how to discover many arguments, by which they show that a line cannot be divided *ad infinitum;* and indeed it is not less absurd to suppose that corporeal substance is composed of bodies or parts than to suppose that a body is composed of surfaces, surfaces of lines, and that lines, finally, are composed of points. Everyone who knows that clear reason is infallible ought to admit this, and especially those who deny that a vacuum can exist. For if corporeal substance could be so divided that its parts could be really distinct, why could not one part be annihilated, the rest remaining, as before, connected with one another? And why must all be so fitted together that there can be no vacuum? For of things which are really distinct the one from the other, one can be and remain in its own position without the other. Since, therefore, it is supposed that there is no vacuum in nature (about which I will speak at another time), but that all the parts must be united, so that no vacuum can exist, it follows that they cannot be really distinguished; that is to say, that corporeal substance, in so far as it is substance, cannot be divided. If, nevertheless, anyone should now ask why there is a natural tendency to consider quantity as capable of division, I reply that quantity is conceived by us in two ways: either abstractly or superficially; that is to say, as we imagine it, or else as substance, in which way it is conceived by the intellect alone. If, therefore, we regard quantity (as we do very often and easily) as it exists in the imagination, we find it to be finite, divisible, and composed of parts; but if we regard it as it exists in the intellect, and conceive it in so far as it is substance, which is very difficult, then, as we have already sufficiently demonstrated, we find it to be infinite, one, and indivisible. This will be plain enough to all who know how to distinguish between the imagination and the intellect, and more especially if we remember that matter is everywhere the same, and that, except in so far as we regard it as affected in different ways, parts are not distinguished in it; that is to say, they are distinguished with regard to mode, but not with regard to reality. For example, we conceive water as being divided, in so far as it is water, and that its parts are separated from one another; but in so far as it is corporeal substance we cannot thus conceive it, for as such it is neither separated nor divided. Moreover, water, in so far as it is water, is begotten and destroyed; but in so far as it is substance, it is neither begotten nor destroyed. By this reasoning I think that I have also answered the second argument, since that too is based upon the assumption that matter, considered as substance, is divisible and composed of parts. And even if what I have urged were not true, I do not know why matter should be unworthy of the divine nature, since (PROP. 14) outside God no substance can exist from which the divine nature could suffer. All things, I say, are in God, and everything which takes place takes place by the laws alone of the infinite nature of God, and follows (as I shall presently show) from the necessity of His essence. Therefore in no way whatever can it be asserted that God suffers from anything, or that substance extended, even if it be supposed divisible, is unworthy of the divine nature, provided only it be allowed that it is eternal and infinite. But enough on this point for the present.

PROPOSITION 16 *From the necessity of the divine nature infinite numbers of things in infinite ways (that is to say, all things which can be conceived by the infinite intellect) must follow.*

Demonstration This proposition must be plain to everyone who considers that from the given definition of anything a number of properties necessarily following from it (that is to say, following from the essence of the thing itself) are inferred by the intellect, and just in proportion as the definition of the thing expresses a greater reality, that is to say, just in proportion as the essence of the thing defined involves a greater reality, will more properties be inferred. But the divine nature possesses absolutely infinite attributes (DEF. 6), each one of which expresses infinite essence in its own kind, and therefore, from the necessity of the divine nature, infinite numbers of things in infinite ways (that is to say, all things which can be conceived by the infinite intellect) must necessarily follow. Q.E.D.

Corollary 1 Hence it follows that God is the efficient cause of all things which can fall under the infinite intellect.

Corollary 2 It follows, secondly, that God is cause through Himself, and not through that which is contingent.

Corollary 3 It follows, thirdly, that God is absolutely the first cause.

PROPOSITION 17 *God acts from the laws of His own nature only, and is compelled by no one.*

Demonstration We have just shown (PROP. 16) that from the necessity, or (which is the same thing) from the laws only of the divine nature, infinite numbers of things absolutely follow; and we have demonstrated (PROP. 15) that nothing can be, nor can be conceived, without God, but that all things are in God. Therefore, outside Himself, there can be nothing by which He may be determined or compelled to act; and therefore He acts from the laws of His own nature only, and is compelled by no one. Q.E.D.

Corollary 1 Hence it follows, firstly, that there is no cause, either external to God or within Him, which can excite Him to act except the perfection of His own nature.

Corollary 2 It follows, secondly, that God alone is a free cause; for God alone exists from the necessity alone of His own nature (PROP. 11, and *Corol. 1*, PROP. 14), and acts from the necessity alone of His own nature (PROP. 17). Therefore (DEF. 7) He alone is a free cause. Q.E.D.

Note There are some who think that God is a free cause because He can, as they think, bring about that those things which we have said follow from His nature—that is to say, those things which are in His power—should not be, or should not be produced by Him. But this is simply saying that God could bring about that it should not follow from the nature of a triangle that its three angles should be equal to two right angles, or that from a given cause an effect should not follow, which is absurd. But I shall show farther on, without the help of this proposition, that neither intellect nor will pertains to the nature of God.

I know, indeed, that there are many who think themselves able to demonstrate that intellect of the highest order and freedom of will both pertain to the nature of God, for they say that they know nothing more perfect which they can attribute to Him than that which is the chief perfection in ourselves. But although they conceive God as actually possessing the highest intellect, they nevertheless do not believe that He can bring about that all those things should exist which are actually in His intellect, for they think that by such a supposition they would destroy His power. If He had created, they say, all things which are in His intellect, He could have created nothing more, and this, they believe, does not accord with God's omnipotence; so then they prefer to consider God as indifferent to all things, and creating nothing excepting that which He has decreed to create by a certain absolute will. But I think that I have shown with sufficient clearness (PROP. 16) that from the supreme power of God, or from His infinite nature, infinite things in infinite ways, that is to say, all things, have necessarily flowed, or continually follow by the same necessity, in the same way as it follows from the nature of a triangle, from eternity and to eternity, that its three angles are equal to two right angles. The omnipotence of God has therefore been actual from eternity, and in the same actuality will remain to eternity. In this way the omnipotence of God, in my opinion, is far more firmly established. My adversaries, indeed (if I may be permitted to speak plainly), seem to deny the omnipotence of God, inasmuch as they are forced to admit that He has in His mind an infinite number of things which might be created, but which, nevertheless, He will never be able to create, for if He were to create all things which He has in His mind, He would, according to them, exhaust His omnipotence and make Himself imperfect. Therefore, in order to make a perfect God, they are compelled to make Him incapable of doing all those things to which His power extends, and anything more absurd than this, or more opposed to God's omnipotence, I do not think can be imagined. Moreover—to say a word, too, about the intellect and will which we commonly attribute to God—if intellect and will pertain to His eternal essence, these attributes cannot be understood in the sense in which men generally use them, for the intellect and will which could constitute His essence would have to differ entirely from our intellect and will, and could resemble ours in nothing except in name. There could be no further likeness than that between the celestial constellation of the Dog and the animal which barks. This I will demonstrate as follows. If intellect pertains to the divine nature, it cannot, like our intellect, follow the things which are its object (as many suppose), nor can it be simultaneous in its nature with them, since God is prior to all things in causality (*Corol. 1,* PROP. 16); but, on the contrary, the truth and formal essence of things is what it is, because as such it exists objectively in God's intellect. Therefore the intellect of God, in so far as it is conceived to constitute His essence, is in truth the cause of things, both of their essence and of their existence—a truth which seems to have been understood by those who have maintained that God's intellect, will, and power are one and the same thing. Since, therefore, God's in-

396

tellect is the sole cause of things, both of their essence and of their existence (as we have already shown), it must necessarily differ from them with regard both to its essence and existence; for an effect differs from its cause precisely in that which it has from its cause. For example, one man is the cause of the existence but not of the essence of another, for the essence is an eternal truth; and therefore with regard to essence the two men may exactly resemble one another, but with regard to existence they must differ. Consequently if the existence of one should perish, that of the other will not therefore perish; but if the essence of one could be destroyed and become false, the essence of the other would be likewise destroyed. Therefore a thing which is the cause both of the essence and of the existence of any effect must differ from that effect both with regard to its essence and with regard to its existence. But the intellect of God is the cause both of the essence and existence of our intellect; therefore the intellect of God, so far as it is conceived to constitute the divine essence, differs from our intellect both with regard to its essence and its existence, nor can it coincide with our intellect in anything except the name, which is what we essayed to prove. The same demonstration may be applied to the will, as anyone may easily see for himself.

PROPOSITION 18   *God is the immanent, and not the transitive cause of all things.*

Demonstration   All things which are, are in God and must be conceived through Him (PROP. 15), and therefore (*Corol. 1*, PROP. 16) He is the cause of the things which are in Himself. This is the first thing which was to be proved. Moreover, outside God there can be no substance (PROP. 14), that is to say (DEF. 3), outside Him nothing can exist which is in itself. This was the second thing to be proved. God, therefore, is the immanent, but not the transitive cause of all things. Q.E.D.

PROPOSITION 19   *God is eternal, or, in other words, all His attributes are eternal.*

Demonstration   For God (DEF. 6) is substance, which (PROP. 11) necessarily exists, that is to say (PROP. 7), a substance to whose nature it pertains to exist, or (which is the same thing) a substance from the definition of which it follows that it exists, and therefore (DEF. 8) He is eternal. Again, by the attributes of God is to be understood that which (DEF. 4) expresses the essence of the divine

397

substance, that is to say, that which pertains to substance. It is this,
I say, which the attributes themselves must involve. But eternity
pertains to the nature of substance (PROP. 7). Therefore each of
the attributes must involve eternity, and therefore all are eternal.
Q.E.D.

Note This proposition is as clear as possible, too, from the
manner in which (PROP. 11) I have demonstrated the existence of
God. From that demonstration I say it is plain that the existence
of God, like His essence, is an eternal truth. Moreover (PROP. 19 of
the *Principles of the Cartesian Philosophy*), I have demonstrated
by another method the eternity of God, and there is no need to
repeat the demonstration here.

PROPOSITION 20 *The existence of God and His essence are one and
the same thing.*

God (PROP. 19) and all His attributes are eternal; that is to say
(DEF. 8), each one of His attributes expresses existence. The same
attributes of God, therefore, which (DEF. 4) explain the eternal
essence of God, at the same time explain His eternal existence; that
is to say, the very same thing which constitutes the essence of God
constitutes at the same time His existence, and therefore His existence and His essence are one and the same thing. Q.E.D.

Corollary 1 Hence it follows, 1. That the existence of God, like
His essence, is an eternal truth.

Corollary 2 It follows, 2. That God is immutable, or (which is
the same thing) all His attributes are immutable; for if they were
changed as regards their existence, they must be changed also as
regards their essence (PROP. 20); that is to say (as is self-evident),
from being true, they would become false, which is absurd.

PROPOSITION 21 *All things which follow from the absolute nature
of any attribute of God must forever exist, and must be infinite; that
is to say, through that same attribute they are eternal and infinite.*

Demonstration Conceive, if possible (supposing that the truth
of the proposition is denied), that in some attribute of God something which is finite and has a determinate existence or duration
follows from the absolute nature of that attribute; for example, an
idea of God in thought. But thought, since it is admitted to be an
attribute of God, is necessarily (PROP. 11) in its nature infinite. But
so far as it has the idea of God it is by supposition finite. But (DEF.

2) it cannot be conceived as finite unless it be determined by thought itself. But it cannot be determined by thought itself so far as it constitutes the idea of God, for so far by supposition it is finite. Therefore it must be determined by thought so far as it does not constitute the idea of God, but which, nevertheless (PROP. 11), necessarily exists. Thought, therefore, exists which does not form the idea of God, and therefore from its nature, in so far as it is absolute thought, the idea of God does not necessarily follow (for it is conceived as forming and as not forming the idea of God), which is contrary to the hypothesis. Therefore, if an idea of God in thought, or anything else in any attribute of God, follow from the necessity of the absolute nature of that attribute (for the demonstration being universal will apply in every case), that thing must necessarily be infinite, which was the first thing to be proved.

Again, that which thus follows from the necessity of the nature of any attribute cannot have a determinate duration. For, if the truth of this be denied, let it be supposed that in some attribute of God a thing exists which follows from the necessity of the nature of the attribute—for example, an idea of God in thought—and let it be supposed that at some time it has either not existed or will not exist. But since thought is supposed to be an attribute of God, it must exist both necessarily and unchangeably (PROP. 11, and *Corol. 2,* PROP. 20). Therefore, beyond the limits of the duration of the idea of God (for it is supposed that at some time it has either not existed or will not exist), thought must exist without the idea of God; but this is contrary to hypothesis, for the supposition is that thought being given, the idea of God necessarily follows. Therefore neither an idea of God in thought, nor anything else which necessarily follows from the absolute nature of any attribute of God, can have a determinate duration, but through the same attribute is eternal; which was the second thing to be proved. Observe that what we have affirmed here is true of everything which in any attribute of God necessarily follows from the absolute nature of God.

PROPOSITION 22 *Whatever follows from any attribute of God, in so far as it is modified by a modification which through the same attribute exists necessarily and infinitely, must also exist necessarily and infinitely.*

Demonstration This proposition is demonstrated in the same manner as the preceding proposition.

PROPOSITION 23 *Every mode which exists necessarily and infinitely must necessarily follow either from the absolute nature of some attribute of God, or from some attribute modified by a modification which exists necessarily and infinitely.*

Demonstration Mode is that which is in something else through which it must be conceived (DEF. 5), that is to say (PROP. 15), it is in God alone and by God alone can be conceived. If a mode, therefore, be conceived to exist necessarily and to be infinite, its necessary existence and infinitude must be concluded from some attribute of God or perceived through it, in so far as it is conceived to express infinitude and necessity of existence, that is to say (DEF. 8), eternity, or, in other words (DEF. 6 and PROP. 19), in so far as it is considered absolutely. A mode, therefore, which exists necessarily and infinitely must follow from the absolute nature of some attribute of God, either immediately (PROP. 21), or mediately through some modification following from His absolute nature, that is to say (PROP. 22), a modification which necessarily and infinitely exists. Q.E.D.

PROPOSITION 24 *The essence of things produced by God does not involve existence.*

This is evident from the first DEFINITION; for that thing whose nature (considered, that is to say, in itself) involves existence, is the cause of itself and exists from the necessity of its own nature alone.

Corollary Hence it follows that God is not only the cause of the commencement of the existence of things, but also of their continuance in existence. For if we consider the essence of things, whether existing or non-existing, we discover that it neither involves existence nor duration, and therefore the essence of existing things cannot be the cause of their existence nor of their duration, but God only is the cause, to whose nature alone existence pertains (*Corol. 1,* PROP. 14).

PROPOSITION 25 *God is not only the efficient cause of the existence of things, but also of their essence.*

Demonstration Suppose that God is not the cause of the essence of things; then (AX. 4) the essence of things can be conceived without God, which (PROP. 15) is absurd. Therefore God is the cause of the essence of things. Q.E.D.

Note This proposition more clearly follows from PROP. 16. For from this proposition it follows that, from the existence of the divine nature, both the essence of things and their existence must necessarily be concluded, or, in a word, in the same sense in which God is said to be the cause of Himself He must be called the cause of all things. This will appear still more clearly from the following corollary.

Corollary Individual things are nothing but modifications or modes of God's attributes, expressing those attributes in a certain and determinate manner. This is evident from PROP. 15 and DEF. 5.

PROPOSITION 26 *A thing which has been determined to any action was necessarily so determined by God, and that which has not been thus determined by God cannot determine itself to action.*

Demonstration That by which things are said to be determined to any action is necessarily something positive (as is self-evident); and therefore God, from the necessity of His nature, is the efficient cause both of its essence and of its existence (PROPS. 25 and 16), which was the first thing to be proved. From this also the second part of the proposition follows most clearly. For if a thing which has not been determined by God could determine itself, the first part of the proposition would be false, and to suppose this possible is an absurdity, as we have shown.

PROPOSITION 27 *A thing which has been determined by God to any action cannot render itself indeterminate.*

Demonstration This proposition is evident from the third AXIOM.

PROPOSITION 28 *An individual thing, or a thing which is finite and which has a determinate existence, cannot exist nor be determined to action unless it be determined to existence and action by another cause which is also finite and has a determinate existence; and again, this cause cannot exist nor be determined to action unless by another cause which is also finite and determined to existence and action, and so on ad infinitum.*

Demonstration Whatever is determined to existence and action is thus determined by God (PROP. 26 and *Corol.*, PROP. 24). But that which is finite and which has a determinate existence could not be produced by the absolute nature of any attribute of God, for

401

whatever follows from the absolute nature of any attribute of God is infinite and eternal (PROP. 21). The finite and determinate must therefore follow from God, or from some attribute of God, in so far as the latter is considered to be affected by some mode, for besides substance and modes nothing exists (AX. 1, and DEFS. 3 and 5), and modes (*Corol.,* PROP. 25) are nothing but modifications of God's attributes. But the finite and determinate could not follow from God, or from any one of His attributes, so far as that attribute is affected with a modification which is eternal and infinite (PROP. 22). It must, therefore, follow or be determined to existence and action by God, or by some attribute of God, in so far as the attribute is modified by a modification which is finite, and which has a determinate existence. This was the first thing to be proved. Again, this cause or this mode (by the same reasoning by which we have already demonstrated the first part of this proposition) must be determined by another cause, which is also finite, and which has a determinate existence, and this last cause (by the same reasoning) must, in its turn, be determined by another cause, and so on continually (by the same reasoning) *ad infinitum.*

Note Since certain things must have been immediately produced by God, that is to say, those which necessarily follow from His absolute nature; these primary products being the mediating cause for those things which, nevertheless, without God can neither be nor can be conceived; it follows, firstly, that of things immediately produced by God He is the proximate cause absolutely, and not in their own kind, as we say; for effects of God can neither be nor be conceived without their cause (PROP. 15, and *Corol.,* PROP. 24).

It follows, secondly, that God cannot be properly called the remote cause of individual things, unless for the sake of distinguishing them from the things which He has immediately produced, or rather which follow from His absolute nature. For by a remote cause we understand that which is in no way joined to its effect. But all things which are, are in God, and so depend upon Him that without Him they can neither be nor be conceived.

PROPOSITION 29 *In nature there is nothing uncertain, but all things are determined from the necessity of the divine nature to exist and act in a certain manner.*

Demonstration Whatever is, is in God (PROP. 15); but God cannot be called an uncertain thing, for (PROP. 11) He exists necessarily

402

and not uncertainly. Moreover, the modes of the divine nature have followed from it necessarily and not uncertainly (PROP. 16), and that, too, whether it be considered absolutely (PROP. 21), or as determined to action in a certain manner (PROP. 27). But God is the cause of these modes, not only in so far as they simply exist (*Corol.*, PROP. 24), but also (PROP. 26) in so far as they are considered as determined to any action. And if they are not determined by God (by the same proposition), it is an impossibility and not an uncertainty that they should determine themselves; and, on the other hand (PROP. 27), if they are determined by God, it is an impossibility and not an uncertainty that they should render themselves indeterminate. Wherefore all things are determined from a necessity of the divine nature, not only to exist, but to exist and act in a certain manner, and there is nothing uncertain. Q.E.D.

Note Before I go any further, I wish here to explain, or rather to recall to recollection, what we mean by *natura naturans* and what by *natura naturata.** For, from what has gone before, I think it is plain that by *natura naturans* we are to understand that which is in itself and is conceived through itself, or those attributes of substance which express eternal and infinite essence, that is to say (*Corol. 1,* PROP. 14, and *Corol. 2,* PROP. 17), God in so far as He is considered as a free cause. But by *natura naturata* I understand everything which follows from the necessity of the nature of God, or of any one of God's attributes, that is to say, all the modes of God's attributes in so far as they are considered as things which are in God, and which without God can neither be nor can be conceived.

PROPOSITION 30 *The actual intellect, whether finite or infinite, must comprehend the attributes of God and the modifications of God, and nothing else.*

Demonstration A true idea must agree with that of which it is the idea (AX. 6), that is to say (as is self-evident), that which is objectively contained in the intellect must necessarily exist in nature. But in nature (*Corol. 1,* PROP. 14) only one substance exists, namely, God, nor any modifications (PROP. 15) excepting those which are in God, and which (by the same proposition) can neither

* The two Latin expressions distinguish between nature as the *active* system of laws and forces (*natura naturans*) which produce all the specific results, and the whole, more *passive,* collection of results produced (*natura naturata*). Spinoza uses the terms to distinguish between the creating substance and the created modes.

be nor be conceived without God. Therefore the actual intellect, whether finite or infinite, must comprehend the attributes of God and the modifications of God, and nothing else. Q.E.D.

PROPOSITION 31 *The actual intellect, whether it be finite or infinite, together with the will, desire, love, etc., must be referred to the* natura naturata *and not to the* natura naturans.

Demonstration For by the intellect (as is self-evident) we do not understand absolute thought, but only a certain mode of thought, which mode differs from other modes, such as desire, love, etc., and therefore (DEF. 5) must be conceived through absolute thought, that is to say (PROP. 15 and DEF. 6), it must be conceived through some attribute of God which expresses the eternal and infinite essence of thought in such a manner that without that attribute it can neither be nor can be conceived. Therefore (*Note,* PROP. 29) the actual intellect, etc., must be referred to the *natura naturata,* and not to the *natura naturans,* in the same manner as all other modes of thought. Q.E.D.

Note I do not here speak of the *actual* intellect because I admit that any intellect *potentially* exists, but because I wish, in order that there may be no confusion, to speak of nothing excepting of that which we perceive with the utmost clearness, that is to say, the understanding itself, which we perceive as clearly as we perceive anything. For we can understand nothing through the intellect which does not lead to a more perfect knowledge of the understanding.

PROPOSITION 32 *The will cannot be called a free cause, but can only be called necessary.*

Demonstration The will is only a certain mode of thought, like the intellect, and therefore (PROP. 28) no volition can exist or be determined to action unless it be determined by another cause, and this again by another, and so on *ad infinitum.* And if the will be supposed infinite, it must be determined to existence and action by God, not in so far as He is substance absolutely infinite, but in so far as He possesses an attribute which expresses the infinite and eternal essence of thought (PROP. 23). In whatever way, therefore, the will be conceived, whether as finite or infinite, it requires a cause by which it may be determined to existence and action, and therefore (DEF. 7) it cannot be called a free cause, but only necessary or compelled. Q.E.D.

Corollary 1 Hence it follows, firstly, that God does not act from freedom of the will.

Corollary 2 It follows, secondly, that will and intellect are related to the nature of God as motion and rest, and absolutely as all natural things, which (PROP. 29) must be determined by God to existence and action in a certain manner. For the will, like all other things, needs a cause by which it may be determined to existence and action in a certain manner, and although from a given will or intellect infinite things may follow, God cannot on this account be said to act from freedom of will, any more than He can be said to act from freedom of motion and rest by reason of the things which follow from motion and rest (for from motion and rest infinite numbers of things follow). Therefore, will does not appertain to the nature of God more than other natural things, but is related to it as motion and rest and all other things are related to it; these all following, as we have shown, from the necessity of the divine nature, and being determined to existence and action in a certain manner.

PROPOSITION 33 *Things could have been produced by God in no other manner nor in any other order than that in which they have been produced.*

Demonstration All things have necessarily followed from the given nature of God (PROP. 16), and from the necessity of His nature have been determined to existence and action in a certain manner (PROP. 29). If, therefore, things could have been of another nature, or could have been determined in another manner to action, so that the order of nature would have been different, the nature of God might then be different from that which it now is, and hence (PROP. 11) that different nature would necessarily exist, and there might consequently be two or more Gods, which (*Corol. 1,* PROP. 14) is absurd. Therefore, things could be produced by God in no other manner nor in any other order than that in which they have been produced. Q.E.D.

Note 1 Since I have thus shown, with greater clearness than that of noonday light, that in things there is absolutely nothing by virtue of which they can be called uncertain, I wish now to explain in a few words what is to be understood by *uncertain,* but firstly, what is to be understood by *necessary* and *impossible.* A thing is called necessary either in reference to its essence or its cause. For the existence of a thing necessarily follows either from the essence and definition of the thing itself, or from a given efficient cause. In the same way a thing is said to be impossible either because the essence of the thing itself or its definition involves a contradiction, or because no external cause exists determinate to the production of such a thing. But a thing cannot be called uncertain unless with reference to a deficiency in our knowledge. For if we do not know that the essence of a thing involves a contradiction, or if we actually know that it involves no contradiction, and nevertheless we can affirm nothing with certainty about its existence because the order of causes is concealed from us, that thing can never appear to us either as necessary or impossible, and therefore we call it either uncertain or possible.

Note 2 From what has gone before it clearly follows that things have been produced by God in the highest degree of perfection, since they have necessarily followed from the existence of a most perfect nature. Nor does this doctrine accuse God of any imperfection, but, on the contrary, His perfection has compelled us to affirm it. Indeed, from its contrary would clearly follow, as I have shown above, that God is not absolutely perfect, since, if things had been produced in any other fashion, another nature would have had to be assigned to Him, different from that which the consideration of the most perfect Being compels us to assign to Him. I do not doubt that many will reject this opinion as ridiculous, nor will they care to apply themselves to its consideration, and this from no other reason than that they have been in the habit of assigning to God another liberty widely different from that absolute will which (DEF. 6) we have taught. On the other hand, I do not doubt, if they were willing to study the matter and properly to consider the series of our demonstrations, that they will altogether reject this liberty which they now assign to God, not only as of no value, but as a great obstacle to knowledge. Neither is there any need that I should here repeat those things which are said in the note to PROP. 17. But for the sake of those who differ from me, I will here show that although it be granted that will pertains to God's essence, it follows nevertheless from His perfection that things could be created in no other mode or order by Him. This it will be easy to show if we first consider that which my opponents themselves admit, that it depends upon the decree and will of God alone that each thing should be what it is, for otherwise God would not be the cause of all things.

It is also admitted that all God's decrees were decreed by God Himself from all eternity, for otherwise imperfection and inconstancy would be proved against Him. But since in eternity there is no *when* nor *before* nor *after,* it follows from the perfection of God alone that He neither can decree nor could ever have decreed anything else than that which He has decreed; that is to say, God has not existed before His decrees, and can never exist without them. But it is said that although it be supposed that God had made the nature of things different from that which it is, or that from eternity He had decreed something else about nature and her order, it would not thence follow that any imperfection exists in God. But if this be said, it must at the same time be allowed that God can change His decrees. For if God had decreed something about nature and her order other than that which He has decreed—that is to say, if He had willed and conceived something else about nature—He would necessarily have had an intellect and a will different from those which He now has. And if it be allowed to assign to God another intellect and another will without any change of His essence and of His perfections, what is the reason why He cannot now change His decrees about creation and nevertheless remain equally perfect? For His intellect and will regarding created things and their order remain the same in relationship to His essence and perfection in whatever manner His intellect and will are conceived. Moreover, all the philosophers whom I have seen admit that there is no such thing as an intellect existing potentially in God, but only an intellect existing actually. But since His intellect and His will are not distinguishable from His essence, as all admit, it follows from this also that if God had had another intellect actually and another will, His essence would have been necessarily different, and hence, as I showed at the beginning, if things had been produced by God in a manner different from that in which they now exist, God's intellect and will, that is to say, His essence (as has been granted), must have been different, which is absurd.

Since, therefore, things could have been produced by God in no other manner or order, this being a truth which follows from His absolute perfection, there is no sound reasoning which can persuade us to believe that God was unwilling to create all things which are in His intellect with the same perfection as that in which they exist in His intellect. But we shall be told that there is no perfection nor imperfection in things, but that that which is in them by reason of which they are perfect or imperfect and are said to be good or evil depends upon the will of God alone, and therefore if God had willed He could have effected that that which is now perfection should have been the extreme of imperfection, and *vice versa*. But what else would this be than openly to affirm that God, who necessarily understands what He wills, is able by His will to understand things in a manner different from that in which He understands them, which, as I have just shown, is a great absurdity? I can therefore turn the argument on my opponents in this way. All things depend upon the power of God. In order that things may be differently constituted, it would be necessary that God's will should be differently constituted; but God's will cannot be other than it is, as we have lately most clearly deduced from His perfection. Things therefore cannot be differently constituted. I confess that this opinion, which subjects all things to a certain indifferent God's will, and affirms that all things depend upon God's good pleasure, is at a less distance from the truth than the opinion of those who affirm that God does everything for the sake of the Good. For these seem to place something outside of God which is independent of Him, to which He looks while He is at work as to a model, or at which He aims as if at a certain mark. This is indeed nothing else than to subject God to fate, the most absurd thing which can be affirmed of Him whom we have shown to be the first and only free cause of the essence of all things as well as of their existence. Therefore it is not worth while that I should waste time in refuting this absurdity.

PROPOSITION 34   *The power of God is His essence itself.*

Demonstration   From the necessity alone of the essence of God it follows that God is the cause of Himself (PROP. 11), and (PROP. 16 and its *Corol.*) the cause of all things. Therefore the power of God, by which He Himself and all things are and act, is His essence itself. Q.E.D.

PROPOSITION 35   *Whatever we conceive to be in God's power necessarily exists.*

Demonstration   For whatever is in God's power must (PROP. 34) be so comprehended in His essence that it necessarily follows from it, and consequently exists necessarily. Q.E.D.

PROPOSITION 36   *Nothing exists from whose nature an effect does not follow.*

ETHICS

Demonstration Whatever exists expresses the nature or the essence of God in a certain and determinate manner (*Corol.,* PROP. 25); that is to say (PROP. 34), whatever exists expresses the power of God, which is the cause of all things, in a certain and determinate manner, and therefore (PROP. 16) some effect must follow from it.

APPENDIX

I HAVE NOW EXPLAINED the nature of God and its properties. I have shown that He necessarily exists; that He is one God; that from the necessity alone of His own nature He is and acts; that He is, and in what way He is, the free cause of all things; that all things are in Him, and so depend upon Him that without Him they can neither be nor can be conceived; and, finally, that all things have been predetermined by Him, not indeed from a freedom of will or from absolute good pleasure, but from His absolute nature or infinite power.

Moreover, wherever an opportunity was afforded, I have endeavored to remove prejudices which might hinder the perception of the truth of what I have demonstrated; but because not a few still remain which have been and are now sufficient to prove a very great hindrance to the comprehension of the connection of things in the manner in which I have explained it, I have thought it worth while to call them up to be examined by reason. But all these prejudices which I here undertake to point out depend upon this solely: that it is commonly supposed that all things in nature, like men, work to some end; and indeed it is thought to be certain that God Himself directs all things to some sure end, for it is said that God has made all things for man, and man that he may worship God. This, therefore, I will first investigate by inquiring, firstly, why so many rest in this prejudice, and why all are so naturally inclined to embrace it? I shall then show its falsity, and, finally, the manner in which there have arisen from it prejudices concerning *good* and *evil, merit* and *sin, praise* and *blame, order* and *disorder, beauty* and *deformity,* and so forth. This, however, is not the place to deduce these things from the nature of the human mind. It will be sufficient if I here take as an axiom that which no one ought to dispute, namely, that man is born ignorant of the causes of things, and that he has a desire, of which he is conscious, to seek that which is profitable to him. From this it follows, firstly, that he thinks him-

409

self free because he is conscious of his wishes and appetites, while at the same time he is ignorant of the causes by which he is led to wish and desire, not dreaming what they are; and, secondly, it follows that man does everything for an end, namely, for that which is profitable to him, which is what he seeks. Hence it happens that he attempts to discover merely the final causes of that which has happened; and when he has heard them he is satisfied, because there is no longer any cause for further uncertainty. But if he cannot hear from another what these final causes are, nothing remains but to turn to himself and reflect upon the ends which usually determine him to the like actions, and thus by his own mind he necessarily judges that of another. Moreover, since he discovers, both within and without himself, a multitude of means which contribute not a little to the attainment of what is profitable to himself —for example, the eyes, which are useful for seeing, the teeth for mastication, plants and animals for nourishment, the sun for giving light, the sea for feeding fish, etc.—it comes to pass that all natural objects are considered as means for obtaining what is profitable. These too being evidently discovered and not created by man, hence he has a cause for believing that some other person exists, who has prepared them for man's use. For having considered them as means it was impossible to believe that they had created themselves, and so he was obliged to infer from the means which he was in the habit of providing for himself that some ruler or rulers of nature exist, endowed with human liberty, who have taken care of all things for him, and have made all things for his use. Since he never heard anything about the mind of these rulers, he was compelled to judge of it from his own, and hence he affirmed that the gods direct everything for his advantage, in order that he may be bound to them and hold them in the highest honor. This is the reason why each man has devised for himself, out of his own brain, a different mode of worshiping God, so that God might love him above others, and direct all nature to the service of his blind cupidity and insatiable avarice.

Thus has this prejudice been turned into a superstition and has driven deep roots into the mind—a prejudice which was the reason why everyone has so eagerly tried to discover and explain the final causes of things. The attempt, however, to show that nature does nothing in vain (that is to say, nothing which is not profitable to man), seems to end in showing that nature, the gods, and man are alike mad.

Do but see, I pray, to what all this has led. Amidst so much in nature that is beneficial, not a few things must have been observed which are injurious, such as storms, earthquakes, diseases, and it was affirmed that these things happened either because the gods were angry because of wrongs which had been inflicted on them by man, or because of sins committed in the method of worshiping them; and although experience daily contradicted this, and showed by an infinity of examples that both the beneficial and the injurious were indiscriminately bestowed on the pious and the impious, the inveterate prejudices on this point have not therefore been abandoned. For it was much easier for a man to place these things aside with others of the use of which he was ignorant, and thus retain his present and inborn state of ignorance, than to destroy the whole superstructure and think out a new one. Hence it was looked upon as indisputable that the judgments of the gods far surpass our comprehension; and this opinion alone would have been sufficient to keep the human race in darkness to all eternity, if mathematics, which does not deal with ends, but with the essences and properties of forms, had not placed before us another rule of truth. In addition to mathematics, other causes also might be assigned, which it is superfluous here to enumerate, tending to make men reflect upon these universal prejudices, and leading them to a true knowledge of things.

I have thus sufficiently explained what I promised in the first place to explain. There will now be no need of many words to show that nature has set no end before herself, and that all final causes are nothing but human fictions. For I believe that this is sufficiently evident both from the foundations and causes of this prejudice, and from PROP. 16 and *Corol.,* PROP. 32, as well as from all those propositions in which I have shown that all things are begotten by a certain eternal necessity of nature and in absolute perfection. Thus much, nevertheless, I will add, that this doctrine concerning an end altogether overturns nature. For that which is in truth the cause it considers as the effect, and *vice versa.* Again, that which is first in nature it puts last; and, finally, that which is supreme and most perfect it makes the most imperfect. For (passing by the first two assertions as self-evident) it is plain from PROPS.

411

21, 22, and 23, that that effect is the most perfect which is immediately produced by God, and in proportion as intermediate causes are necessary for the production of a thing is it imperfect. But if things which are immediately produced by God were made in order that He might obtain the end He had in view, then the last things for the sake of which the first exist must be the most perfect of all. Again, this doctrine does away with God's perfection. For if God works to obtain an end, He necessarily seeks something of which He stands in need. And although theologians and metaphysicians distinguish between the end of want and the end of assimilation, they confess that God has done all things for His own sake, and not for the sake of the things to be created, because before the creation they can assign nothing excepting God for the sake of which God could do anything; and therefore they are necessarily compelled to admit that God stood in need of and desired those things for which He determined to prepare means. This is self-evident. Nor is it here to be overlooked that the adherents of this doctrine, who have found a pleasure in displaying their ingenuity in assigning the ends of things, have introduced a new species of argument, not the *reductio ad impossibile,** but the *reductio ad ignorantiam,*† to prove their position, which shows that it had no other method of defense left. For, by way of example, if a stone has fallen from some roof on somebody's head and killed him, they will demonstrate in this manner that the stone has fallen in order to kill the man. For if it did not fall for that purpose by the will of God, how could so many circumstances concur through chance (and a number often simultaneously do concur)? You will answer, perhaps, that the event happened because the wind blew and the man was passing that way. But, they will urge, why did the wind blow at that time, and why did the man pass that way precisely at the same moment? If you again reply that the wind rose then because the sea on the preceding day began to be stormy, the weather hitherto having been calm, and that the man had been invited by a friend, they will urge again—because there is no end of questioning—But why was the sea agitated? why was the man invited at that time? And so they will not cease from asking the causes of causes, until at last you fly to the will of God, the refuge for ignorance.

* Reduction to the impossible.
† Reduction to ignorance.

412

So, also, when they behold the structure of the human body, they are amazed; and because they are ignorant of the causes of such art, they conclude that the body was made not by mechanical but by a supernatural or divine art, and has been formed in such a way so that the one part may not injure the other. Hence it happens that the man who endeavors to find out the true causes of miracles, and who desires as a wise man to understand nature, and not to gape at it like a fool, is generally considered and proclaimed to be a heretic and impious by those whom the vulgar worship as the interpreters both of nature and the gods. For these know that if ignorance be removed, amazed stupidity, the sole ground on which they rely in arguing or in defending their authority, is taken away also. But these things I leave and pass on to that which I determined to do in the third place.

After man has persuaded himself that all things which exist are made for him, he must in everything adjudge that to be of the greatest importance which is most useful to him, and he must esteem that to be of surpassing worth by which he is most beneficially affected. In this way he is compelled to form those notions by which he explains nature; such, for instance, as *good, evil, order, confusion, heat, cold, beauty,* and *deformity,* etc.; and because he supposes himself to be free, notions like those of *praise* and *blame, sin* and *merit,* have arisen. These latter I shall hereafter explain when I have treated of human nature; the former I will here briefly unfold.

It is to be observed that man has given the name *good* to everything which leads to health and the worship of God; on the contrary, everything which does not lead thereto he calls *evil.* But because those who do not understand nature affirm nothing about things themselves, but only imagine them, and take the imagination to be understanding, they therefore, ignorant of things and their nature, firmly believe an *order* to be in things; for when things are so placed that, if they are represented to us through the senses, we can easily imagine them, and consequently easily remember them, we call them well arranged; but if they are not placed so that we can imagine and remember them, we call them badly arranged or *confused.* Moreover, since those things are more especially pleasing to us which we can easily imagine, men therefore prefer order to confusion, as if order were something in nature apart from our own imagination; and they say that God has created everything in order, and in this manner they ignorantly attribute imagination to God, unless they mean perhaps that God, out of consideration for the human imagination, has disposed things in the manner in which they can most easily be imagined. No hesitation seems to be caused by the fact that an infinite number of things are discovered which far surpass our imagination, and very many which confound it through its weakness. But enough of this. The other notions which I have mentioned are nothing but modes in which the imagination is affected in different ways, and nevertheless they are regarded by the ignorant as being specially attributes of things, because, as we have remarked, men consider all things as made for themselves, and call the nature of a thing good, evil, sound, putrid, or corrupt, just as they are affected by it. For example, if the motion by which the nerves are affected by means of objects represented to the eye conduces to well-being, the objects by which it is caused are called *beautiful;* while those exciting a contrary motion are called *deformed.* Those things, too, which stimulate the senses through the nostrils are called sweet-smelling or stinking; those which act through the taste are called sweet or bitter, full-flavored or insipid; those which act through the touch, hard or soft, heavy or light; those, lastly, which act through the ears are said to make a noise, sound, or harmony, the last having caused men to lose their senses to such a degree that they have believed that God even is delighted with it. Indeed, philosophers may be found who have persuaded themselves that the celestial motions beget a harmony. All these things sufficiently show that everyone judges things by the constitution of his brain, or rather accepts the modifications of his imagination in the place of things. It is not, therefore, to be wondered at, as we may observe in passing, that all those controversies which we see have arisen among men, so that at last skepticism has been the result. For although human bodies agree in many things, they differ in more, and therefore that which to one person is good will appear to another evil, that which to one is well arranged to another is confused, that which pleases one will displease another, and so on in other cases which I pass by both because we cannot notice them at length here, and because they are within the experience of everyone. For everyone has heard the expressions: So many heads, so many ways of thinking; Everyone is satisfied with his own way of thinking; Differences of brains are not less common than differences of taste—all which maxims show that men decide upon matters according to the constitution of their brains, and imagine rather than understand things. If men understood things, they would, as mathematics prove, at least be all alike convinced if they were not all alike attracted. We see, therefore, that all those methods by which the common people are in the habit of explaining nature are only different sorts of imaginations, and do not reveal the nature of anything in itself, but only the constitution of the imagination; and because they have names as if they were entities existing apart from the imagination, I call them entities not of the reason but of the imagination. All argument, therefore, urged against us based upon such notions can be easily refuted. Many people, for instance, are accustomed to argue thus: If all things have followed from the necessity of the most perfect nature of God, how is it that so many imperfections have arisen in nature—corruption, for instance, of things till they stink; deformity, exciting disgust; confusion, evil, crime, etc.? But, as I have just observed, all this is easily answered. For the perfection of things is to be judged by their nature and power alone; nor are they more or less perfect because they delight or offend the human senses, or because they are beneficial or prejudicial to human nature. But to those who ask why God has not created all men in such a manner that they might be controlled by the dictates of reason alone, I give but this answer: Because to Him material was not wanting for the creation of everything, from the highest down to the very lowest grade of perfection; or, to speak more properly, because the laws of His nature were so ample that they sufficed for the production of everything which can be conceived by an infinite intellect, as I have demonstrated in PROP. 16.

These are the prejudices which I undertook to notice here. If any others of a similar character remain, they can easily be rectified with a little thought by anyone.

[*In* PART TWO, *Spinoza deals with the "nature and origin of the mind," and in* PART THREE *with the "origin and nature of the emotions." His basic approach and final conclusions can be seen in the sections of* PART FOUR *and the whole of* PART FIVE *which follow.*]

Of Human Bondage or
of the Strength of the Emotions

PREFACE

THE IMPOTENCE OF MAN to govern or restrain the emotions I call bondage, for a man who is under their control is not his own master, but is mastered by fortune, in whose power he is, so that he is often forced to follow the worse, although he sees the better before him. I propose in this part to demonstrate why this is, and also to show what of good and evil the emotions possess. But before I begin I should like to say a few words about perfection and imperfection, and about good and evil. If a man has proposed to do a thing and has accomplished it, he calls it perfect, and not only he, but everyone else who has really known or has believed that he has known the mind and intention of the author of that work will call it perfect too. For example, having seen some work (which I suppose to be as yet not finished), if we know that the intention of the author of that work is to build a house, we shall call the house imperfect; while, on the other hand, we shall call it perfect as soon as we see the work has been brought to the end which the author had determined for it. But if we see any work such as we have never seen before, and if we do not know the mind of the workman, we shall then not be able to say whether the work is perfect or imperfect.* This seems to have been the first signification of these words; but afterward men began to form universal ideas, to think out for themselves types of houses, buildings, castles, and to prefer some types of things to others; and so it happened that each person called a thing perfect which seemed to agree with the universal idea which he had formed of that thing, and, on the other hand, he called a thing imperfect which seemed to agree less with his typal conception, although, according to the

---

* A translation cannot show the etymology of the word *perfect* as it is shown in the original Latin, so that this passage may perhaps seem rather obscure. It is only necessary, however, to bear in mind that *perfect* and *accomplished* are expressible by the same word in Latin, and that *accomplish* is the primary meaning of *perficere.*—TRANS.

416

intention of the workman, it had been entirely completed. This appears to be the only reason why the words *perfect* and *imperfect* are commonly applied to natural objects which are not made with human hands; for men are in the habit of forming, both of natural as well as of artificial objects, universal ideas which they regard as types of things, and which they think nature has in view, setting them before herself as types too; it being the common opinion that she does nothing except for the sake of some end. When, therefore, men see something done by nature which does not altogether answer to that typal conception which they have of the thing, they think that nature herself has failed or committed an error, and that she has left the thing imperfect. Thus we see that the custom of applying the words *perfect* and *imperfect* to natural objects has arisen rather from prejudice than from true knowledge of them. For we have shown in the APPENDIX to PART ONE of this work that nature does nothing for the sake of an end, for that eternal and infinite Being whom we call God or Nature acts by the same necessity by which He exists; for we have shown that He acts by the same necessity of nature as that by which He exists (PROP. 16, PART ONE). The reason or cause, therefore, why God or nature acts and the reason why He exists are one and the same. Since, therefore, He exists for no end, He acts for no end; and since He has no principle or end of existence, He has no principle or end of action. A final cause, as it is called, is nothing, therefore, but human desire, in so far as this is considered as the principle or primary cause of anything. For example, when we say that the having a house to live in was the final cause of this or that house, we merely mean that a man, because he imagined the advantages of a domestic life, desired to build a house. Therefore, having a house to live in, in so far as it is considered as a final cause, is merely this particular desire, which is really an efficient cause, and is considered as primary, because men are usually ignorant of the causes of their desires; for, as I have often said, we are conscious of our actions and desires, but ignorant of the causes by which we are determined to desire anything. As for the vulgar opinion that nature sometimes fails or commits an error, or produces imperfect things, I class it amongst those fictions mentioned in the APPENDIX to PART ONE.

Perfection, therefore, and imperfection are really only modes of thought; that is to say, notions which we are in the habit of forming from the comparison with one another of individuals of the same species or genus, and this is the reason why I have said that by reality and perfection I understand the same thing; for we are in the habit of referring all individuals in nature to one genus, which is called the most general; that is to say, to the notion of being, which embraces absolutely all the individual objects in nature. In so far, therefore, as we refer the individual objects in nature to this genus, and compare them one with another, and discover that some possess more being or reality than others, in so far do we call some more perfect than others; and in so far as we assign to the latter anything which, like limitation, termination, impotence, etc., involves negation, shall we call them imperfect, because they do not affect our minds so strongly as those we call perfect, but not because anything which really belongs to them is wanting, or because nature has committed an error. For nothing belongs to the nature of anything excepting that which follows from the necessity of the nature of the efficient cause, and whatever follows from the necessity of the nature of the efficient cause necessarily happens.

With regard to good and evil, these terms indicate nothing positive in things considered in themselves, nor are they anything else than modes of thought, or notions which we form from the comparison of one thing with another. For one and the same thing may at the same time be both good and evil or indifferent. Music, for example, is good to a melancholy person, bad to one mourning, while to a deaf man it is neither good nor bad. But although things are so, we must retain these words. For since we desire to form for ourselves an idea of man upon which we may look as a model of human nature, it will be of service to us to retain these expressions in the sense I have mentioned. By *good*, therefore, I understand in the following pages everything which we are certain is a means by which we may approach nearer and nearer to the model of human nature we set before us. By *evil,* on the contrary, I understand everything which we are certain hinders us from reaching that model. Again, I shall call men more or less perfect or imperfect in so far as they approach more or less nearly to this same model. For it is to be carefully observed, that when I say that an individual passes from a less to a greater perfection and *vice versa,* I do not understand that from one essence or form he is changed into another (for a horse, for instance, would be as much destroyed if it were changed into a man as if it were changed into an insect), but rather we conceive that his power of action, in so far as it is understood by his own nature. is increased or diminished. Finally, by perfection generally, I understand, as I have said, reality; that is to say, the essence of any object in so far as it exists and acts in a certain manner, no regard being paid to its duration. For no individual thing can be said to be more perfect because for a longer time it has persevered in existence; inasmuch as the duration of things cannot be determined by their essence, the essence of things involving no fixed or determined period of existence; any object, whether it be more or less perfect, always being able to persevere in existence with the same force as that with which it commenced existence. All things, therefore, are equal in this respect.

DEFINITIONS

1 By good, I understand that which we certainly know is useful to us.

2 By evil, on the contrary, I understand that which we certainly know hinders us from possessing anything that is good.

3 I call individual things uncertain in so far as we discover nothing, while we attend to their essence alone, which necessarily posits their existence or which necessarily excludes it.

4 I call these individual things possible, in so far as we are ignorant, while we attend to the causes from which they must be produced, whether these causes are determined to the production of these things. In *Note,* PROP. 33, PART ONE, I made no difference between possible and uncertain, because there was no occasion there to distinguish them accurately.

5 By contrary emotions, I understand in the following pages those which, although they may be of the same kind, draw a man in different directions; such as voluptuousness and avarice, which are both a species of love, and are not contrary to one another by nature, but only by accident. . . .

7 By end for the sake of which we do anything, I understand appetite.

8 By virtue and power, I understand the same thing; that is to say, virtue, in so far as it is related to man, is the essence itself or nature of the man in so far as it has the power of effecting certain things which can be understood through the laws of its nature alone.

AXIOM

There is no individual thing in nature which is not surpassed in strength and power by some other thing, but any individual thing being given, another and a stronger is also given, by which the former can be destroyed.

PROPOSITION 1   *Nothing positive contained in a false idea is removed by the presence of the true in so far as it is true.*

Demonstration   Falsity consists in nothing but the privation of knowledge which inadequate ideas involve, nor do they possess anything positive on account of which they are called false; on the contrary, in so far as they are related to God, they are true. If, therefore, anything positive contained in a false idea were removed by the presence of the true in so far as it is true, a true idea would be removed by itself, which is absurd. Nothing positive, therefore, etc. Q.E.D.

Note   For an imagination is an idea which indicates the present constitution of the human body rather than the nature of an external body, not indeed distinctly but confusedly, so that the mind is said to err. For example, when we look at the sun, we imagine its distance from us to be about two hundred feet, and in this we are deceived so long as we remain in ignorance of the true distance. When this is known, the error is removed, but not the imagination, that is to say, the idea of the sun which explains its nature in so far only as the body is affected by it; so that although we know its true distance, we nevertheless imagine it close to us. For, as we have shown, it is not because we are ignorant of the sun's true distance that we imagine it to be so close to us, but because the mind conceives the magnitude of the sun just in so far as the body is affected by it. So when the rays of the sun falling upon a surface of water are reflected to our eyes, we imagine it to be in the water, although its true place is known to us. So with the other imaginations by which the mind is deceived; whether they indicate the natural constitution of the body or an increase or diminution in its power of action, they are not opposed to the truth, nor do they disappear with the presence of the truth. We know that when we groundlessly fear any evil, the fear vanishes when we hear correct intelligence; but we also know, on the other hand, that when we fear an evil which will actually come upon us, the fear vanishes when we hear false intelligence, so that the imaginations do not disappear with the presence of the truth, in so far as it is true, but because other imaginations arise which are stronger, and which exclude the present existence of the objects we imagine.

PROPOSITION 2   *We suffer in so far as we are a part of nature, which part cannot be conceived by itself nor without the other parts.*

Demonstration   We are said to suffer when anything occurs in us of which we are only the partial cause, that is to say, anything which cannot be deduced from the laws of our own nature alone; we suffer, therefore, in so far as we are a part of nature, which part cannot be conceived by itself nor without the other parts. Q.E.D.

PROPOSITION 3   *The force by which man perseveres in existence is limited, and infinitely surpassed by the power of external causes.*

Demonstration   This is evident from the AXIOM, PART FOUR. For any man being given, there is given something else—for example, A —more powerful than he is, and A being given, there is again given something, B, more powerful than A, and so on *ad infinitum*. Hence the power of man is limited by the power of some other object, and is infinitely surpassed by the power of external causes. Q.E.D.

PROPOSITION 4   *It is impossible that a man should not be a part of nature, and that he should suffer no changes but those which can be understood through his own nature alone, and of which he is the adequate cause.*

Demonstration   The power by which individual things and consequently man preserve their being is the actual power of God or nature (*Corol.,* PROP. 24, PART ONE), not in so far as it is infinite, but in so far as it can be explained by the actual essence of man. The power therefore of man, in so far as it is explained by his actual essence, is part of the infinite power of God or nature, that is to say (PROP. 34, PART ONE), part of His essence. This was the first thing to be proved. Again, if it were possible that man could suffer no changes but those which can be understood through his nature alone, it would follow that he could not perish, but that he would exist forever necessarily; and this necessary existence must result from a cause whose power is either finite or infinite, that is to say, either from the power of man alone, which would be able to place at a distance from himself all other changes which could take their origin from external causes, or it must result from the infinite power of nature by which all individual things would be so directed that man could suffer no changes but those tending to his preservation. But the first case (by the preceding proposition, whose demonstration is universal and capable of application to all individual

421

objects) is absurd; therefore if it were possible for a man to suffer no changes but those which could be understood through his own nature alone, and consequently (as we have shown) that he should always necessarily exist, this must follow from the infinite power of God; and therefore (PROP. 16, PART ONE) from the necessity of the divine nature, in so far as it is considered as affected by the idea of any one man, the whole order of nature, in so far as it is conceived under the attributes of thought and extension, would have to be deduced. From this it would follow (PROP. 21, PART ONE) that man would be infinite, which (by the first part of this demonstration) is an absurdity. It is impossible, therefore, that a man can suffer no changes but those of which he is the adequate cause. Q.E.D.

Corollary Hence it follows that a man is necessarily always subject to passions, and that he follows and obeys the common order of nature, accommodating himself to it as far as the nature of things requires.

PROPOSITION 5 *The force and increase of any passion and its perseverance in existence are not limited by the power by which we endeavor to persevere in existence, but by the power of an external cause compared with our own power.*

Demonstration The essence of a passion cannot be explained by our essence alone; that is to say, the power of a passion cannot be limited by the power by which we endeavor to persevere in our being, but must necessarily be limited by the power of an external cause compared with our own power. Q.E.D.

PROPOSITION 6 *The other actions or power of a man may be so far surpassed by force of some passion or emotion, that the emotion may obstinately cling to him.*

Demonstration The force and increase of any passion and its perseverance in existence are limited by the power of an external cause compared with our own power (PROP. 5, PART FOUR), and therefore (PROP. 3, PART FOUR) may surpass the power of man. Q.E.D.

PROPOSITION 7 *An emotion cannot be restrained nor removed unless by an opposed and stronger emotion.*

Demonstration An emotion, in so far as it is related to the mind, is an idea by which the mind affirms a greater or less power of existence for its body than the body possessed before. Whenever, therefore, the mind is agitated by any emotion, the body is at the same time affected with a modification by which its power of action is increased or diminished. Again, this modification of the body (PROP. 5, PART FOUR) receives from its own cause a power to persevere in its own being, a power, therefore, which cannot be restrained nor removed unless by a bodily cause affecting the body with a modification contrary to the first, and stronger than it (AX., PART FOUR). Thus the mind is affected by the idea of a modification stronger than the former and contrary to it; that is to say (by the general definition of the emotions), it will be affected with an emotion stronger than the former and contrary to it, and this stronger emotion will exclude the existence of the other or remove it. Thus an emotion cannot be restrained nor removed unless by an opposed and stronger emotion. Q.E.D.

Corollary An emotion, in so far as it is related to the mind, cannot be restrained nor removed unless by the idea of a bodily modification opposed to that which we suffer and stronger than it. For the emotion which we suffer cannot be restrained nor removed unless by an opposed and stronger emotion (PROP. 7, PART FOUR); that is to say (by the general definition of the emotions), it cannot be removed unless by the idea of a bodily modification stronger than that which affects us, and opposed to it.

PROPOSITION 8 *Knowledge of good or evil is nothing but an emotion of joy or sorrow in so far as we are conscious of it.*

Demonstration We call a thing good which contributes to the preservation of our being, and we call a thing evil if it is an obstacle to the preservation of our being (DEFS. 1 and 2, PART FOUR); that is to say, a thing is called by us good or evil as it increases or diminishes, helps or restrains, our power of action. In so far, therefore, as we perceive that any object affects us with joy or sorrow do we call it good or evil, and therefore the knowledge of good or evil is nothing but an idea of joy or sorrow which necessarily follows from the emotion itself of joy or sorrow. But this idea is united to the emotion in the same way as the mind is united to the body, or, in other words, this idea is not actually distinguished from the emotion itself; that is to say (by the general definition of the emotions), it is not actually distinguished from the idea of the modification of the body, unless in conception alone. This knowledge, therefore, of good and evil is nothing but the emotion itself of joy and sorrow in so far as we are conscious of it. Q.E.D.

PROPOSITION 9   *If we imagine the cause of an emotion to be actually present with us, that emotion will be stronger than if we imagined the cause not to be present.*

Demonstration   The imagination is an idea by which the mind contemplates an object as present, an idea which nevertheless indicates the constitution of the human body rather than the nature of the external object. Imagination, therefore (by the general definition of the emotions), is an emotion in so far as it indicates the constitution of the body. But the imagination increases in intensity in proportion as we imagine nothing which excludes the present existence of the external object. If, therefore, we imagine the cause of an emotion to be actually present with us, that emotion will be intenser or stronger than if we imagined the cause not to be present. Q.E.D.

Corollary 1   When I said that we are affected by the image of an object in the future or the past with the same emotion with which we should be affected if the object we imagined were actually present, I was careful to warn the reader that this was true in so far only as we attend to the image alone of the object itself, for this is of the same nature whether we have imagined the object or not; but I have not denied that the image becomes weaker when we contemplate as present other objects which exclude the present existence of the future object. This exception I neglected to make, because I had determined to treat in this part of my work of the strength of the emotions.

Corollary 2   The image of a past or future object, that is to say, of an object which we contemplate in relation to the past or future to the exclusion of the present, other things being equal, is weaker than the image of a present object, and consequently the emotion toward a future or past object, other things being equal, is weaker then than the emotion toward a present object.

PROPOSITION 10   *We are affected with regard to a future object which we imagine will soon be present more powerfully than if we imagine that the time at which it will exist is further removed from the present, and the memory of an object which we imagine has but just passed away also affects us more powerfully than if we imagine the object to have passed away some time ago.*

Demonstration   In so far as we imagine that an object will quickly be present or has not long since passed away, do we

424

imagine something which excludes the presence of the object less than if we imagine that the time of its existence is at a great distance from the present, either in the future or the past (as is self-evident), and therefore (PROP. 9, PART FOUR) so far shall we be affected more strongly with regard to it. Q.E.D.

Note From the observations which we made upon DEF. 6, PART FOUR, it follows that all objects which are separated from the present time by a longer interval than our imagination has any power to determine affect us equally slightly, although we know them to be separated from one another by a large space of time.

PROPOSITION 11 *The emotion toward an object which we imagine as necessary, other things being equal, is stronger than that toward an object that is possible, uncertain, or not necessary.*

Demonstration In so far as we imagine any object to be necessary do we affirm its existence, and, on the other hand, we deny its existence in so far as we imagine it to be not necessary (PROP. 33, PART ONE), and therefore (PROP. 9, PART FOUR) the emotion toward a necessary object, other things being equal, is stronger than that which we feel toward one that is not necessary.

PROPOSITION 12 *The emotion toward an object which we know does not exist in the present, and which we imagine as possible, other things being equal, is stronger than the emotion toward an uncertain object.*

Demonstration In so far as we imagine an object as uncertain, we are not affected by the image of any other object which posits the existence of the first (DEF. 3, PART FOUR), but, on the contrary (by hypothesis), we imagine some things which exclude its present existence. But in so far as we imagine any object in the future to be possible do we imagine some things which posit its existence (DEF. 4, PART FOUR), that is to say, things which foster hope or fear, and therefore the emotion toward a possible object is stronger, etc. Q.E.D.

Corollary The emotion toward an object which we know does not exist in the present, and which we imagine as uncertain, is much weaker than if we imagined that the object were present to us.

Demonstration The emotion toward an object which we imagined to exist in the present is stronger than if we imagined it as future (*Corol.*, PROP. 9, PART FOUR), and is much stronger if we imagined the future to be at no great distance from the present time

425

(PROP. 10, PART FOUR). The emotion, therefore, toward an object which we imagine will not exist for a long time is so much feebler than if we imagined it as present, and nevertheless (PROP. 12, PART FOUR) is stronger than if we imagined it as uncertain; and therefore the emotion toward an uncertain object is much feebler than if we imagined the object to be present to us. Q.E.D.

PROPOSITION 13 *The emotion toward an uncertain object which we know does not exist in the present, other things being equal, is much weaker than the emotion toward a past object.*

Demonstration In so far as we imagine an object as uncertain, we are affected with no image of any other object which posits the existence of the first (DEF. 3, PART FOUR). On the contrary, we imagine (by hypothesis) certain things which exclude its present existence. But in so far as we imagine it in relationship to past time are we supposed to imagine something which brings it back to the memory or which excites its image, and therefore so far causes us to contemplate it as present. Therefore (PROP. 9, PART FOUR), the emotion toward an uncertain object which we know does not exist in the present, other things being equal, will be weaker than the emotion toward a past object. Q.E.D.

PROPOSITION 14 *No emotion can be restrained by the true knowledge of good and evil in so far as it is true, but only in so far as it is considered as an emotion.*

Demonstration An emotion is an idea by which the mind affirms a greater or less power of existence for the body than it possessed before (by the general definition of the emotions); and therefore (PROP. 1, PART FOUR) this idea has nothing positive which can be removed by the presence of the truth, and consequently the true knowledge of good and evil, in so far as it is true, can restrain no emotion. But in so far as it is an emotion (see PROP. 8, PART FOUR) will it restrain any other emotion, provided that the latter be the weaker of the two (PROP. 7, PART FOUR). Q.E.D.

APPENDIX

MY OBSERVATIONS IN THIS PART concerning the true method of life have not been arranged so that they could be seen at a glance, but have been demonstrated here and there according as I could more easily deduce one from another. I have determined, therefore, here to collect them, and reduce them under principal heads.

I

All our efforts or desires follow from the necessity of our nature in such a manner that they can be understood either through it alone as their proximate cause, or in so far as we are a part of nature, which part cannot be adequately conceived through itself and without the other individuals.

II

The desires which follow from our nature in such a manner that they can be understood through it alone, are those which are related to the mind, in so far as it is conceived to consist of adequate ideas. The remaining desires are not related to the mind, unless in so far as it conceives things inadequately, whose power and increase cannot be determined by human power, but by the power of objects which are outside us. The first kind of desires, therefore, are properly called actions, but the latter passions; for the first always indicate our power, and the latter, on the contrary, indicate our impotence and imperfect knowledge.

III

Our actions, that is to say, those desires which are determined by man's power or reason, are always good; the others may be good as well as evil.

IV

It is therefore most profitable to us in life to make perfect the intellect or reason as far as possible, and in this one thing consists the highest happiness or blessedness of man; for blessedness is nothing but the peace of mind which springs from the intuitive knowledge of God, and to perfect the intellect is nothing but to understand God, together with the attributes and actions of God, which flow from the necessity of His nature. The final aim, therefore, of a man who is guided by reason, that is to say, the chief desire by which he strives to govern all his other desires, is that by which he is led adequately to conceive himself and all things which can be conceived by his intelligence.

427

V

There is no rational life, therefore, without intelligence, and things are good only in so far as they assist man to enjoy that life of the mind which is determined by intelligence. Those things alone, on the other hand, we call evil which hinder man from perfecting his reason and enjoying a rational life.

VI

But because all those things of which man is the efficient cause are necessarily good, it follows that no evil can happen to man except from external causes, that is to say, except in so far as he is a part of the whole of nature, whose laws human nature is compelled to obey—compelled also to accommodate himself to this whole of nature in almost an infinite number of ways.

VII

It is impossible that a man should not be a part of nature and follow her common order; but if he be placed among individuals who agree with his nature, his power of action will by that very fact be assisted and supported. But if, on the contrary, he be placed among individuals who do not in the least agree with his nature, he will scarcely be able without great change on his part to accommodate himself to them.

VIII

Anything that exists in nature which we judge to be evil or able to hinder us from existing and enjoying a rational life, we are allowed to remove from us in that way which seems the safest; and whatever, on the other hand, we judge to be good or to be profitable for the preservation of our being or the enjoyment of a rational life, we are permitted to take for our use and use in any way we may think proper; and absolutely, everyone is allowed by the highest right of nature to do that which he believes contributes to his own profit.

IX

Nothing, therefore, can agree better with the nature of any object than other individuals of the same kind, and so (see § VII) there is nothing more profitable to man for the preservation of his being and the enjoyment of a rational life than a man who is guided by reason. Again, since there is no single thing we know which is more excellent than a man who is guided by reason, it follows that there is nothing by which a person can better show how much skill and talent he possesses than by so educating men that at last they will live under the direct authority of reason.

X

In so far as men are carried away by envy or any emotion of hatred toward one another, so far are they contrary to one another, and consequently so much the more are they to be feared, as they have more power than other individuals of nature.

XI

Minds, nevertheless, are not conquered by arms, but by love and generosity.

XII

Above all things is it profitable to men to form communities and to unite themselves to one another by bonds which may make all of them as one man; and absolutely, it is profitable for them to do whatever may tend to strengthen their friendships.

XIII

But to accomplish this, skill and watchfulness are required; for men are changeable (those being very few who live according to the laws of reason), and nevertheless generally envious and more inclined to vengeance than pity. To bear with each, therefore, according to his disposition and to refrain from imitating his emotions require a singular power of mind. But those, on the contrary, who know how to revile men, to denounce vices rather than teach virtues, and not to strengthen men's minds but to weaken them, are injurious both to themselves and others, so that many of them through an excess of impatience and a false zeal for religion prefer living with brutes rather than among men; just as boys or youths, unable to endure with equanimity the rebukes of their parents, fly to the army, choosing the discomforts of war and the rule of a tyrant rather than the comforts of home and the admonitions of a father, suffering all kinds of burdens to be imposed upon them in order that they may revenge themselves upon their parents.

429

XIV

Although, therefore, men generally determine everything by their pleasure, many more advantages than disadvantages arise from their common union. It is better, therefore, to endure with equanimity the injuries inflicted by them, and to apply our minds to those things which subserve concord and the establishment of friendship.

XV

The things which beget concord are those which are related to justice, integrity, and honor; for besides that which is unjust and injurious, men take ill also anything which is esteemed base, or that anyone should despise the received customs of the State. But in order to win love, those things are chiefly necessary which have reference to religion and piety.

XVI

Concord, moreover, is often produced by fear, but it is without good faith. It is to be observed, too, that fear arises from impotence of mind, and therefore is of no service to reason; nor is pity, although it seems to present an appearance of piety.

XVII

Men also are conquered by liberality, especially those who have not the means wherewith to procure what is necessary for the support of life. But to assist everyone who is needy far surpasses the strength or profit of a private person, for the wealth of a private person is altogether insufficient to supply such wants. Besides, the power of any one man is too limited for him to be able to unite everyone with himself in friendship. The care, therefore, of the poor is incumbent on the whole of society and concerns only the general profit.

XIX

The love of a harlot, that is to say, the lust of sexual intercourse, which arises from mere external form, and absolutely all love which recognizes any other cause than the freedom of the mind, easily passes into hatred, unless, which is worse, it becomes a species of delirium, and thereby discord is cherished rather than concord.

XX

With regard to marriage, it is plain that it is in accordance with reason, if the desire of connection is engendered not merely by external form, but by a love of begetting children and wisely educating them; and if, in addition, the love both of the husband and wife has for its cause not external form merely, but chiefly liberty of mind.

XXI

Flattery, too, produces concord, but only by means of the disgraceful crime of slavery or perfidy; for there are none who are more taken by flattery than the proud, who wish to be first and are not so.

XXII

There is a false appearance of piety and religion in dejection; and although dejection is the opposite of pride, the humble dejected man is very near akin to the proud.

XXIII

Shame also contributes to concord, but only with regard to those matters which cannot be concealed. Shame, too, inasmuch as it is a kind of sorrow, does not belong to the service of reason.

XXIV

The remaining emotions of sorrow which have man for their object are directly opposed to justice, integrity, honor, piety, and religion; and although indignation may seem to present an appearance of equity, yet there is no law where it is allowed to everyone to judge the deeds of another, and to vindicate his own or another's right.

XXV

Affability, that is to say, the desire of pleasing men, which is determined by reason, is related to piety. But if affability arise from an emotion, it is ambition or desire, by which men, generally under a false pretense of piety, excite discords and seditions. For he who desires to assist other people, either by advice or by deed, in order that they may together enjoy the highest good, will strive, above all

431

things, to win their love, and not to draw them into admiration, so that a doctrine may be named after him, nor absolutely to give any occasion for envy. In common conversation, too, he will avoid referring to the vices of men, and will take care only sparingly to speak of human impotence, while he will talk largely of human virtue or power, and of the way by which it may be made perfect, so that men being moved not by fear or aversion, but solely by the notion of joy, may endeavor as much as they can to live under the rule of reason.

XXVI

Excepting man, we know no individual thing in nature in whose mind we can take pleasure, nor anything which we can unite with ourselves by friendship or any kind of intercourse, and therefore the law of our own profit does not demand that we should preserve anything which exists in nature excepting men, but teaches us to preserve it or destroy it in accordance with its varied uses, or to adapt it to our own service in any way whatever.

XXVII

The profit which we derive from objects outside us, over and above the experience and knowledge which we obtain because we observe them and change them from their existing forms into others, is chiefly the preservation of the body, and for this reason those objects are the most profitable to us which can feed and nourish the body, so that all its parts are able properly to perform their functions. For the more capable the body is of being affected in many ways, and affecting external bodies in many ways, the more capable of thinking is the mind. But there seem to be very few things in nature of this kind, and it is consequently necessary for the requisite nourishment of the body to use many different kinds of food; for the human body is composed of a great number of parts of different nature, which need constant and varied food in order that the whole of the body may be equally adapted for all those things which can follow from its nature, and consequently that the mind also may be equally adapted to conceive many things.

XXVIII

The strength of one man would scarcely suffice to obtain these things if men did not mutually assist one another. As money has presented us with an abstract of everything, it has come to pass that its image above every other usually occupies the mind of the multitude, because they can imagine hardly any kind of joy without the accompanying idea of money as its cause.

XXIX

This, however, is a vice only in those who seek money not from poverty or necessity, but because they have learned the arts of gain, by which they keep up a grand appearance. As for the body itself, they feed it in accordance with custom, but sparingly, because they believe that they lose so much of their goods as they spend upon the preservation of their body. Those, however, who know the true use of money, and regulate the measure of wealth according to their needs, live contented with few things.

XXX

Since, therefore, those things are good which help the parts of the body to perform their functions, and since joy consists in this, that the power of man, in so far as he is made up of mind and body, is helped or increased, it follows that all those things which bring joy are good. But inasmuch as things do not work to this end—that they may affect us with joy—nor is their power of action guided in accordance with our profit, and finally, since joy is generally related chiefly to some one part of the body, it follows that generally the emotions of joy (unless reason and watchfulness be present), and consequently the desires which are begotten from them, are excessive. It is to be added, that an emotion causes us to put that thing first which is sweet to us in the present, and that we are not able to judge the future with an equal emotion of the mind.

XXXI

Superstition, on the contrary, seems to affirm that what brings sorrow is good, and, on the contrary, that what brings joy is evil. But no one excepting an envious man is delighted at my impotence or disadvantage, for the greater the joy with which we are affected, the greater the perfection to which we pass, and consequently the more do we participate in the divine nature; nor can joy ever be evil which is controlled by a true consideration for our own profit. On the other hand, the man who is led by fear, and does what is good that he may avoid what is evil, is not guided by reason.

XXXII

But human power is very limited, and is infinitely surpassed by the power of external causes, so that we do not possess an absolute power to adapt to our service the things which are outside us. Nevertheless we shall bear with equanimity those things which happen to us contrary to what a consideration of our own profit demands, if we are conscious that we have performed our duty, that the power we have could not reach so far as to enable us to avoid those things, and that we are a part of the whole of nature, whose order we follow. If we clearly and distinctly understand this, the part of us which is determined by intelligence, that is to say, the better part of us, will be entirely satisfied therewith, and in that satisfaction will endeavor to persevere; for, in so far as we understand, we cannot desire anything excepting what is necessary, nor absolutely, can we be satisfied with anything but the truth. Therefore in so far as we understand these things properly will the efforts of the better part of us agree with the order of the whole of nature.

PART FIVE

Of the Power of the Intellect, or of Human Liberty

PREFACE

I PASS AT LENGTH to the other part of ethics which concerns the method or way which leads to liberty. In this part, therefore, I shall treat of the power of reason, showing how much reason itself can control the emotions, and then what is freedom of mind or blessedness. Thence we shall see how much stronger the wise man is than the ignorant. In what manner and in what way the intellect should be rendered perfect, and with what art the body is to be cared for in order that it may properly perform its functions, I have nothing to do with here; for the former belongs to logic, the latter to medicine. I shall occupy myself here, as I have said, solely with the power of the mind or of reason, first of all showing the extent and nature of the authority which it has over the emotions in restraining them and governing them; for that we have not absolute authority over them we have already demonstrated. The Stoics indeed thought that the emotions depend absolutely on our will, and that we are absolutely masters over them; but they were driven, by the contradiction of experience, though not by their own principles, to confess that not a little practice and study are required in order to restrain and govern the emotions. This one of them attempted to illustrate, if I remember rightly, by the example of two dogs, one of a domestic and the other of a hunting breed; for he was able by habit to make the house dog hunt, and the hunting dog, on the contrary, to desist from running after hares. To the Stoical opinion Descartes much inclines. He affirms that the soul or mind is united specially to a certain part of the brain called the pineal gland, which the mind by the mere exercise of the will is able to move in different ways, and by whose help the mind perceives all the movements which are excited in the body and external objects. This gland he affirms is suspended in the middle of the brain in such a manner that it can be moved by the least motion of the animal spirits. Again, he affirms that any variation in the manner in which the animal spirits impinge upon this gland is followed by a variation in the manner in which it is suspended in the middle of the brain, and moreover that the number of different impressions on the gland is the same as that of the different external objects which propel the animal spirits toward it. Hence it comes to pass that if the gland, by the will of the soul moving it in different directions, be afterward suspended in this or that way in which it had once been suspended by the spirits agitated in this or that way, then the gland itself will propel and determine the animal spirits themselves in the same way as that in which they had before been repelled by a similar suspension of the gland. Moreover, he affirmed that each volition of the mind is united in nature to a certain motion of the gland. For example, if a person wishes to behold a remote object, this volition will cause the pupil of the eye to dilate, but if he thinks merely of the dilation of the pupil, to have that volition will profit him nothing, because nature has not connected a motion of the gland which serves to impel the animal spirits toward the optic nerve in a way suitable for dilation or contraction of the pupil with the volition of dilation or contraction, but only with the volition of beholding objects afar off or close at hand. Finally, he maintained that although each motion of this gland appears to be connected by nature from the commencement of our life with an individual thought, these motions can nevertheless be connected by habit with other thoughts, a proposition which he attempts to demonstrate in his *Passions of the Soul,* ART. 50, PART ONE.

From this he concludes that there is no mind so feeble that it cannot, when properly directed, acquire absolute power over its passions; for passions, as defined by him, are "perceptions, or sensations, or emotions of the soul which are related to it specially, and which are produced, preserved, and strengthened by some motion of the spirits." (See the *Passions of the Soul,* ART. 27, PART ONE.) But since it is possible to join to a certain volition any motion of the gland, and consequently of the spirits, and since the determination of the will depends solely on our power, we shall be able to acquire absolute mastery over our passions provided only we determine our will by fixed and firm decisions by which we desire to direct our actions and bind with these decisions the movements of the passions we wish to have. So far as I can gather from his own words, this is the opinion of that distinguished man, and I could scarcely have believed it possible for one so great to have put it forward if it had been less subtle. I can hardly wonder enough that a philosopher who firmly resolved to make no deduction except from self-evident principles, and to affirm nothing but what he clearly and distinctly perceived, and who blamed all the schoolmen because they desired to explain obscure matters by occult qualities, should accept a hypothesis more occult than any occult quality. What does he understand, I ask, by the union of the mind and body? What clear and distinct conception has he of thought intimately connected with a certain small portion of matter? I wish that he had explained this union by its proximate cause. But he conceived the mind to be so distinct from the body that he was able to assign no single cause of this union, nor of the mind itself, but was obliged to have recourse to the cause of the whole universe, that is to say, to God. Again, I should like to know how many degrees of motion the mind can give to that pineal gland, and with how great a power the mind can hold it suspended. For I do not understand whether this gland is acted on by the mind more slowly or more quickly than by the animal spirits, and whether the movements of the passions, which we have so closely bound with firm decisions, might not be separated from them again by bodily causes, from which it would follow that although the mind had firmly determined to meet danger, and had joined to this decision the motion of boldness, the sight of the danger might cause the gland to be suspended in such a manner that the mind could think of nothing but flight. Indeed, since there is no relation between the will and motion, so there is no comparison between the power or strength of the body and that of the mind, and consequently the strength of the body can never be determined by the strength of the mind. It is to be remembered also that this gland is not found to be so situated in the middle of the brain that it can be driven about so easily and in so many ways, and that all the nerves are not extended to the cavities of the brain. Lastly, I omit all that Descartes asserts concerning the will and the freedom of the will, since I have shown over and over again that it is false. Therefore, inasmuch as the power of the mind, as I have shown above, is determined by intelligence alone, we shall determine by the knowledge of the mind alone the remedies against the emotions—remedies which everyone, I believe, has experienced, although there may not have been any accurate observation or distinct perception of them, and from this knowledge of the mind alone shall we deduce everything which relates to its blessedness.

AXIOMS

1 If two contrary actions be excited in the same subject, a change must necessarily take place in both, or in one alone, until they cease to be contrary.

2 The power of an emotion is limited by the power of its cause, in so far as the essence of the emotion is explained or limited by the essence of the cause itself.

PROPOSITION 1 *As thoughts and the ideas of things are arranged and connected in the mind, exactly so are the modifications of the body or the images of things arranged and connected in the body.*

Demonstration The order and connection of ideas is the same as the order and connection of things, and *vice versa,* the order and connection of things is the same as the order and connection of ideas. Therefore, as the order and connection of ideas in the mind is according to the order and connection of the modifications of the body, it follows, *vice versa,* that the order and connection of the modifications of the body is according to the order and connection in the mind of the thoughts and ideas of things. Q.E.D.

PROPOSITION 2 *If we detach an emotion of the mind from the thought of an external cause and connect it with other thoughts, then the love or hatred toward the external cause and the fluctuations of the mind which arise from these emotions will be destroyed.*

Demonstration That which constitutes the form of love or hatred is joy or sorrow, accompanied with the idea of an external cause. If this idea therefore be taken away, the form of love or hatred is also removed, and therefore these emotions and any others which arise from them are destroyed. Q.E.D.

PROPOSITION 3 *An emotion which is a passion ceases to be a passion as soon as we form a clear and distinct idea of it.*

Demonstration An emotion which is a passion is a confused idea (by the general definition of the emotions). If, therefore, we form a clear and distinct idea of this emotion, the idea will not be distinguished—except by reason—from this emotion, in so far as the emotion is related to the mind alone, and therefore the emotion will cease to be a passion. Q.E.D.

Corollary In proportion, then, as we know an emotion better is it more within our control, and the less does the mind suffer from it.

PROPOSITION 4 *There is no modification of the body of which we cannot form some clear and distinct conception.*

Demonstration Those things which are common to all cannot be otherwise than adequately conceived, and therefore there is no modification of the body of which we cannot form some clear and distinct conception. Q.E.D.

Corollary Hence it follows that there is no emotion of which we cannot form some clear and distinct conception. For an emotion is an idea of a modification of the body (by the general definition of the emotions), and this idea therefore (PROP. 4, PART FIVE) must involve some clear and distinct conception.

Note Since nothing exists from which some effect does not follow (PROP. 36, PART ONE), and since we understand clearly and distinctly everything which follows from an idea which is adequate in us, it is a necessary consequence that everyone has the power, partly at least, if not absolutely, of understanding clearly and distinctly himself and his emotions, and consequently of bringing it to pass that he suffers less from them. We have therefore mainly to strive to acquire a clear and distinct knowledge as far as possible of each emotion, so that the mind may be led to pass from the emotion to think those things which it perceives clearly and distinctly, and with which it is entirely satisfied, and to strive also that the emotion may be separated from the thought of an external cause and connected with true thoughts. Thus not only love, hatred, etc., will be destroyed (PROP. 2, PART FIVE), but also the appetites or desires to which the emotion gives rise cannot be excessive. For it is above everything to be observed that the appetite by which a man is said to act is one and the same appetite as that by which he is said to suffer. For example, we have shown that human nature is so constituted that everyone desires that other people should live according to his way of thinking, a desire which in a man who is not guided by reason is a passion which is called ambition, and is not very different from pride; while, on the other hand, in a man who lives according to the dictates of reason it is an action or virtue which is called piety. In the same manner, all the appetites or desires are passions only in so far as they arise from inadequate ideas, and are classed among the virtues whenever they are excited or begotten by adequate ideas; for all the desires by which we are determined to any action may arise either from adequate or inadequate ideas. To return, therefore, to the point from which we set out: there is no remedy within our power which can be conceived more excellent for the emotions than that which consists in a true knowledge of them, since the mind possesses no other power than that of thinking and forming adequate ideas, as we have shown above.

PROPOSITION 5 *An emotion toward an object which we do not imagine as necessary, possible, or uncertain, but which we simply imagine, is, other things being equal, the greatest of all.*

Demonstration The emotion toward an object which we imagine to be free is greater than toward one which is necessary, and consequently still greater than toward one which we imagine as possible or uncertain (PROP. 11, PART FOUR). But to imagine an object as free can be nothing else than to imagine it simply, while we know not the causes by which it was determined to action. An emotion, therefore, toward an object which we simply imagine is, other things being equal, greater than toward one which we imagine as necessary, possible, or uncertain, and consequently greatest of all. Q.E.D.

PROPOSITION 6 *In so far as the mind understands all things as necessary, so far has it greater power over the emotions, or suffers less from them.*

439

Baruch Spinoza

Demonstration The mind understands all things to be necessary (PROP. 29, PART ONE), and determined by an infinite chain of causes to existence and action (PROP. 28, PART ONE), and therefore (PROP. 5, PART FIVE) so far enables itself to suffer less from the emotions which arise from these things, and to be less affected toward them. Q.E.D.

Note The more this knowledge that things are necessary is applied to individual things which we imagine more distinctly and more vividly, the greater is this power of the mind over the emotions —a fact to which experience also testifies. For we see that sorrow for the loss of anything good is diminished if the person who has lost it considers that it could not by any possibility have been preserved. So also we see that nobody pities an infant because it does not know how to speak, walk, or reason, and lives so many years not conscious, as it were, of itself; but if a number of human beings were born adult, and only a few here and there were born infants, everyone would pity the infants, because we should then consider infancy not as a thing natural and necessary, but as a defect or fault of nature. Many other facts of a similar kind we might observe.

PROPOSITION 7 *The emotions which spring from reason or which are excited by it are, if time be taken into account, more powerful than those which are related to individual objects which we contemplate as absent.*

Demonstration We do not contemplate an object as absent by reason of the emotion by which we imagine it, but by reason of the fact that the body is affected with another emotion, which excludes the existence of that object (PROP. 17, PART TWO). The emotion, therefore, which is related to an object which we contemplate as absent, is not of such a nature as to overcome the other actions and power of man (concerning these things see PROP. 6, PART FOUR), but, on the contrary, is of such a nature that it can in some way be restrained by those modifications which exclude the existence of its external cause (PROP. 9, PART FOUR). But the emotion which arises from reason is necessarily related to the common properties of things, which we always contemplate as present (for nothing can exist which excludes their present existence), and which we always imagine in the same way. This emotion, therefore, always remains the same, and consequently (AX. 1, PART FIVE), the emotions which are contrary to it, and which are not maintained by their external cause, must more and more accommodate themselves to it until they are no longer contrary to it. So far, therefore, the emotion which springs from reason is the stronger. Q.E.D.

PROPOSITION 8 *The greater the number of the causes which simultaneously concur to excite any emotion, the greater it will be.*

Demonstration A number of simultaneous causes can do more than if they were fewer, and therefore (PROP. 5, PART FOUR) the greater the number of the simultaneous causes by which an emotion is excited, the greater it is. Q.E.D.

Note This proposition is also evident from AX. 2, PART FIVE.

PROPOSITION 9 *If we are affected by an emotion which is related to many and different causes, which the mind contemplates at the same time with the emotion itself, we are less injured, suffer less from it, and are less affected therefore toward each cause than if we were affected by another emotion equally great which is related to one cause only or to fewer causes.*

Demonstration An emotion is bad or injurious only in so far as it hinders the mind from thinking, and therefore that emotion by which the mind is determined to the contemplation of a number of objects at the same time is less injurious than another emotion equally great which holds the mind in the contemplation of one object alone or of a few objects, so that it cannot think of others. This is the first thing we had to prove. Again, since the essence of the mind, that is to say, its power, consists in thought alone, the mind suffers less through an emotion by which it is determined to the contemplation of a number of objects at the same time than through an emotion equally great which holds it occupied in the contemplation of one object alone or of a few objects. This is the second thing we had to prove. Finally, this emotion, in so far as it is related to a number of external causes, is therefore less toward each. Q.E.D.

PROPOSITION 10 *So long as we are not agitated by emotions which are contrary to our nature do we possess the power of arranging and connecting the modifications of the body according to the order of the intellect.*

Demonstration The emotions which are contrary to our nature, that is to say, which are evil, are evil so far as they hinder the mind from understanding. So long, therefore, as we are not agitated by emotions which are contrary to our nature, so long the power of

441

the mind by which it endeavors to understand things is not hindered, and therefore so long does it possess the power of forming clear and distinct ideas, and of deducing them, the one from the other. So long, consequently (PROP. 1, PART FIVE), do we possess the power of arranging and connecting the modifications of the body according to the order of the intellect. Q.E.D.

Note Through this power of properly arranging and connecting the modifications of the body we can prevent ourselves from being easily affected by evil emotions. For (PROP. 7, PART FIVE) a greater power is required to restrain emotions which are arranged and connected according to the order of the intellect than is required to restrain those which are uncertain and unsettled. The best thing, therefore, we can do, so long as we lack a perfect knowledge of our emotions, is to conceive a right rule of life, or sure maxims of life— to commit these latter to memory, and constantly to apply them to the particular cases which frequently meet us in life, so that our imagination may be widely affected by them, and they may always be ready to hand. For example, among the maxims of life we have placed this, that hatred is to be conquered by love or generosity, and is not to be met with hatred in return. But in order that we may always have this prescript of reason in readiness whenever it will be of service, we must think over and often meditate upon the common injuries inflicted by men, and consider how and in what way they may best be repelled by generosity; for thus we shall connect the image of injury with the imagination of this maxim, and it will be at hand whenever an injury is offered to us. If we also have at hand the law of our own true profit and good which follows from mutual friendship and common fellowship, and remember that the highest peace of mind arises from a right rule of life, and also that man, like other things, acts according to the necessity of nature, then the injury or the hatred which usually arises from that necessity will occupy but the least part of the imagination, and will be easily overcome: or supposing that the anger which generally arises from the greatest injuries is not so easily overcome, it will nevertheless be overcome, although not without fluctuation of mind, in a far shorter space of time than would have been necessary if we had not possessed those maxims on which we had thus meditated beforehand. This is evident from PROPS. 6, 7, and 8, PART FIVE.

Concerning strength of mind, we must reflect in the same way for the purpose of getting rid of fear, that is to say, we must often enumerate and imagine the common dangers of life, and think upon the manner in which they can best be avoided and overcome by presence of mind and courage. It is to be observed, however, that in the ordering of our thoughts and images we must always look to those qualities which in each thing are good, so that we may be determined to action always by an emotion of joy.

For example, if a man sees that he pursues glory too eagerly, let him think on its proper use, for what end it is to be followed, and by what means it can be obtained; but let him not think upon its abuse and vanity, and on the inconstancy of men and things of this sort, about which no one thinks unless through disease of mind; for with such thoughts do those who are ambitious greatly torment themselves when they despair of obtaining the honors for which they are striving; and while they vomit forth rage, wish to be thought wise. Indeed it is certain that those covet glory the most who are loudest in declaiming against its abuse and the vanity of the world. Nor is this a peculiarity of the ambitious, but is common to all to whom fortune is adverse and who are impotent in mind; for we see that a poor and avaricious man is never weary of speaking about the abuse of money and the vices of the rich, thereby achieving nothing save to torment himself and show to others that he is unable to bear with equanimity not only his own poverty but also the wealth of others. So also a man who has not been well received by his mistress thinks of nothing but the fickleness of women, their faithlessness, and their other oft-proclaimed failings—all of which he forgets as soon as he is taken into favor by his mistress again. He, therefore, who desires to govern his emotions and appetites from a love of liberty alone will strive as much as he can to know virtues and their causes, and to fill his mind with that joy which springs from a true knowledge of them. Least of all will he desire to contemplate the vices of men and disparage men, or to delight in a false show of liberty. He who will diligently observe these things (and they are not difficult), and will continue to practice them, will assuredly in a short space of time be able for the most part to direct his actions in accordance with the command of reason.

PROPOSITION 11 *The greater the number of objects to which an image is related, the more constant is it, or the more frequently does it present itself, and the more does it occupy the mind.*

Demonstration The greater the number of objects to which an image or emotion is related, the greater is the number of causes by which it can be excited and cherished. All these causes the mind contemplates simultaneously by means of the emotion (by hypothesis), and therefore the more constant is the emotion, or the more frequently does it present itself, and the more does it occupy the mind (PROP. 8, PART FIVE). Q.E.D.

PROPOSITION 12 *The images of things are more easily connected with those images which are related to things which we clearly and distinctly understand than with any others.*

Demonstration Things which we clearly and distinctly understand are either the common properties of things or what are deduced from them, and consequently (PROP. 11, PART FIVE) are more frequently excited in us; and therefore it is easier for us to contemplate other things together with these which we clearly and distinctly understand than with any others, and consequently, it is easier to connect things with these which we clearly and distinctly understand than with any others.

PROPOSITION 13 *The greater the number of other things with which any image is connected, the more frequently does it present itself.*

Demonstration For the greater the number of other things with which an image is connected, the greater is the number of causes by which it may be excited. Q.E.D.

PROPOSITION 14 *The mind can cause all the modifications of the body or the images of things to be related to the idea of God.*

Demonstration There is no modification of the body of which the mind cannot form some clear and distinct conception (PROP. 4, PART FIVE), and therefore (PROP. 15, PART ONE) it can cause all the modifications of the body to be related to the idea of God. Q.E.D.

PROPOSITION 15 *He who clearly and distinctly understands himself and his emotions loves God, and loves Him better the better he understands himself and his emotions.*

Demonstration He who clearly and distinctly understands himself and his emotions rejoices, and his joy is attended with the idea of God (PROP. 14, PART FIVE); therefore he loves God, and (by the same reasoning) loves Him better the better he understands himself and his emotions. Q.E.D.

PROPOSITION 16 *This love of God above everything else ought to occupy the mind.*

444

Demonstration For this love is connected with all the modifications of the body (PROP. 14, PART FIVE), by all of which it is cherished (PROP. 15, PART FIVE), and therefore (PROP. 11, PART FIVE) above everything else ought to occupy the mind. Q.E.D.

PROPOSITION 17 *God is free from passions, nor is He affected with any emotion of joy or sorrow.*

Demonstration All ideas, in so far as they are related to God, are true; that is to say, are adequate, and therefore (by the general definition of the emotions) God is free from passions. Again, God can neither pass to a greater nor to a less perfection (*Corol. 2*, PROP. 20, PART ONE), and therefore He cannot be affected with any emotion of joy or sorrow. Q.E.D.

Corollary Properly speaking, God loves no one and hates no one; for God (PROP. 17, PART FIVE) is not affected with any emotion of joy or sorrow, and consequently He neither loves nor hates anyone.

PROPOSITION 18 *No one can hate God.*

Demonstration The idea of God which is in us is adequate and perfect, and therefore in so far as we contemplate God do we act, and consequently no sorrow can exist with the accompanying idea of God; that is to say, no one can hate God. Q.E.D.

Corollary Love of God cannot be turned into hatred.

Note But some may object, that if we understand God to be the cause of all things, we do for that very reason consider Him to be the cause of sorrow. But I reply, that in so far as we understand the causes of sorrow, it ceases to be a passion, that is to say, it ceases to be sorrow; and therefore in so far as we understand God to be the cause of sorrow do we rejoice.

PROPOSITION 19 *He who loves God cannot strive that God should love him in return.*

Demonstration If a man were to strive after this, he would desire (*Corol.*, PROP. 17, PART FIVE) that God, whom he loves, should not be God, and consequently he would desire to be sad, which is absurd. Therefore he who loves God, etc. Q.E.D.

PROPOSITION 20 *This love of God cannot be defiled either by the emotion of envy or jealousy, but is the more strengthened the more people we imagine to be connected with God by the same bond of love.*

445

Demonstration This love of God is the highest good which we can seek according to the dictate of reason; is common to all men; and we desire that all may enjoy it. It cannot, therefore, be sullied by the emotion of envy, nor (PROP. 18, PART FIVE) by that of jealousy, but, on the contrary, it must be the more strengthened the more people we imagine to rejoice in it. Q.E.D.

Note It is possible to show in the same manner that there is no emotion directly contrary to this love and able to destroy it, and so we may conclude that this love of God is the most constant of all the emotions, and that, in so far as it is related to the body, it cannot be destroyed unless with the body itself. What its nature is, in so far as it is related to the mind alone, we shall see hereafter.

I have, in what has preceded, included all the remedies for the emotions, that is to say, everything which the mind, considered in itself alone, can do against them. It appears therefrom that the power of the mind over the emotions consists—

1 In the knowledge itself of the emotions. (See *Note*, PROP. 4, PART FIVE.)

2 In the separation by the mind of the emotions from the thought of an external cause, which we imagine confusedly. (See PROP. 2, PART FIVE, and *Note*, PROP. 4, PART FIVE.)

3 In duration, in which the modifications which are related to objects we understand surpass those related to objects conceived in a mutilated or confused manner. (PROP. 7, PART FIVE.)

4 In the multitude of causes by which the modifications which are related to the common properties of things or to God are nourished. (PROPS. 9 and 11, PART FIVE.)

5 In the order in which the mind can arrange its emotions and connect them one with the other. (*Note*, PROP. 10, PART FIVE, and see also PROPS. 12, 13, and 14, PART FIVE.)

But that this power of the mind over the emotions may be better understood, it is to be carefully observed that we call the emotions great when we compare the emotion of one man with that of another, and see that one man is agitated more than another by the same emotion, or when we compare the emotions of one and the same man, and discover that he is affected or moved more by one emotion than by another.

For (PROP. 5, PART FOUR) the power of any emotion is limited by the power of the external cause as compared with our own power. But the power of the mind is limited solely by knowledge, while impotence or passion is estimated solely by privation of knowledge, or, in other words, by that through which ideas are called inadequate; and it therefore follows that that mind suffers the most whose largest part consists of inadequate ideas, so that it is distinguished rather by what it suffers than by what it does, while, on the contrary, that mind acts the most whose largest part consists of adequate ideas, so that although it may possess as many inadequate ideas as the first, it is nevertheless distinguished rather by those which belong to human virtue than by those which are a sign of human impotence. Again, it is to be observed that our sorrows and misfortunes mainly proceed from too much love toward an object which is subject to many changes, and which we can never possess. For no one is troubled or anxious about any object he does not love; neither do wrongs, suspicions, hatreds, etc., arise except from love toward objects of which no one can be truly the possessor.

From all this we easily conceive what is the power which clear and distinct knowledge, and especially that third kind of knowledge whose foundation is the knowledge itself of God, possesses over the emotions; the power, namely, by which it is able, in so far as they are passions, if not actually to destroy them (see PROP. 3, PART FIVE, with the *Note*, PROP. 4, PART FIVE), at least to make them constitute the smallest part of the mind (see PROP. 14, PART FIVE). Moreover, it begets a love toward an immutable and eternal object (see PROP. 15, PART FIVE) of which we are really partakers; a love which therefore cannot be vitiated by the defects which are in common love, but which can always become greater and greater (PROP. 15, PART FIVE), occupy the largest part of the mind (PROP. 16, PART FIVE), and thoroughly affect it.

I have now concluded all that I had to say relating to this present life. For anyone who will attend to what has been urged in this *Note,* and to the definition of the mind and its emotions, will easily be able to see the truth of what I said in the beginning of the *Note,* that in these few words all the remedies for the emotions are comprehended. It is time, therefore, that I should now pass to the consideration of those matters which appertain to the duration of the mind without relation to the body.

PROPOSITION 21 *The mind can imagine nothing, nor can it recollect anything that is past, except while the body exists.*

447

Demonstration The mind does not express the actual existence of its body, nor does it conceive as actual the modifications of the body, except while the body exists, and consequently it conceives no body as actually existing except while its own body exists. It can therefore imagine nothing, nor can it recollect anything that is past, except while the body exists. Q.E.D.

PROPOSITION 22 *In God, nevertheless, there necessarily exists an idea which expresses the essence of this or that human body under the form of eternity.*

Demonstration God is not only the cause of the existence of this or that human body, but also of its essence (PROP. 25, PART ONE), which therefore must necessarily be conceived through the essence of God itself (AX. 4, PART ONE) and by a certain eternal necessity (PROP. 16, PART ONE). This conception, moreover, must necessarily exist in God. Q.E.D.

PROPOSITION 23 *The human mind cannot be absolutely destroyed with the body, but something of it remains which is eternal.*

Demonstration In God there necessarily exists a conception or idea which expresses the essence of the human body (PROP. 22, PART FIVE). This conception or idea is therefore necessarily something which pertains to the essence of the human mind. But we ascribe to the human mind no duration which can be limited by time, unless in so far as it expresses the actual existence of the body, which is explained through duration, and which can be limited by time, that is to say, we cannot ascribe duration to the mind except while the body exists.

But nevertheless, since this something is that which is conceived by a certain eternal necessity through the essence itself of God (PROP. 22, PART FIVE), this something which pertains to the essence of the mind will necessarily be eternal. Q.E.D.

Note This idea which expresses the essence of the body under the form of eternity is, as we have said, a certain mode of thought which pertains to the essence of the mind, and is necessarily eternal. It is impossible, nevertheless, that we should recollect that we existed before the body, because there are no traces of any such existence in the body, and also because eternity cannot be defined by time, or have any relationship to it. Nevertheless we feel and know by experience that we are eternal. For the mind is no less sensible of those things which it conceives through intelligence than of those which it remembers, for demonstrations are the eyes of the mind by which it sees and observes things.

Although, therefore, we do not recollect that we existed before the body, we feel that our mind, in so far as it involves the essence of the body under the form of eternity, is eternal, and that this existence of the mind cannot be limited by time nor explained by duration. Only in so far, therefore, as it involves the actual existence of the body can the mind be said to possess duration, and its existence be limited by a fixed time, and so far only has it the power of determining the existence of things in time, and of conceiving them under the form of duration.

PROPOSITION 24   *The more we understand individual objects, the more we understand God.*

Demonstration   This is evident from *Corol.*, PROP. 25, PART ONE.

PROPOSITION 25   *The highest effort of the mind and its highest virtue is to understand things by the third kind of knowledge.**

Demonstration   The third kind of knowledge proceeds from an adequate idea of certain attributes of God to an adequate knowledge of the essence of things; and the more we understand things in this manner (PROP. 24, PART FIVE), the more we understand God; and therefore the highest virtue of the mind, that is to say (DEF. 8, PART FOUR), the power or nature of the mind, or its highest effort, is to understand things by the third kind of knowledge. Q.E.D.

PROPOSITION 26   *The better the mind is adapted to understand things by the third kind of knowledge, the more it desires to understand them by this kind of knowledge.*

Demonstration   This is evident; for in so far as we conceive the mind to be adapted to understand things by this kind of knowledge, do we conceive it to be determined to understand things by this kind of knowledge, and consequently the better the mind is adapted to this way of understanding things, the more it desires it. Q.E.D.

* Spinoza distinguishes between three kinds of knowledge: first, crude experience or hearsay which does not grasp the reasons involved; second, knowledge based on observation of causes and reasoning, but without full certainty; third, knowledge which is logically certain, that is, formed from full understanding of basic properties.

PROPOSITION 27 *From this third kind of knowledge arises the highest possible peace of mind.*

Demonstration The highest virtue of the mind is to know God, or to understand things by the third kind of knowledge (PROP. 25, PART FIVE). This virtue is greater the more the mind knows things by this kind of knowledge (PROP. 24, PART FIVE), and therefore he who knows things by this kind of knowledge passes to the highest human perfection, and consequently is affected with the highest joy, which is accompanied with the idea of himself and his own virtue; and therefore from this kind of knowledge arises the highest possible peace of mind. Q.E.D.

PROPOSITION 28 *The effort or the desire to know things by the third kind of knowledge cannot arise from the first kind, but may arise from the second kind of knowledge.*

Demonstration This proposition is self-evident; for everything that we clearly and distinctly understand, we understand either through itself or through something which is conceived through itself; or, in other words, ideas which are clear and distinct in us, or which are related to the third kind of knowledge, cannot follow from mutilated and confused ideas, which are related to the first kind of knowledge, but from adequate ideas, that is to say, from the second and third kinds of knowledge. Therefore the desire of knowing things by the third kind of knowledge cannot arise from the first kind, but may arise from the second. Q.E.D.

PROPOSITION 29 *Everything which the mind understands under the form of eternity, it understands not because it conceives the present actual existence of the body, but because it conceives the essence of the body under the form of eternity.*

Demonstration In so far as the mind conceives the present existence of its body does it conceive duration which can be determined in time, and so far only has it the power of conceiving things in relation to time. But eternity cannot be explained by duration (DEF. 8, PART ONE, and its *Explanation*); therefore the mind so far has not the power of conceiving things under the form of eternity: but because it is the nature of reason to conceive things under the form of eternity, and because it also pertains to the nature of the mind to conceive the essence of the body under the form of eternity (PROP. 23, PART FIVE), and excepting these two things nothing else pertains to the nature of the mind, therefore this power of con-

450

ceiving things under the form of eternity does not pertain to the mind except in so far as it conceives the essence of the body under the form of eternity. Q.E.D.

Note Things are conceived by us as actual in two ways; either in so far as we conceive them to exist with relation to a fixed time and place, or in so far as we conceive them to be contained in God, and to follow from the necessity of the divine nature. But those things which are conceived in this second way as true or real we conceive under the form of eternity, and their ideas involve the eternal and infinite essence of God.

PROPOSITION 30 *Our mind, in so far as it knows itself and the body under the form of eternity, necessarily has a knowledge of God, and knows that it is in God and is conceived through Him.*

Demonstration Eternity is the very essence of God, in so far as that essence involves necessary existence (DEF. 8, PART ONE). To conceive things therefore under the form of eternity, is to conceive them in so far as they are conceived through the essence of God as actually existing things, or in so far as through the essence of God they involve existence. Therefore our mind, in so far as it conceives itself and its body under the form of eternity, necessarily has a knowledge of God, and knows, etc. Q.E.D.

PROPOSITION 31 *The third kind of knowledge depends upon the mind as its formal cause, in so far as the mind itself is eternal.*

Demonstration The mind conceives nothing under the form of eternity, unless in so far as it conceives the essence of its body under the form of eternity (PROP. 29, PART FIVE), that is to say (PROPS. 21 and 23, PART FIVE), unless in so far as it is eternal. Therefore (PROP. 30, PART FIVE) in so far as the mind is eternal it has a knowledge of God, which is necessarily adequate, and therefore in so far as it is eternal it is fitted to know all those things which can follow from this knowledge of God, that is to say, it is fitted to know things by the third kind of knowledge, of which, in so far as the mind is eternal, it is the adequate or formal cause. Q.E.D.

Note As each person therefore becomes stronger in this kind of knowledge, the more is he conscious of himself and of God; that is to say, the more perfect and the happier he is, a truth which will still more clearly appear from what follows. Here, however, it is to be observed, that although we are now certain that the mind

451

is eternal in so far as it conceives things under the form of eternity, yet, in order that what we wish to prove may be more easily explained and better understood, we shall consider the mind, as we have hitherto done, as if it had just begun to be, and had just begun to understand things under the form of eternity. This we can do without any risk of error, provided only we are careful to conclude nothing except from clear premises.

PROPOSITION 32 *In whatever we understand by the third kind of knowledge we delight, and our delight is accompanied with the idea of God as its cause.*

Demonstration From this kind of knowledge arises the highest possible peace of mind, that is to say, the highest joy, attended moreover with the idea of one's self (PROP. 27, PART FIVE), and consequently (PROP. 30, PART FIVE) attended with the idea of God as its cause. Q.E.D.

Corollary From the third kind of knowledge necessarily springs the intellectual love of God. For from this kind of knowledge arises (PROP. 32, PART FIVE) joy attended with the idea of God as its cause, that is to say, the love of God, not in so far as we imagine Him as present (PROP. 29, PART FIVE), but in so far as we understand that He is eternal; and that is what I call the intellectual love of God.

PROPOSITION 33 *The intellectual love of God which arises from the third kind of knowledge is eternal.*

Demonstration The third kind of knowledge (PROP. 31, PART FIVE, and AX. 3, PART ONE) is eternal, and therefore (by the same axiom) the love which springs from it is necessarily eternal. Q.E.D.

Note Although this love of God has no beginning (PROP. 33, PART FIVE), it nevertheless has all the perfections of love, just as if it had originated—as we supposed in the *Corollary,* PROP. 32, PART FIVE. Nor is there here any difference, excepting that the mind has eternally possessed these same perfections which we imagined as now accruing to it, and has possessed them with the accompanying idea of God as the eternal cause. And if joy consist in the passage to a greater perfection, blessedness must indeed consist in this, that the mind is endowed with perfection itself.

PROPOSITION 34 *The mind is subject to emotions which are related to passions only so long as the body exists.*

Demonstration An imagination is an idea by which the mind contemplates any object as present. This idea nevertheless indicates the present constitution of the human body rather than the nature of the external object. An emotion, therefore (by the general definition of the emotions), is an imagination in so far as it indicates the present constitution of the body, and therefore (PROP. 21, PART FIVE) the mind, only so long as the body exists, is subject to emotions which are related to passions. Q.E.D.

Corollary Hence it follows that no love except intellectual love is eternal.

Note If we look at the common opinion of men, we shall see that they are indeed conscious of the eternity of their minds, but they confound it with duration, and attribute it to imagination or memory, which they believe remain after death.

PROPOSITION 35 *God loves Himself with an infinite intellectual love.*

God is absolutely infinite (DEF. 6, PART ONE), that is to say, the nature of God delights in infinite perfection accompanied with the idea of Himself, that is to say (PROP. 11, and DEF. 1, PART ONE), with the idea of Himself as cause, and this is what, in *Corol.*, PROP. 32, PART FIVE, we have called intellectual love.

PROPOSITION 36 *The intellectual love of the mind toward God is the very love with which He loves Himself, not in so far as He is infinite, but in so far as He can be explained through the essence of the human mind considered under the form of eternity; that is to say, the intellectual love of the mind toward God is part of the infinite love with which God loves Himself.*

Demonstration This love of the mind must be related to the actions of the mind (*Corol.*, PROP. 32, PART FIVE), and it is therefore an action by which the mind contemplates itself; and which is accompanied with the idea of God as cause (PROP. 32, PART FIVE, with the *Corol.*); that is to say (*Corol.*, PROP. 25, PART ONE), it is an action, by which God, in so far as He can be explained by the human mind, contemplates Himself, the action being accompanied with the idea of Himself; and therefore (PROP. 35, PART FIVE), this love of the mind is part of the infinite love with which God loves Himself. Q.E.D.

Corollary Hence it follows that God, in so far as He loves Himself, loves men, and consequently that the love of God toward men

453

and the intellectual love of the mind toward God are one and the same thing.

Note Hence we clearly understand that our salvation, or blessedness, or liberty consists in a constant and eternal love toward God, or in the love of God toward men. This love or blessedness is called Glory in the sacred writings, and not without reason. For whether it be related to God or to the mind, it may properly be called repose of mind, which is, in truth, not distinguished from glory. For in so far as it is related to God, it is (PROP. 35, PART FIVE) joy (granting that it is allowable to use this word), accompanied with the idea of Himself, and it is the same thing when it is related to the mind (PROP. 27, PART FIVE). Again, since the essence of our mind consists in knowledge alone, whose beginning and foundation is God (PROP. 15, PART ONE), it is clear to us in what manner and by what method our mind, with regard both to essence and existence, follows from the divine nature, and continually depends upon God. I thought it worth while for me to notice this here, in order that I might show, by this example, what that knowledge of individual objects which I have called intuitive or of the third kind is able to do, and how much more potent it is than the universal knowledge, which I have called knowledge of the second kind. For although I have shown generally in PART ONE that all things, and consequently also the human mind, depend upon God both with regard to existence and essence, yet that demonstration, although legitimate, and placed beyond the possibility of a doubt, does not, nevertheless, so affect our mind as a proof from the essence itself of any individual object which we say depends upon God.

PROPOSITION 37 *There is nothing in nature which is contrary to this intellectual love, or which can negate it.*

This intellectual love necessarily follows from the nature of the mind, in so far as it is considered, through the nature of God, as an eternal truth (PROPS. 33 and 29, PART FIVE). If there were anything, therefore, contrary to this love, it would be contrary to the truth, and consequently whatever might be able to negate this love would be able to make the true false, which (as is self-evident) is absurd. There exists, therefore, nothing in nature, etc. Q.E.D.

Note The axiom of PART FOUR refers only to individual objects, in so far as they are considered in relation to a fixed time and place. This, I believe, no one can doubt.

PROPOSITION 38 *The more objects the mind understands by the second and third kinds of knowledge, the less it suffers from those emotions which are evil, and the less it fears death.*

Demonstration The essence of the mind consists in knowledge. The more things, therefore, the mind knows by the second and third kinds of knowledge, the greater is that part which abides (PROP. 29 and 23, PART FIVE), and consequently (PROP. 37, PART FIVE) the greater is that part which is not touched by emotions which are contrary to our nature, that is to say, which are evil. The more things, therefore, the mind understands by the second and third kinds of knowledge, the greater is that part which remains unharmed, and the less consequently does it suffer from the emotions.

Note We are thus enabled to understand that death is by so much the less injurious to us as the clear and distinct knowledge of the mind is greater, and consequently as the mind loves God more. Again, since (PROP. 27, PART FIVE) from the third kind of knowledge there arises the highest possible peace, it follows that it is possible for the human mind to be of such a nature that that part of it which we have shown perishes with its body (PROP. 21, PART FIVE), in comparison with the part of it which remains, is of no consequence. But more fully upon this subject presently.

PROPOSITION 39 *He who possesses a body fit for many things possesses a mind of which the greater part is eternal.*

Demonstration He who possesses a body fitted for doing many things is least of all agitated by those emotions which are evil, that is to say, by emotions which are contrary to our nature, and therefore (PROP. 10, PART FIVE) he possesses the power of arranging and connecting the modifications of the body according to the order of the intellect, and consequently (PROP. 14, PART FIVE) of causing all the modifications of the body to be related to the idea of God (PROP. 15, PART FIVE); in consequence of which he is affected with a love of God, which (PROP. 16, PART FIVE) must occupy or form the greatest part of his mind, and therefore (PROP. 33, PART FIVE) he possesses a mind of which the greatest part is eternal.

Note Inasmuch as human bodies are fit for many things, we

455

cannot doubt the possibility of their possessing such a nature that they may be related to minds which have a large knowledge of themselves and of God, and whose greatest or principal part is eternal, so that they scarcely fear death. To understand this more clearly, it is to be here considered that we live in constant change, and that according as we change for the better or the worse we are called happy or unhappy. For he who passes from infancy or childhood to death is called unhappy, and, on the other hand, we consider ourselves happy if we can pass through the whole period of life with a sound mind in a sound body. Moreover, he who, like an infant or child, possesses a body fit for very few things, and almost altogether dependent on external causes, has a mind which, considered in itself alone, is almost entirely unconscious of itself, of God, and of objects. On the other hand, he who possesses a body fit for many things possesses a mind which, considered in itself alone, is largely conscious of itself, of God, and of objects. In this life, therefore, it is our chief endeavor to change the body of infancy, so far as its nature permits and is conducive thereto, into another body which is fitted for many things, and which is related to a mind conscious as much as possible of itself, of God, and of objects; so that everything which is related to its memory or imagination, in comparison with the intellect, is scarcely of any moment, as I have already said in the note of the preceding proposition.

PROPOSITION 40 *The more perfection a thing possesses, the more it acts and the less it suffers, and conversely the more it acts the more perfect it is.*

Demonstration The more perfect a thing is, the more reality it possesses, and consequently the more it acts and the less it suffers. Inversely also it may be demonstrated in the same way that the more a thing acts the more perfect it is. Q.E.D.

Corollary Hence it follows that that part of the mind which abides, whether great or small, is more perfect than the other part. For the part of the mind which is eternal (PROPS. 23 and 29, PART FIVE) is the intellect, through which alone we are said to act, but that part which, as we have shown, perishes, is the imagination itself (PROP. 21, PART FIVE), through which alone we are said to suffer. Therefore (PROP. 40, PART FIVE) that part which abides, whether great or small, is more perfect than the latter. Q.E.D.

Note These are the things I proposed to prove concerning the

456

mind, in so far as it is considered without relation to the existence of the body, and from these, taken together with PROP. 21, PART ONE, and other propositions, it is evident that our mind, in so far as it understands, is an eternal mode of thought, which is determined by another eternal mode of thought, and this again by another, and so on *ad infinitum,* so that all taken together form the eternal and infinite intellect of God.

PROPOSITION 41 *Even if we did not know that our mind is eternal, we should still consider as of primary importance Piety and Religion, and absolutely everything which in PART FOUR we have shown to be related to strength of mind and generosity.*

Demonstration The primary and sole foundation of virtue or of the proper conduct of life is to seek our own profit. But in order to determine what reason prescribes as profitable, we had no regard to the eternity of the mind, which we did not recognize till we came to PART FIVE. Therefore, although we were at that time ignorant that the mind is eternal, we considered as of primary importance those things which we have shown are related to strength of mind and generosity; and therefore, even if we were now ignorant of the eternity of the mind, we should consider those commands of reason as of primary importance. Q.E.D.

Note The creed of the multitude seems to be different from this; for most persons seem to believe that they are free in so far as it is allowed them to obey their lusts, and that they give up a portion of their rights, in so far as they are bound to live according to the commands of divine law. Piety, therefore, and religion, and absolutely all those things that are related to greatness of soul, they believe to be burdens which they hope to be able to lay aside after death; hoping also to receive some reward for their bondage, that is to say, for their piety and religion. It is not merely this hope, however, but also and chiefly fear of dreadful punishments after death, by which they are induced to live according to the commands of divine law, that is to say, as far as their feebleness and impotent mind will permit; and if this hope and fear were not present to them, but if they, on the contrary, believed that minds perish with the body, and that there is no prolongation of life for miserable creatures exhausted with the burden of their piety, they would return to ways of their own liking; they would prefer to let everything be controlled by their own passions, and to obey fortune rather than themselves.

This seems to me as absurd as if a man, because he does not believe that he will be able to feed his body with good food to all eternity, should desire to satiate himself with poisonous and deadly drugs; or as if, because he sees that the mind is not eternal or immortal, he should therefore prefer to be mad and to live without reason—absurdities so great that they scarcely deserve to be repeated.

PROPOSITION 42 *Blessedness is not the reward of virtue, but is virtue itself; nor do we delight in blessedness because we restrain our lusts; but, on the contrary, because we delight in it, therefore are we able to restrain them.*

Demonstration Blessedness consists in love toward God (PROP. 36, PART FIVE, and its *Note*), which arises from the third kind of knowledge (*Corol.,* PROP. 32, PART FIVE), and this love, therefore, must be related to the mind in so far as it acts. Blessedness, therefore (DEF. 8, PART FOUR), is virtue itself, which was the first thing to be proved. Again, the more the mind delights in this divine love or blessedness, the more it understands (PROP. 32, PART FIVE), that is to say (*Corol.,* PROP. 3, PART FIVE), the greater is the power it has over its emotions, and (PROP. 38, PART FIVE) the less it suffers from emotions which are evil. Therefore, it is because the mind delights in this divine love or blessedness that it possesses the power of restraining the lusts; and because the power of man to restrain the emotions is in the intellect alone, no one, therefore, delights in blessedness because he has restrained his emotions, but, on the contrary, the power of restraining his lusts springs from blessedness itself. Q.E.D.

Note I have finished everything I wished to explain concerning the power of the mind over the emotions and concerning its liberty. From what has been said we see what is the strength of the wise man, and how much he surpasses the ignorant who is driven forward by lust alone. For the ignorant man is not only agitated by external causes in many ways, and never enjoys true peace of soul, but lives also ignorant, as it were, both of God and of things, and as soon as he ceases to suffer ceases also to be. On the other hand, the wise man, in so far as he is considered as such, is scarcely ever moved in his mind, but, being conscious by a certain eternal necessity of himself, of God, and of things, never ceases to be, and always enjoys true peace of soul. If the way which, as I have shown, leads hither seem very difficult, it can nevertheless be found. It must indeed be difficult since it is so seldom discovered; for if salvation lay ready to hand and could be discovered without great labor, how could it be possible that it should be neglected almost by everybody? But all noble things are as difficult as they are rare.

Martin Luther

REFUSES
TO RECANT
BEFORE THE
DIET OF WORMS

April 18, 1521

HERE I STAND. I cannot do otherwise. God help me. Amen."
These famous words, expressive at once of sturdy determination and humility, do not appear in the official transcript of the proceedings. But because they were reported by witnesses and because they reverberate with Luther's personal accents, we allow them to stand as his own and to conclude the great speech.

The moment is one of those which a thousand years, as we look back upon them, seem to have unwittingly prepared and from which subsequent history seems to have been formed along unanticipated lines. This is the moment from which the Reformation in Northern Europe took its strongest impulse.

The city of Worms on the Rhine in the province of Hesse is the place. The hour is late afternoon on the eighteenth of April, 1521. The city is full of distinguished persons from all over Europe, and their servants and private guards and equipage choke the streets and inn yards. One of the troops of soldiers we know to have been under special orders to stand ready to quell any untoward disturbance. Frederick the Wise, Elector of Saxony, is a friend of Luther, and he means to assure that the safe-conduct under which the monk has come to Worms shall not be violated.

A great hall in the city is the meeting place of the first Diet or parliament of the German nation to assemble in the reign of Charles V, the nineteen-year-old monarch who for several months now has been Emperor of the Holy Roman Empire. The Emperor is seated in a chair of state; beside him is his brother, the Archduke Ferdinand. Below them sit deputies of the Pope, sent especially to hear the German monk who has written both works of noble faith and works scandalous to the Holy Church. Among the more than two hundred in attendance are six Electors of the Empire, whose descendants almost all are to become kings; eighty dukes, the rulers of semi-independent territories; thirty archbishops and other prelates; many princes, barons, counts and knights; seven ambassadors, including those of France and England; and the nuncios of Pope Leo X.

The Emperor Charles, who, many years later, is to relinquish the throne for a monk's habit and tonsure, is at this moment the greatest Christian ruler since Charlemagne. Grandson of Ferdinand and Isabella of Spain, he is the descendant of the long line of Hapsburgs; he is lord of Austria, Burgundy, the Low Countries, Spain and Naples. As Holy Roman Emperor he symbolizes the medieval unity of church and state; he is brother and arm of the papacy.

"I neither can nor will retract. . . ."

And before Charles is brought the Augustinian friar, Martin Luther: monk, priest, university lecturer, doctor of theology, subprior of his monastery, accused heretic against whom the writ of excommunication is already prepared, son of a humble miner and smelterer of Thuringia.

Strangely enough, this monk, whom history is to look to as the man who shivered the unity of Western Christianity into the countless sects and eventually the secularism of modern thought, is less modern than his opponents. Through him, puritan North Europe accuses shining Rome of worldliness; through him the single-minded faith of the Dark Ages condemns the intellectual enlightenment of the Renaissance. This monk, whom history is to look to as the creator of the modern nationalistic state, supposes himself to be acting as the defender of the Kingdom of Heaven against the corruptions of earthly kingdoms.

THE NEW MOSES

CURIOUS TO MODERN EARS are the allusions by which he reveals that he feels, at this moment, like Moses brought before Pharaoh, like Moses a humble man forced to bear God's great mandate. This attitude is apparent in his opening words. Like Moses, he is not skillful in speech; he may forget, he says, the proper forms of address for princes of this world; he is a child of his cloister.

Then, when he has distinguished with care between those of his works which are tacitly acknowledged to serve in the propagation of the faith and those which he admits sow dissension, he speaks exactly as Moses might have spoken, promising plagues upon Egypt. "Do not forget that God is wonderful and terrible in his counsels. Tremble lest, if you disdain the divine word, that word may produce a deluge of evils." He proceeds then to warn his listeners of what he calls the error of Pharaoh and of the kings of Israel, the error of enforcing iniquity in the name of peace.

JUSTIFICATION BY FAITH

And what was Luther being required to recant? What opinions did he hold in opposition to his Church? Luther's most important doctrine is that of justification by faith, and his most famous quarrel with the papacy derives from it—his quarrel over the abuse of indulgences.

Luther had pondered long on Saint Paul's *Epistle to the Romans*, I:16–17, which says in part, "For I am not ashamed of the gospel of Christ: for it is the power of God unto salvation to every one that believeth. . . . For therein is the righteousness of God revealed from faith to faith: as it is written, The just shall live by faith." Luther became convinced that the sinfulness of man's nature was too great to be redeemed by the means which the Church prescribed for redemption; he could not convince himself that man's penitence, to say nothing of the penitential works which the Church imposed, was sufficient to procure him forgiveness from a God who is perfect in righteousness and who requires perfection.

What came in answer to the theologian's questings of soul was the thrill of conviction that God himself confers on the penitential sinner the bounteous grace which he can neither conceive in his sinful nature nor earn in the sinful world. Only his faith, not his works, will suffice him unto salvation.

From the enunciation of this doctrine proceeded as a natural consequence the celebrated Ninety-Five Theses Against the Abuse of Indulgences, which Luther posted on the door of the Castle church at Wittenberg in 1517. Indulgences were originally writs issued by the Christian martyrs which applied the spiritual benefits from the martyr's sufferings to a penitent sinner, thereby releasing the penitent from temporal punishment incurred by his sin. In the early days of the Church a sinner was frequently excluded from the Christian community until he had performed a penance—a number of days of fasting, recitation of the psalms on his knees for so many days or almsgiving. Thus it is plain that the effectiveness of indulgences depended upon the doctrine that salvation might be earned by the sinner. Over the years the privilege of the indulgence was abused. And by the year 1500 the sale of indulgences by some mercenary ecclesiastics had become widespread. In Luther's own diocese a scandal arose out of the sale of indulgences to pay the moneylenders whose loans had made it possible for Albert of Brandenburg to hold the offices of two bishops and an archbishop, all at the same time.

THE PLAIN ANSWER

To the German monk, the faithful of his country were the Israelites whom he was required by God to lead out of the Egypt of papal Rome. So intent was he upon the explanation of his calling that he seems not to have been aware that he had not answered the plain question of whether or not he would retract his writings.

Then, his mission avowed, Martin Luther gave a direct answer to Emperor and Pope at once: "Unless I shall be convinced of error . . . I never can nor will retract, for I must not go against my conscience."

Edwin Blois Barrett
Hamilton College

466

M OST SERENE EMPEROR, illustrious princes, very good lords, I stand before you at the time appointed, beseeching your majesty and your highnesses to hear me, as I hope, with justice and kindness. If in my replies I forget to give you the titles which are due to you, if I offend against the ceremonial of courts, forgive me, for I have not been brought up in palaces; I am but a poor monk, the child of my cloister, and I assure you that I have never preached or written anything except in the simplicity of my heart, and for the glory of God, and the honor of the Gospel.

"Most serene emperor, princes of the empire, to the two questions put to me yesterday, if I acknowledged to be mine the books published in my name, and if I persisted in defending them, I say that I do persist; and I shall persist in this reply to the hour of my death. Yes, these are my books, the books which I have published or which have been published in my name. I acknowledge them, I admit and shall ever admit them to be mine, provided that malice, trickery, or unseasonable prudence do not effect any alteration in them. I acknowledge that what my hand has written has been matured by my reflection.

"Before replying to the second question, I entreat your majesty and the Orders of the empire to consider that my books do not all treat of the same matter. There are some of them didactic, intended for the edification of the faithful, for the advancement of piety and the improvement of morals, which the bull, acknowledging the innocence of similar treatises, has not in the slightest condemned. If I were to disown them, what should I be doing? I should be denouncing an instruction admitted by all Christians, thus setting myself up against the universal voice of the faithful.

"There is another sort of writings in which I attack the papacy and the opinions of the papists, as monstrosities, as the ruin of sound doctrines, and the damnation of body and soul. Ah! I cannot deny it, and no one more than I, so loudly do the voice and testimony of conscience speak. The decretals of the popes have thrown disorder into Christianity, have entrapped, imprisoned, tortured the faith of the faithful, and devoured as a prey this noble Germany, which has never ceased to protest against false doctrines contrary to the Gospel and to the judgment of the fathers. If I were to deny these writings, I should lend fresh force and audacity to the tyranny of Rome, I should take away from the torrent of impiety an embankment by which it would overflow the Christian world. My recantation would only serve to extend and increase the kingdom of iniquity; especially when it should be known that it was by orders of his majesty and the very serene princes my lords that I made this recantation.

"Finally, there is another series of works published in my name; I allude to those polemical books suggested and written against some of my adversaries, supporters of the tyranny of Rome. I shall readily admit that I have shown myself more violent in them than is becoming a man of my calling; I do not act the saint here, I do not dispute upon my conduct, but rather upon Christ's doctrines. I cannot, moreover, consent to disavow these writings, because Rome would avail itself of my admission to extend her kingdom and oppress souls.

"Being a man, and not God, I cannot protect my books with any other patronage than that with which Christ protected his doctrines. When interrogated before Annas as to what he taught, and his face was buffeted by a servant: 'If I have spoken evil,' said he, 'show me how.' If the Lord Jesus, who knew that he was without sin, did not repel the testimony which the vilest lips gave of his divine word, ought not I, the scum of the earth, who am only able to sin, to solicit an examination of my doctrines?

"In the name of the living God, then, I entreat your sacred majesty, you illustrious Orders, every human creature, to come and bear witness against me, and convince me of error, with the Prophets and the Gospel in hand. I am ready to disown my errors, if they convince me of falsehood, and to throw my books in the fire.

"Of this be assured, I have weighed the dangers, the troubles, the afflictions, the animosities which my doctrines will bring to the world. I am delighted to see that the word of God is about to produce discords and dissensions; it is the portion and destiny of the divine word, for the Lord has said: 'I am come, not to bring peace but the sword; I am come to separate the son from the father.'

"Do not forget that God is wonderful and terrible in his counsels. Tremble lest, if you disdain the divine word, that word may produce a deluge of evils, and the kingdom of this noble youth, upon whom after God all our hopes rest, be soon disturbed.

"I might here, by examples drawn from the sacred books, point out to you Pharaoh, the king of Egypt, and the kings of Israel, losing themselves in the desire to reign by peace and what they termed wisdom. For God confounds the hypocrite in his hypocrisy, and overturns the mountains before they know their fall. Fear is the work of God.

"Not that I seek here to give counsel to such mighty and powerful minds; I owe this testimony of love to my native Germany. I conclude by commending myself to your sacred majesty and your highnesses, and I humbly implore you not to permit my adversaries to make me an object of hatred here. I have done."

Then the official rose and said that Luther had not answered the question; that it was not a question of discussing opinions already condemned by the councils; that he demanded a simple and conclusive answer, whether he would or would not retract? Luther resumed still more boldly:

"Since your sacred majesty and your highnesses demand a simple reply, I shall give it. It shall neither be involved nor polished; and it is this: unless I shall be convicted of error by the testimony of the Scriptures or evident reason (for I do not believe in the sole authority of the pope and the councils, which so often have erred or have contradicted themselves, and I acknowledge no master but the Bible and the word of God), I neither can nor will retract, for I must not go against my conscience.

"Such is my profession of faith; expect nothing else from me. God help me. Amen."

469

THE

CLOUDS

TRANSLATED BY *Thomas Mitchell*

by

Aristophanes

NOTE: *The translator's summaries of various omitted passages appear italicized and in brackets throughout the text.*

HOME COURSE APPRECIATION

THERE CAN BE NO QUESTION that the plays of Aeschylus, Sophocles and Euripides are unsurpassed in the history of tragedy; the plays of Aristophanes can hardly be said to hold a lesser place in the annals of comedy. They combine wit, intellect and imagination, expressed in poetry of the highest order.

Each year in Athens two festivals honored Bacchus (Dionysus). One, the City Dionysia, was held in March and was devoted primarily to tragedy and satyr-plays, although comedies were also performed on one of the five festival days. The other great festival, the Lenaea, which took place during the winter, was devoted to comedy. The plays were extravagant productions, with the actors wearing elaborate costumes, amusing and frequently grotesque masks and low-heeled shoes, called "socks." All the actors were men and, in Aristophanes' plays at least, the casts were relatively large, with a chorus numbering twenty-four. As with the tragedies, comedies by various authors were presented on a competitive basis, a prize being awarded to the one judged the best. Aristophanes several times received the first prize.

In the history of Greek comedy, Aristophanes' work belongs to the earliest, or Old Comedy, period. This school of writing held sway in Athens for roughly sixty years, from approximately 450 to 390 B.C. Its origin and early development are somewhat obscure, but, like tragedy, it seems to have had its beginnings in the revels honoring Bacchus, the god of rebirth and vegetation, particularly the grape. From these celebrations Old Comedy took its mood of joy and optimism. In addition, Old Comedy seems to have been influenced by the Sicilian mime, a rude kind of farce, conspicuous mainly for its coarse humor and its attacks on the foibles of individuals. The earliest comedies apparently developed in rural sections and were, in great part, spontaneous performances on the part of the actors.

473

However, with the appearance of Cratinus, the first notable writer of comedy, in the middle of the fifth century B.C., the revels were molded into a literary form and became popular in the city as well as in the outlying regions. Altogether, some forty Greek playwrights have been referred to as comedians; of them three stand out: Cratinus, Eupolis and Aristophanes. Only the works of Aristophanes have had the good fortune to be preserved for the present day.

THE PLAYS RECORD THE MAN

O F ARISTOPHANES HIMSELF, very little is known. The year of his birth is usually set at 448 B.C. and his death is believed to have occurred some sixty-five years later. He was an Athenian citizen, the son of a landowner. Apparently he was a precocious youth, for his first play, *The Banqueteers,* was produced when he was about twenty-one years of age. All told, his comedies numbered between forty and fifty, but only eleven are now in existence. Of these, *The Frogs* and *The Clouds* have proved to be the favorites of most readers, although *Lysistrata* (a hilarious story of a woman's device for ending warfare) and *The Birds* (a satire on Utopias) are also popular. From what we can determine from the extant plays and from the records of ancient commentators, there seems to be little doubt that Aristophanes' art marks the high point in Old Comedy. Almost immediately after his death the style in comedy changed. To it the form known as Middle Comedy briefly succeeded, being replaced finally by New Comedy, the predecessor of the modern comedy of manners.

Although we have so little information about the external details of Aristophanes' life, almost all that we would want to know about his philosophy is recorded in his plays. His works testify, more convincingly perhaps than might a formal biography, to his genuine patriotism, his concern for the welfare of Athens, his hatred of war, his loathing of bad government. From his comedies we learn of his nostalgia for the past, for the "good old days" of the early fifth century B.C. He was an inveterate conservative, uncomfortable in an age of ever-widening change. Clinging to orthodox beliefs, he loudly declaimed the spirit of speculation and inquiry that was pervading the religion and thought of his day. He could not help regarding the new literature, education, philosophy and political institutions as the signs of a decadent age. We require some caution, therefore, in reading Aristophanes, to avoid accepting his plays as impartial or historically accurate pictures of late fifth-century Athens. On the other

474

Aristophanes of Athens, master of Greek comedy.

hand, there is little reason to doubt that Athens, by Aristophanes' time, was beset by usurers, grafters and self-styled philosophers. The bright light of the glorious past was already beginning to dim and would soon be dark. Yet whether we regard Aristophanes as a belated moralist or as a jaundiced pessimist, we must admire the way he fulfills the prime role of the comic poet: the outspoken critic of the mores and manners of his times.

THE NATURE OF GREEK COMEDY

Aristophanes' plays are rather different from the comedies of the twentieth century, or those of any other period for that matter. One reason may be that few comic writers have so wide a range to their humor. Aristophanes could be funny in the most profound or sophisticated sense at one moment and then could shift suddenly to burlesque and farce. He concerned himself with issues that really mattered in his day, making such particular reference to men and events that modern readers are often needlessly distressed because they do not know the specific facts of his allusions. Yet with the aid of a few footnotes and the imagination to transfer events from the past into the present it is easy to see that Aristophanes' criticisms of the democracy of his day may well apply to modern institutions.

Aristophanes' satire exposes, in a most brilliant manner, some of the evils gnawing away at the foundations of Athenian society. This is especially the case in the attacks on the stupidity of war and on the demagogic Cleon, the leader of the Athenian democracy after Pericles' death. Aristophanes was most fortunate to have lived during the flowering of Greek democracy, for there was hardly another period in the history of the ancient world that would have tolerated, let alone have awarded poetic prizes to, a man who so forcefully and so openly decried the existing state of affairs.

Another evidence of Aristophanes' genius is his handling of poetic symbols. We tend to forget that the poet uses Cloud-worship for more than its comic appeal in describing a state of mind; or that he has Socrates hanging in a basket, suspended between two worlds, for more than its comic effect. Aristophanes explored all the physical properties of the natural world (and, in *The Frogs,* the mythical properties of the Underworld), in his comedies. Few comic writers have ever used such a vast and imaginative field to expound their themes.

476

O N THE MOST BASIC LEVEL, tragedy ends with a definition of the great man, comedy with a definition of the ordinary man. The "heroes" of most comedies seem to be the men who, like epic or tragic heroes, go in quest of knowledge or happiness: Bacchus (or Dionysus) in *The Frogs* and Strepsiades in *The Clouds*. Yet Bacchus is constantly overshadowed by Euripides and Aeschylus, just as Strepsiades is overwhelmed by Socrates.

In the end, all is well. Bacchus, after going to Hades in search of a "true poet," returns with Aeschylus, and his purpose is resolved. Strepsiades, after wanting his son, Pheidippides, to learn sophistic methods of debate in order to escape their creditors, sees his purpose achieved—though it backfires when Pheidippides beats him, and justifies his cruelty by the same sophistry. Strepsiades gets his revenge, however, by burning down the hall of the sophists.

There are several devices used in *The Clouds* that are typical of Aristophanic comedy. One of these is a special form of the choral interlude, called the *parabasis,* a speech in which the chorus addresses the audience directly, speaking in the author's name and discussing subjects which have no necessary connection with either the action of the play or its theme. In *The Clouds* the subject matter of the *parabasis* includes Aristophanes' consideration of his own works, his opinion of Cleon and his views of religion. The political and social circumstances in Athens form the main theme of the *parabasis* in *The Frogs,* which was a later play.

SATIRE AND LYRIC POETRY

A second device frequently used by Aristophanes, and found in the middle section of *The Clouds,* is the *agon,* a verbal debate, or sometimes an actual fight, which involves the central topic of the play. Thus, in the one comedy, there is a debate between the representatives of the old and new methods of education, and in the other play, between representatives of the old and new kinds of literature. Such passages afford ample room for the dramatist to display his cleverness and develop the play's theme.

So much is made of Aristophanes' brilliant ideas one sometimes neglects the way in which he presents them. His comedies have become classics because they combine clever comic verses with lyric poetry of the highest quality. Frequently his poetic genius comes to the fore in the choral interludes, as in the beautiful chant of the Chorus of Votaries in *The Frogs*. In other places, individuals will soar on wings of lyric melody, as happens in the stirring speech made by Dicaeologos (right logic) in *The Clouds*. There have been many successful writers of comedy since Aristophanes' time, but few of them have been able to blend their comic gifts with such notable poetry. Perhaps the only other dramatist to succeed in any comparable way was Shakespeare.

"THE CLOUDS"—SOPHIST MIASMA

The Clouds, as we read it today, is the second draft of a comedy that had been performed for the first time in 423 B.C. In it several separate points are at issue. To begin, Aristophanes takes the Sophists to task for their use of rhetoric. Oratory had been a much respected accomplishment among the Athenians before this time, but the Sophists had degraded it. They developed and refined the techniques of rhetoric to the end that they could argue successfully on either side of a question. Their attention was not focused on the truth of a proposition under discussion, but rather on the process of persuasion for its own sake. Although some of the villainies of which the Sophists have been accused are probably little more than malicious gossip, it seems to be the case that many of those who joined the movement were decidedly lacking in a sense of social or moral responsibility and did enjoy "making the worse appear the better cause." Aristophanes, at least, had no doubt at all that such was the influence of Sophistry. Hence, Strepsiades goes to the school of the Sophists to learn to talk himself out of having to pay his legal debts.

Another bone of contention in *The Clouds* is the question of philosophical inquiry and speculation. Aristophanes regarded such investigation as leading to one of two possible results, both of which were bad: either it would provide nothing but useless information, or it would pervert the mind, drawing it away from the truths of the old religion. Thus, Strepsiades finds Socrates, the master Sophist of the play, engaged in scientifically determining how far a flea can jump, or how a gnat buzzes. Still later, when he enters the school, he discovers Socrates worshiping a set of new deities, the Clouds. These are in reality only fog, mist and air; but in the distorted view of the Sophists, they are legitimate divinities, while the Olympian gods are nothing but unreal myths. To the orthodox Aristophanes, such doctrine represented the ultimate in intellectual perversion.

478

PHILOSOPHY VERSUS RELIGION

Still a third aspect of the central theme in the play comes to light in the *agon,* or debate, on the subject of the new education versus the old. The argument itself is an example of Sophistry in practice, since Adicaeologos (wrong logic) argues for a cause that is clearly the worse of the two. But in addition, the opposing points of view represent Aristophanes' opinions of the educative system that was in operation and of the defunct system of the golden days of the past. Dicaeologos cites as the glory of the old education its modest, virtuous, well-disciplined young men who were absorbed in athletics and scornful of a lazy life of idleness and empty jest. These were the youths who ran the Marathon and participated in the other games and contests. Adicaeologos answers his opponent's arguments with the most illogical and specious reasoning imaginable, attempting to convince Pheidippides that idleness, levity and immorality are the greatest virtues.

In each of his attacks on the prevailing attitudes of his time, Aristophanes makes Socrates bear the burden of guilt: he is the master of false argumentation, the leading "scientific" inquirer and the foremost advocater of the new education. Actually, the philosopher was himself an outspoken enemy of Sophism who specifically disavowed any interest in scientific inquiry. That he questioned commonly accepted beliefs is true, of course; but his motive, it should be remembered, was not to destroy all orthodoxy, but rather to redefine and clarify the meaning of words and concepts. Significantly enough, however, the charges of impiety and of misleading the young, which the dramatist brings against Socrates, are precisely those used against him later and for which he was condemned to death.

AN EVALUATION

Naturally, time has robbed much of the pungency from his allusions to contemporary people and events. Modern readers tend to feel that the dramatist leans too heavily on comic references to functions of the body. He is criticized for his attacks on philosophers and tragedians. Yet Aristophanes' fame rightly endures despite these attacks. He has given the world a personal vision of the foibles of his now dead society; his vision has lived on. Any evaluation of Aristophanes cannot detract from his position as "the father of comedy."

Cast of Characters

STREPSIADES.

PHEIDIPPIDES, *his son.*

BOY, *servant of Strepsiades.*

DISCIPLES OF SOCRATES.

SOCRATES.

CHORUS OF CLOUDS.

DICAEOLOGOS (*Right logic*).

ADICAEOLOGOS (*Wrong logic*).

PASIAS, *a usurer.*

AMYNIAS, *another usurer.*

WITNESSES.

CHAEREPHON.

Cast of Characters

SCENE: *Athens.* STREPSIADES *is discovered in his chamber,* PHEIDIPPIDES *sleeping in his bed. Time, before break of day.*

STREPSIADES (*stretching and yawning*)

Ah me, ah me! will this night never end?
Oh kingly Jove, will there be no more day?
And yet the cock sang out long time ago;
I heard him—but my people lie and snore,
Snore in defiance, for the rascals know
It is their privilege in time of war,
Which with its other plagues brings this upon us,
That we mayn't rouse these vermin with a cudgel.
There's my young hopeful too, he sleeps it through,
Snug under five fat blankets at least.
Would I could sleep so sound! but my poor eyes
Have no sleep in them; what with debts and duns
And stablekeepers' bills, which this fine spark
Heaps on my back, I lie awake the while:
And what does he care but to coil up his locks,
Ride, drive his horses, dream of them all night,
While I, poor devil, may go hang—for now
The moon in her last quarter * wains apace,

* Bills were payable at the end of the month.

And my usurious creditors are gaping.
What ho! a light! bring me my tablets, boy!
That I may set down all, and sum them up,
Debts, creditors, and interest upon interest—
(BOY *enters with a light and tablets.*)
Let me see where I am and what the total—
Fifty dollars to Pasias—Ha! to Pasias fifty!
Blast it, and for what? A horse indeed,
Very noble by his marks—Curse such marks!
Would I had given this eye from out my head,
Before I'd have paid for such a nag!

PHEIDIPPIDES

Shame on you, Philo! Keep within your ring.

STREPSIADES

There it is! that's it! the bane of all my peace—
He's racing even in his sleep!

PHEIDIPPIDES

A heat—a heat!
How many turns to a heat?

STREPSIADES

More than enough;
You've given me plenty of turns—I'm jaded.
But to my list—What name stands next to Pasias?
Amynias—twelve good dollars—still for the race—
A chariot mounted on its wheels complete.

PHEIDIPPIDES

Dismount! unharness and away!

STREPSIADES

I thank you;
You have unharnessed me: I am dismounted,
And with a vengeance—All my goods are in pawn,
Fines, forfeiture and penalties in plenty.

PHEIDIPPIDES (*wakes*)

My father! why so restless? who has vexed you?

484

THE CLOUDS

STREPSIADES

The sheriff vexes me; he breaks my sleep.

PHEIDIPPIDES

Peace, self-tormentor, let me sleep!

STREPSIADES

Sleep on!
But take this with you; all these debts of mine
Will double on your head: a plague confound
That cursed matchmaker, who drew me in
To wed that precious mother of yours.
I lived at ease in the country, coarsely clad,
Rough, free, and just as full as oil and honey
And store of stock could fill me, till I took,
Clown as I was, this limb of the Alcmaeons,*
This vain, extravagant, high-blooded dame:
Rare bedfellows and dainty—were we not?
I, smelling of the wine vat, figs and fleeces,
The produce of my farm; all essence she,
Saffron and harlot's kisses, paint and washes,
A pampered wanton—Idle I'll not call her;
She took great pains to work my ruin,
Which made me tell her, pointing to this cloak,
Now threadbare on my shoulders—see, goodwife,
This is your work—in truth you toil too hard.

BOY

Master, the lamp has drunk up all its oil.

STREPSIADES

Yes, it's a drunken lamp; the more fault yours;
Whelp, you shall howl for this.

BOY

Why? for what fault?

* Noble family of Athens, of which Megacles was a member

485

STREPSIADES

For cramming such a greedy wick with oil.

(Exit BOY.*)*

Well! in good time this hopeful heir was born;
Then I and my beloved fell to wrangling
About the naming of the brat—My wife
Would dub her colt Xanthippus or Charippus,
Or it might be Callipides, she didn't care
As long as the name was noble—but I
Stuck for his grandfather Pheidonides;
At last when neither could prevail, the matter
Was compromised by calling him Pheidippides:
Then she began to fondle her sweet babe,
And taking him by the hand—Lambkin, she cried,
When you are some years older you shall drive,
Like Megacles, your chariot to the city,
Robed in a saffron mantle—No, said I,
Not so, my boy, but you shall drive your goats,
When you are able, from the fields of Phelle,
Clad in a woolen jacket like your father:
But he is deaf to all these frugal rules,
And drives me on the gallop to my ruin;
Therefore all night I call my thoughts to council,
And after long debate find one chance left,
To which, if I can lead him, all is safe,
If not—but soft: it's time that I should wake him.
But how to soothe him to the task? (*speaking in a soft gentle tone*)
    Pheidippides!
Precious Pheidippides!

PHEIDIPPIDES

What now, my father?

STREPSIADES

Kiss me, my boy! give me your hand—

PHEIDIPPIDES

Tell me, what do you want?

486

The Clouds

STREPSIADES

Do you love me, sir? speak!

PHEIDIPPIDES

Yes, by equestrian Neptune!

STREPSIADES (*angrily*)

Don't name him,
Don't name that charioteer; he is my bane,
The source of all my sorrow—but, my son,
If you love me, prove it by obedience.

PHEIDIPPIDES

What must I obey?

STREPSIADES

Reform your habits;
Quit them at once, and what I shall prescribe,
Do that!

PHEIDIPPIDES

And what is it that you prescribe?

STREPSIADES

But will you do it?

PHEIDIPPIDES

Yes, by Dionysus!

STREPSIADES

Good: get up! come here, boy! look outside!
That little wicket and the hut close by—
Do you see them?

PHEIDIPPIDES

Clearly. What about that hut?

STREPSIADES

Why that's the council chamber of all wisdom:
There the choice spirits dwell, who teach the world

487

That heaven's great concave is one mighty oven,
And men its burning embers; they are the ones
Who can show lawyers how to twist a cause,
So you'll pay them for it, right or wrong.

PHEIDIPPIDES

And how do you call them?

STREPSIADES

Indeed, I don't know that,
But they are men, who take a world of pains;
Very good men and able.

PHEIDIPPIDES

Away with them!
Poor rogues, I know them now; you mean those scabs,
Those squalid, barefoot, beggarly impostors,
The mighty evil spirits of whose sect
Are Socrates and Chaerephon. Away!

STREPSIADES

Hush, hush! be still; don't speak such foolish prattle;
But if you'll take my advice, join their college
And quit your riding school.

PHEIDIPPIDES

Not I, so help me
Even if you bribed me
With all the racers that Leogaras
Breeds from his swiftest stud.

STREPSIADES

Dear, darling lad,
Try to be ruled, and learn.

PHEIDIPPIDES

What shall I learn?

STREPSIADES

They have a choice of logic; this for justice,
That for injustice: learn the latter art,

488

THE CLOUDS

And all these creditors who now pester me
Shall never touch a penny that I owe them.

PHEIDIPPIDES

I'll learn from no such masters, nor be made
A scarecrow and a may-game to my comrades;
I don't want to starve to death!

STREPSIADES

And I don't either!
No feasting you and your fine pampered cattle
At free cost any longer—Horse and foot
To the crows I bequeath you. So be gone!

PHEIDIPPIDES

Well, sir, I have an uncle who's rich and noble;
Megacles won't let me be unhorsed;
I'll go to him; I'll trouble you no longer.   (*Exit* PHEIDIPPIDES.)

STREPSIADES (*alone*)

He has thrown me to the ground, but I'll not lie there;
I'll get up and, with permission of the gods,
See if I can't learn these arts myself:
But being old, sluggish and dull of wit,
How am I sure these subtleties won't escape me?
Well! I'll try it: what's the use of complaining?
Why don't I knock and enter?—Ho! in there!—
　　(*Knocks violently at the door of Socrates' humble dwelling.*)

DISCIPLE (*half-opening the door*)

Go, hang yourself! and give the crows a dinner—
What noisy fellow are you at the door?

STREPSIADES

Strepsiades of Cicynna,* son of Pheidon.

DISCIPLE

Whoever you are, before Heaven, you're a fool
Not to respect these doors; battering so loud,
* Similar in connotation to Podunk

And kicking with such vengeance, you have marred
The ripe conception of my pregnant brain,
And brought on a miscarriage.

STREPSIADES

Oh! the pity!—
Pardon my ignorance: I'm countrybred
And far afield have come: I pray you tell me
What curious thought my luckless din has strangled,
Just as your brain was hatching.

DISCIPLE

These are things
We never speak of but among ourselves.

STREPSIADES

Speak boldly then to me, for I have come
To be among you, and share the secrets
Of your profound academy.

DISCIPLE

Enough!
I'll tell you, but think of it as being
Among our mysteries—This is the question,
As it was put just now to Chaerephon,
By our great master Socrates, to answer—
How many of his own lengths at one spring
A flea can hop—for we saw one vault
From Chaerephon's black eyebrow to the head
Of the philosopher.

STREPSIADES

And how did the other
Contrive to measure this?

DISCIPLE

Most accurately:
He dipped the insect's feet in melted wax,
Which, hardening into sandals as it cooled,
Gave him the space by rule infallible.

490

STREPSIADES

Imperial Jove! what subtlety of thought!

DISCIPLE

But there's a deeper question yet behind;
What would you say to that?

STREPSIADES

I beg you, tell me.

DISCIPLE

It was put to Socrates, if he could say,
When a gnat hummed, whether the sound issued
From mouth or tail.

STREPSIADES

Yes, indeed; what did he say?

DISCIPLE

He said your gnat blows his trumpet backward
From a sonorous cavity within him,
Which being filled with breath, and forced along
The narrow pipe or rectum of his body,
Vents itself in a loud hum behind.

STREPSIADES

Ha! then I see the podex of your gnat
Is trumpet-fashioned—Oh! the blessings on him
For this discovery; well may he escape
The law's strict scrutiny, who thus develops
The anatomy of a gnat.

DISCIPLE

Nor is this all;
Another grand experiment was blasted
By a cursed cat.

STREPSIADES

And how, good sir? please tell me.

DISCIPLE

One night as he was gazing at the moon,
Curious and all intent upon her motions,
A cat on the house ridge was at her needs,
And squirted in his face.

STREPSIADES

Curses on her for it!
Yet I must laugh a bit to think a cat
Should so bespatter Socrates.

DISCIPLE

Last night
We were bilked of our supper.

STREPSIADES

Were you, indeed?
What did your master substitute instead?

DISCIPLE

Why to tell the truth, he sprinkled a few ashes
Upon the board, then with a little pin,
Neatly bent, he went over to the gym
And neatly filched away a discarded cloak.

STREPSIADES

Why do we talk then of Thales? * Open,
Open the school, and let me see your master:
I'm on fire to enter—Come, unbar!
(*The door of the school is unbarred. The Socratic scholars are
seen in various grotesque situations and positions.* STREPSIADES,
*with signs of astonishment, draws back a pace or two, then ex-
claims:*)
O Hercules, defend me! who are these?
What kind of cattle have we here?

DISCIPLE

Why are you so amazed? What do they resemble?
* Popular philosopher

492

The Clouds

STREPSIADES

I think they're chained like our Spartan prisoners,
Captured at Pylos. What are they in search of?
Why are their eyes so riveted on the earth?

DISCIPLE

There their researches center.

STREPSIADES

Is it for onions
They are looking? Come, boys, give up your search;
I'll show you what you want, a fine onion field,
All round and sound—but hey! why do those men
Dip their heads so low?

DISCIPLE

Their studies lead that way: They are now diving
Into the dark realms of Hell and Night.

STREPSIADES

But why are their cruppers mounted up?

DISCIPLE

To practice star-gazing, and teach them
Their proper elevations—but no more:
   (*addressing himself to some of his fellow students, who were
   crowding about the newcomer*)
In, fellow students, in: if the master should come
And find us here—

STREPSIADES

No indeed, let 'em stay
And advise me in my business.

DISCIPLE

Impossible; they cannot give the time.

STREPSIADES

Now for the love of Heaven, what have we here?
Tell me what that is!   (*observing the apparatus*)

493

DISCIPLE

This machine
Is for astronomy—

STREPSIADES

And this?

DISCIPLE

For geometry.

STREPSIADES

How?

DISCIPLE

For measuring the earth.

STREPSIADES

Indeed!
By the acre?

DISCIPLE

No, sir, by the lump;
Even the whole globe at once.

STREPSIADES

Well said, indeed.
Then everyone can get a piece.

DISCIPLE

Look now, this line marks the circumference
Of the whole earth, do you see? This spot is Athens—

STREPSIADES

Athens! how? I don't see any courts sitting;
Therefore I can't believe you.

DISCIPLE

Yes, yes indeed,
This very state is Attica.

494

THE CLOUDS

STREPSIADES

And where,
Where is my hometown, Cicynna?

DISCIPLE

Here it lies:
And here's Euboea—Look how far it runs—

STREPSIADES

How far it runs! Yes, Pericles has made it
Run far enough from us—Where's Sparta?

DISCIPLE

Here; close to Athens.

STREPSIADES

Ah! much too close!
Please, good friends, take that bad neighbor away from us.

DISCIPLE

That's not for us to do.

STREPSIADES

The worse luck yours!
But look! (*casting up his eyes*) who's this suspended in a basket?

DISCIPLE (*with solemnity*)

HIMSELF. HE.

STREPSIADES

HE? HE who?

DISCIPLE

Why, Socrates.

STREPSIADES

Ha! Socrates!—(*to the scholar*) Shout up to him and
Bid him come down! roar lustily.

495

DISCIPLE

Not I:
Do it yourself; I've other things to do.   (*Exit* DISCIPLE.)

STREPSIADES

Ho! Socrates—Hey there, my little Socrates!

SOCRATES

Mortal! insect of a day,
What do you call me for?

STREPSIADES

I want to know what you're doing.

SOCRATES

I tread the air, contemplating the sun.

STREPSIADES

Ah! that's why you're basketed so high.
Up there you look down upon the Gods—But I hope
You'll put your feet on earth.

SOCRATES

Sublime in air,
Sublime in thought I carry my mind with me,
Its cogitations all assimilated
To the pure atmosphere in which I float;
Lower me to earth, and my mind's subtle powers,
Seized by contagious dullness, lose their spirit;
For the dry earth drinks up the generous sap,
The vegetating vigor of philosophy,
And leaves it a mere husk.

STREPSIADES

What do you say?
Philosophy has sapped your vigor?
But come, my precious fellow, come down quickly,
And teach me those fine things I'm here in quest of.

496

THE CLOUDS

SOCRATES

And what fine things are they?

STREPSIADES

A new formula
For sending off my creditors, and foiling them
By learning how to debate;
By debts, pawns, pledges, usuries, executions,
I am racked and rent in tatters.

SOCRATES

Why permit it?
What strange infatuation seized your senses?

STREPSIADES

The horse consumption, a devouring plague;
But if you'll enter me among your scholars,
And tutor me like them to cheat my creditors,
Name your own price, and by the Gods I swear
I'll pay you to the last cent.

SOCRATES

By what Gods?
Answer that first; for your Gods are not mine.

STREPSIADES

By what do you swear then? As the Byzantines swear
By their debased iron coin?

SOCRATES

Are you ambitious
To be instructed in celestial matters,
And taught to know them clearly?

STREPSIADES

Yes, yes indeed,
As long as they serve my purpose, and seem celestial.

SOCRATES

What if I bring you to a conference
With my own Goddesses, the Clouds?

STREPSIADES

That's what I wish indeed!

SOCRATES

Come, sit down;
Repose yourself upon this couch.

STREPSIADES

It's done.

SOCRATES

Now take this chaplet—wear it.

STREPSIADES

Why this chaplet?
Would you make me another Athamas,
And sacrifice me to a cloud? *

SOCRATES

Fear nothing;
It is an indispensable ceremony
At OUR initiations.

STREPSIADES

What am I to gain?
(STREPSIADES *gets flour poured on him, making him fear even
more strongly that he is a sacrificial victim.*)

SOCRATES

It will sift your faculties as fine as powder,
Bolt 'em like meal, grind 'em as light as dust;
Only be patient.
* Athamas married a cloud.

498

THE CLOUDS

STREPSIADES

Truly, you'll go near
To making your words good; if you pound me so,
You'll make me dust and nothing else.

SOCRATES (*assuming all the magical solemnity and tone
of voice of a priest*)

Keep silence, then, and listen to a prayer
Which fits the gravity of age to hear—
Oh! Air, all powerful Air, which does enfold
This pendant globe, you vault of flaming gold.
You sacred Clouds, who bid the thunder roll,
Shine forth, approach, and cheer your suppliant's soul!

STREPSIADES

Keep them off awhile, till I am ready.
Ah! luckless me, I wish I had brought my raincap,
And so escaped a soaking.

SOCRATES

Come, come away!
Fly swift, you Clouds, and give yourselves to view!
Whether on high Olympus' sacred top
Snow-crowned you sit, or in the azure vales
Of your own father Ocean sporting weave
Your misty dance, or dip your golden urns
Into the seven mouths of Nile; whether you dwell
On Thracian Mimas, or Moeotis' lake,
Hear me, yes hear, and thus invoked approach!

(*Thunder is heard. A large and shapeless* CLOUD *is seen floating
in the air, from which the following song is heard.*)

CLOUD

Ascend, you watery Clouds, on high,
Daughters of Ocean, climb the sky,
And over the mountain's pine-capped brow
Towering, your fleecy mantle throw:
From there let us scan the wide-stretched scene,
Groves, lawns, and rilling streams between,

499

And stormy Neptune's vast expanse,
And grasp all nature at a glance.
Now the dark tempest flits away,
And lo! the glittering orb of day
Darts from his clear ethereal beam,
Come let us snatch the joyous gleam.

SOCRATES

Yes, you Divinities, whom I adore,
I hail you now, propitious to my prayer.
Did you hear them speak in thunder to me?

STREPSIADES (*kneeling, and, with various acts of buffoonery, affecting terror and embarrassment*)

And I too am your Cloudships' most obedient,
And promise to adore your thunder:
No (*turning to* SOCRATES), take it how you may, my frights and
    fears
Have pinched and choliced my poor bowels so,
That I can't choose but treat their holy nostrils
With an unsavory sacrifice.

SOCRATES

Put aside
These gross scurrilities, which for low buffoons
And mountebanks are more fitting. Hush! be still,
Listen to the chorus of their heavenly voices,
For music is the language they delight in.

CHORUS OF CLOUDS (*approaching nearer*)

You Clouds replete with fruitful showers,
Here let us seek Minerva's towers,
The cradle of old Cecrops' race,
The world's chief ornament and grace;
Here mystic shrines and rites divine
And lamps in sacred splendor shine;
Here the Gods dwell in marble domes,
Feasted with costly hecatombs,
That round their votive statues blaze,
While crowded temples ring with praise;

500

The Clouds

And pompous sacrifices here
Make holidays throughout the year,
And when gay springtime comes again,
Dionysus calls his sportive train,
And pipe and song and choral dance
Hail the soft hours as they advance.

STREPSIADES

Now, in the name of Jove, tell me,
Who are these ranting women, who talk so high?
They're Amazons, no doubt.

SOCRATES

Not so,
Not women, but celestial clouds, friendly powers
To men of sluggish parts; from these we draw
Sense, apprehension, volubility,
Wit to confute, and cunning to ensnare.

STREPSIADES

Ah! that's why my heart leapt within me
For sympathy when I first heard them:
Now I can prattle shrewdly of first causes,
And spin out metaphysical cobwebs finely,
And dogmatize most rarely, and dispute
And paradox it with the best of you:
So, come what may, I must and will behold them;
Show me their faces, I implore you.

SOCRATES

Look,
Look toward that hilltop where I point—There, there!
Now they descend the hill; I see them plainly,
As plain as can be.

STREPSIADES

Where, where? Oh, please show me!

SOCRATES

Here! a whole troop of them through woods and hollows,
A byway of their own.

STREPSIADES

What ails my eyes,
That I can't catch a glimpse of them?

SOCRATES

Now look!
Here at the very entrance—

STREPSIADES

I still can't see them clearly.

SOCRATES

Then you must be
Sand-blind or worse.

STREPSIADES

No, by father Jove,
I cannot choose but see them—precious creatures!
For in good faith here's plenty and to spare.

(*Enter* CHORUS OF CLOUDS.)

SOCRATES

And do you doubt that they are goddesses?

STREPSIADES

Not I, so help me! only I'd a notion
That they were fog and dew and dusky vapor.

SOCRATES

For shame! Why, man, these are the nursing mothers
Of all our famous sophists, fortunetellers,
Quacks, medicine-mongers, bards bombastical,
Chorus projectors and star interpreters,
And wonder-making cheats—The gang of idlers,
Who pay them for their feeding with good store
Of flattery and mouth-worship.

STREPSIADES

Now I see
Whom we may thank for driving them along

The Clouds

At such a furious dithyrambic rate,
Sun-shadowing clouds of many-colored hues,
Air-rending tempests, hundred-headed Typhons;
Now rousing, rattling them about our ears,
Now gently wafting them down the sky,
Moist, airy, bending, bursting into showers;
For which fine descriptions these poor knaves
Dine daintily on scraps.

SOCRATES

And proper food;
What better do they merit?

STREPSIADES

And yet,
If these are clouds (do you hear me?)
How were they metamorphosed into women?
Clouds are not such as these.

SOCRATES

And what else are they?

STREPSIADES

Truly, I can't rightly tell, but I should guess
Something like flakes of wool, not women, surely;
And look! these women have noses.

SOCRATES

Listen, friend,
I'll put a question to you.

STREPSIADES

Out with it!
Be quick: let's have it.

SOCRATES

This is it, in short—
Have you never seen a cloud, which you could fancy
Shaped like a centaur, leopard, wolf or bull?

503

STREPSIADES

Yes indeed, I have, and what about it?

SOCRATES

Why then,
Clouds can assume what shapes they will, believe me;
For instance; should they spy some hairy clown
Rugged and rough, like the unlicked cub *
Of Xenophantes, straight they turn to centaurs,
And kick at him for vengeance.

STREPSIADES

Well done, Clouds!
But should they spy that peculating knave,
Simon, that public thief, how would they treat him?

SOCRATES

As wolves—in character most like his own.

STREPSIADES

Yes, there it is now; when they saw Cleonymus,
That dastard runaway, they turned to hinds
In honor of his cowardice.

SOCRATES

And now,
Having seen Cleisthenes, to mock his lewdness
They change themselves to women.

STREPSIADES

Welcome, ladies!
Imperial ladies, welcome! If it pleases
Your Highnesses so far to grace a mortal,
Give me a touch of your celestial voices.

CHORUS

Hail, grandpa! who at this late hour of life
Would go to school for cunning; and all hail,

* Hieronymus, a contemporary figure, as are those following

504

The Clouds

You prince pontifical of quirks and quibbles,
Speak your full mind, make known your wants and wishes!
You and our worthy Prodicus excepted,
Not one of all your sophists have our ear:
Him for his wit and learning we esteem,
You for your proud deportment and high looks,
In barefoot beggary strutting up and down,
Content to suffer mockery for our sake,
And carry a grave face while others laugh.

STREPSIADES

Oh! mother earth, was ever voice like this,
So reverend, so portentous, so divine!

SOCRATES

These are your only deities, all else
I flout at.

STREPSIADES

Wait! Olympian Jupiter—
Is he no god?

SOCRATES

What Jupiter? what god?
Please, no more—away with him at once!

STREPSIADES

Tell me! who gives us rain? answer me that.

SOCRATES

These give us rain; as I will demonstrate:
Come on now—When did you ever see it rain
Without a cloud? If Jupiter gives rain,
Let him rain down his favors in the sunshine,
And not ask the clouds to help him.

STREPSIADES

You've hit it,
It's so; heaven help me! I thought till now,
When it was his godship's pleasure, he made water

Into a sieve and gave the earth a shower.
But, listen to me, who thunders? tell me that;
For it's then I tremble.

SOCRATES

These, these thunder,
When they are tumbled.

STREPSIADES

How, blasphemer, how?

SOCRATES

When they are charged with vapors full to bursting,
And bandied to and fro against each other,
Then with the shock they burst and crack amain.

STREPSIADES

And who is he that jowls them thus together
But Jove himself?

SOCRATES

Jove! it's not Jove who does it,
But the ethereal vortex.

STREPSIADES

What is he?
I never heard of him; isn't he Jove?
Or is Jove put aside, and Vortex crowned
King of Olympus in his state and place?
But let me learn some more of this same thunder.

SOCRATES

Haven't you learned? I told you how the clouds,
Being surcharged with vapor, rush together,
And, in the conflict, shake the poles with thunder.

STREPSIADES

But who believes you?

506

THE CLOUDS

You, as I shall prove it:
Look how when you cram
Your belly full of pottage—if you shake
And stir it lustily about—what then?

Why then it gives a desperate crack;
It bounces like a thunderbolt, the pottage
Keeps such a coil within me—At the first,
Pappax it cries—and then with double force,
Papappax!—when at length *Papappapax*
Out of my sounding entrails thundering bursts.

Think then, if your belly trumpets forth,
How must the vast vault of heaven resound,
When the clouds crack with thunder!

Let that pass,
And tell me of the lightning, whose quick flash
Burns us to cinders; that, at least, great Jove
Keeps in reserve to launch at perjury?

Dunce, dotard! were you born before the flood
To talk of perjury, while Simon breathes,
Theorus and Cleonymus, while they,
Thrice-perjured villains, brave the lightning's stroke,
And gaze at the heavens unscorched? Would these escape?
Why, man, Jove's random fires strike his own shrine,
Strike Sunium's guiltless top, strike the dumb oak,
Who never yet broke faith or falsely swore.

It may be so, in truth! You say this well:
But I want to be taught the natural cause
Of these appearances.

SOCRATES

See when the winds,
In their free courses checked, are pent and pursed
As if within a bladder, stretching then
And struggling for expansion, they burst forth
With crack so fierce it sets the air on fire.

STREPSIADES

The devil they do! why now the murder's out:
So was I served with a damned paunch, I broiled
On last Jove's day, just such a scurvy trick;
Because, not dreaming of your thunder,
I never thought to give the rascal vent,
Bounce! goes the bag, and covers me all over
With filth and ordure till my eyes struck fire.

CHORUS

The envy of all Athens you shall be,
Happy old man, who from our lips do suck
Into your ears true wisdom, so you are
But wise to learn, and studious to retain
What you have learned; patient to bear the blows
And buffets of hard fortune; to persist,
Doing or suffering; firmly to abide
Hunger and cold, not craving where to dine,
To drink, to sport and trifle time away;
But holding that for best, which best becomes
A man who means to carry all things through
Neatly, expertly, perfect at all points
With head, hands, tongue to force his way to fortune.

STREPSIADES

Be confident; I give myself for one
Of a tough heart, watchful as care can make me,
A frugal, pinching fellow, that can sup
Upon a sprig of savory and go to bed;
I am your man for this, hard as an anvil.

The Clouds

It's well, so you will ratify your faith
In our deities—CHAOS and CLOUDS
And SPEECH—to these and only these adhere.

STREPSIADES

If from this hour I ever waste
A single thought on any other gods,
Or give them sacrifice, libation, incense,
No, even common courtesy, renounce me.

CHORUS

Speak your wish boldly then; and you shall prosper
As you obey and worship us, and study
The wholesome art of thriving.

STREPSIADES

Gracious ladies,
I ask no mighty favor, simply this—
Let me outdistance every tongue in Greece,
And run 'em out of sight a hundred lengths.

CHORUS

Is that all? we are your friends to serve you;
We will endow you with such powers of speech,
As after this not a politician in Athens
Shall spout such popular harangues as you.

STREPSIADES

A fig for powers of spouting! give me powers
Of nonsuiting my creditors.

CHORUS

A trifle—
Granted as soon as asked; only be bold,
And show yourself obedient to your teachers.

STREPSIADES

With your help so I will, being undone,
Stripped of my pelf by these high-blooded cattle,

And a fine woman, the torment of my life.
Now let them work their wicked will upon me;
They're welcome to my carcass; let 'em claw it,
Starve it with thirst and hunger, fry it, freeze it,
Nay, flay the very skin off; it's their own;
So that I may but fob my creditors,
Let the world talk; I care not though it call me
A bold-faced, loud-tongued, overbearing bully;
A shameless, vile, prevaricating cheat;
A tricking, quibbling, double-dealing knave;
A prating, pettyfogging limb of the law;
A sly old fox, a perjurer, a hangdog,
A ragamuffin made of shreds and patches,
The leavings of a dunghill—Let 'em rail,
Yes indeed, let 'em turn my guts to fiddle strings,
May my bread be my poison if I care!

CHORUS

This fellow has a prompt and daring spirit—
Come here, sir; do you perceive and feel
What great and glorious fame you shall acquire
By our schooling of you?

STREPSIADES

What, I ask you!

CHORUS

What but to live the envy of mankind
Under our patronage?

STREPSIADES

When shall I see
Those halcyon days?

CHORUS

Then shall your doors be thronged
With clients waiting for your coming forth,
All eager to consult you, pressing all
To catch a word from you, with abstracts, briefs,
And cases ready-drawn for your opinion.

510

The Clouds

But come, begin and lecture this old fellow;
Sift him, that we may see what meal he's made of.

SOCRATES

Listen, let's hear what principles you hold,
That these being known, I may apply such tools
As tally with your stuff.

STREPSIADES

Tools! by the gods;
Are you about to spring a mine upon me?

SOCRATES

Not so, but simply in the way of practice
To try your memory.

STREPSIADES

Oh! as for that,
My memory is of two sorts, long and short:
With them who owe me anything, it never fails;
My creditors indeed complain of it,
As mainly apt to leak and lose its reckoning.

SOCRATES

But let us hear if nature has endowed you
With any grace of speaking.

STREPSIADES

None of speaking.
But a most apt propensity for cheating.

SOCRATES

If this is all, how can you hope to learn?

STREPSIADES

Fear me not, never break your head for that.

SOCRATES

Well then be quick, and when I speak of things
Mysterious and profound, see that you make
No boggling, but—

511

STREPSIADES

I understand your meaning;
You'd have me bolt philosophy by mouthfuls,
Just like a hungry cur.

SOCRATES

Oh! brutal, gross
And barbarous ignorance! I must suspect,
Old as you are, you must be taught with stripes:
Tell me now, when you are beaten, what do you feel?

STREPSIADES

The blows of him who beats me;
But having breathed awhile I lay my action
And cite my witnesses; later on more cool,
I bring my cause into the court, and sue
For damages.

SOCRATES

Strip off your cloak! prepare.

STREPSIADES

Prepare for what? what crime have I committed?

SOCRATES

None; but the rule and custom is with us,
That all shall enter naked.

STREPSIADES

And why naked?
I come with no search warrant; fear me not;
I'll carry nothing away with me.

SOCRATES

No matter;
Conform yourself, and strip.

512

THE CLOUDS

STREPSIADES

And if I do,
Tell me for my encouragement to which
Of all your scholars you will liken me.

SOCRATES

You shall be called a second Chaerephon.

STREPSIADES

Ah! Chaerephon is the name
Of a dead man—excuse me.

SOCRATES

No more words:
Pluck up your courage; don't answer, but follow:
Hurry and be perfected.

STREPSIADES

Give me my dole
Of honey cake in hand, and pass me on;
Never trust me if I don't quake and tremble
As if the cavern of Trophonius * yawned,
And I were stepping in.

SOCRATES

What ails you? enter!
Why do you halt and loiter at the door?

(*Exeunt* SOCRATES *and* STREPSIADES.)

CHORUS

Go, brave adventurer, proceed!
May fortune crown the gallant deed;
Though far advanced in life's last stage,
Spurning the infirmities of age,
You can to youthful labors rise,
And boldly struggle to be wise.

You, who are here spectators of our scene,
Listen with patience to a few plain words,
* Oracle where a dragon was placated by honey cake

And by my patron, mighty Dionysus,
I swear they shall be true ones—Gentle friends,
So may I prosper in your fair esteem,
As I declare in truth that I was moved
To tender you my former comedy,
As deeming it the best of all my works,
And you its judges worthy of that work,
Which I had wrought with my best care and pains:
But fools were found to thrust me from the stage,
And you, whose better wisdom should have saved me
From that most vile cabal, permitted it;
For which I now must chide, yet not so sharply
As to break off from such approved good friends:
No, you have been my patrons from all time,
Even to my first-born issue: when I dropped
My bantling at your door to hide the shame
Of one who called herself a maiden muse,
You charitably took the foundling in,
And gave it worthy training. Now, behold,
This sister comedy, Electra-like,
Comes to see if she may find
Some recognition of a brother lost,
Though but a relic of his well-known hair.
Seemly and modest she appears before you;
Not like our stage buffoons in shaggy hide
To set a mob roaring; she will vent
No foolish jests at baldness, will not dance
The indecent dance; we have no old man
Armed with a staff to practice manual jokes
On the bystanders' ribs, and keep the ring
For them who dance the chorus: you shall see
No howling furies burst upon the stage
Waving their torches; other weapons
Than the muse gives us we shall not employ,
No *ah me, ah me!* will sigh in your ears.
Yet not of this I boast, nor that I scorn
To cater to your palates with some scraps
At second or third hand, but fresh and fair
And still original, as one, who knows,
When he has done a good deed, where to stop;

514

The Clouds

And, having pressed giant Cleon to the ground,
Not to insult his carcass, like those
Who, having once run down Hyperbolus,
Poor devil! mouth and mangle without mercy
Him and his mother too . . . Shame upon such scenes!
Hermippus next *Hyperbolized* amain,
And now the whole pack open in full cry,
Holding the game in chase, which I had roused.
If there are any here, who laugh with these,
Let such not smile with me; but if this night
You crown these scenes with merited applause,
Posterity shall justify your taste.

Semichorus

Great Jove, supreme of Gods, and heaven's high king,
First I invoke; next to him the Trident's lord,
Whose mighty stroke smites the wild waves asunder,
And makes the firm earth tremble; you from whom
We draw our being, all-inspiring Air,
Parent of nature; and you, radiant Sun,
Throned in your flaming chariot, I invoke,
Dear to the gods and by the world adored.

Chorus of Clouds

Most grave and sapient judges, hear the charge,
Which we shall now prefer, of slights ill brooked
By us your wronged appellants: for while we,
The patronesses of your state, the Clouds,
Of all the powers celestial serve you most,
You graceless mortals serve us not at all;
Nor smoke, nor sacrifice ascends from you,
But blank ingratitude and cold neglect.
If some rash enterprise you set on foot,
Some brainless project, straight with rain or thunder,
Sure warnings, we apprise you of your folly:
When late you made that offspring of a tanner,
That Paphlagonian odious to the gods,
The general of your armies, see how fierce
We scowled upon you, and indignant rolled
Our thunders intermixed with flashing fires;

515

The Moon forsook her course, and the vexed Sun
Quenched his bright torch, disdaining to behold
Cleon your chief, yet chief that Cleon was,
(For it should seem a proverb with your people,
That measures badly taken best succeed):
But if you'll learn from us the ready way
To cancel your past errors, and insure
Fame and good fortune for the public weal,
You have nothing else to do, but stop the swallow
Of that wide-gaping cormorant, that thief
Convicted and avowed, with a neat noose
Drawn tight and fitted to his scurvy throat.

SEMICHORUS

You too, Apollo, of your native isle,
Upon your Cinthian mountain throne,
Hear and be present! you, Diana,
Whose golden shrine the Lydian maidens serve
With rich and costly worship; you, Athena,
Armed with the dreadful aegis, virgin queen,
And patroness of Athens; you, who hold
Divided empire on Parnassus' heights,
Lead here your gay train of revelers,
Convivial god, and thus invoked, approach!

CHORUS

As we were journeying here, about midway
We crossed upon the Moon, who for a while
Held us in conversation, and with courteous greeting
To this assembly charged us—This premised,
The tenor of our next instruction points
To anger and complaint for ill returns
On your part to good offices on hers.
First for the loan of her bright silver lamp
So long held out to you, by which you've saved
Your torch and lackey for many a night.
More she could name, if benefits availed;
But you have lost all reckoning of your feasts,
And turned your calendar quite topsy-turvy;
So that the deities, who find themselves

516

The Clouds

Bilked of their dues, and supperless for lack
Of their accustomed sacrifices, rail
At her, poor Moon, and vent their hungry spite,
As if she were at fault; while you, in truth,
Maliciously select our gala days,
When feasting would be welcome, for your suits
And criminal indictments; but when we
Keep fast and put on mourning for the loss
Of Memnon or Sarpedon,* sons of Heaven,
Then, then you mock us with the savory odor
Of smoking dainties, which we may not taste:
Therefore it is, that when this year you chose
Hyperbolus as a member of the city council,
We tore away his crown, and drove him back
To warn you how you slight the Moon again.

(*Enter* SOCRATES.)

SOCRATES (*in violent indignation*)

O vivifying breath, ethereal air,
And you profoundest chaos, witness for me
If ever wretch were seen so gross and dull,
So stupid and perplexed as this old clown,
Whose shallow intellect can entertain
No image nor impression of a thought;
But before you've told it, it is lost and gone!
It's time however he should now come forth
In the broad day—What ho! Strepsiades—
Take up your pallet; bring yourself and it
Into the light.

(*Enter* STREPSIADES.)

STREPSIADES

Yes, if the bugs would let me.

SOCRATES

Quick, quick, I say; set down your load and listen!

STREPSIADES

Lo! here I am.

* Heroes slain in Trojan War

SOCRATES

Come, tell me what it is
That you would learn besides what I have taught you;
Is it measure, verse, or modulation?

STREPSIADES

Measure by all means, for I was robbed
Of two days' dole in the measure of my grain
By a damned knavish huckster.

SOCRATES

Pish! who talks
Of grain? I ask which meter you prefer,
Tetrameter or trimeter.

STREPSIADES

I answer—
Give me a pint pot.

SOCRATES

Yes, but that's no answer.

STREPSIADES

No answer! stake your money, and I'll wager
That your tetrameter is half my pint pot.

SOCRATES

Go to the gallows, blockhead, with your pint pot!
Will nothing stick to you? But come, perhaps
We may try further and fare better with you—
Suppose I spoke to you of modulation;
Do you want to be taught that?

STREPSIADES

Tell me first,
Will I be profited? will I be paid
The grain that I was cheated of? tell me that.

518

THE CLOUDS

SOCRATES

You will be profited by being taught
To bear your part at table in some sort
After a decent fashion; you will learn
Which verse is most commensurate and fit
To the armed chorus in the dance of war,
And which with most harmonious cadence guides
The dactyl in his course poetical.

STREPSIADES

The dactyl,* ha! Sure I know that well.

SOCRATES

And how? tell me.

STREPSIADES

Here, at my fingers' end;
This is my dactyl, and has been my dactyl
Since I could count my fingers.

SOCRATES

Oh the dolt!

STREPSIADES

I wish to be no wiser in these matters.

SOCRATES

What then?

STREPSIADES

Why then, teach me no other art
But the fine art of defrauding.

SOCRATES

Granted; still
There is some previous matter, as for instance
The genders male and female—Can you name them?

* Means 'finger' in Greek and also denotes a poetical 'foot'

519

STREPSIADES

If not, I'm a fool—These are masculine:
Ram, bull, goat, dog and pullet.

SOCRATES

There you're out:
Pullet is male and female.

STREPSIADES

Tell me how?

SOCRATES

Cock and hen pullet—So they should be named.

STREPSIADES

And so they should, by the ethereal air!
You've hit it; for which rare discovery,
Take all the grain this cardopus contains.

SOCRATES

Why there again you sin against the genders.
To call your bolting tub a cardopus,
Making that masculine which should be feminine.

STREPSIADES

How do I make my bolting tub a male?

SOCRATES

Did you not call it cardopus? As well
You might have called Cleonymus a man;
He and your bolting tub alike belong
To the other sex, believe me.

STREPSIADES

Well, my trough
Shall be a cardopa and he Cleonyma; *
Will that content you?
* Greek names ending in a are feminine.

The Clouds

Socrates

Yes, and while you live,
Learn to distinguish sex in proper names.

Strepsiades

I do; the female I am perfect in.

Socrates

Give me the proof.

Strepsiades

Lysilla, she's a female;
Philinna and Demetria and Cleitagora.

Socrates

Now name your males.

Strepsiades

A thousand—as for instance,
Philoxenus, Melesias and Amynias.

Socrates

Do you call these masculine, egregious dunce?

Strepsiades

Are they not such with you?

Socrates

No; just think if
You and Amynias meet—how will you greet him?

Strepsiades

Why, thus for instance—Hip! holla! Amynia!

Socrates

There, there! you make a woman of him at once.

STREPSIADES

And right it is for one who shuns the field;
A coward ought not to be called a man;
Why teach me what is known to all the world?

SOCRATES

Yes, why indeed?—but come, repose yourself.

STREPSIADES

Why so?

SOCRATES

For meditation's sake: lie down.

STREPSIADES

Not on this pallet I beg you, sir;
But if I must lie down, let me repose
On the bare earth and meditate.

SOCRATES

Away!
There's nothing but this bed will cherish thought.

STREPSIADES

It cherishes, alas! a host of bugs,
That show no mercy on me.

SOCRATES

Come, begin,
Cudgel your brains and turn yourself about;
Now ruminate awhile, and if you start
A thought that puzzles you, try the other side,
And turn to something else, but not to sleep;
Suffer not sleep to close your eyes one moment.

STREPSIADES (*after a considerable pause*)
Ah! woe is me; ah, woeful, well-a-day!

SOCRATES

What ails you? why this moaning?

The Clouds

Strepsiades

I am lost;
I've roused the natives from their hiding holes;
A colony of bugs in ambuscade
Have fallen upon me: belly, back and ribs;
No part is free: I feed a commonwealth.

Socrates

Don't take your sufferings too much to heart.

Strepsiades

How can I choose—a wretch made up of wants!
Here I am, penniless and spiritless,
Without a skin, Heaven knows, without a shoe;
And to complete my miseries here I lie,
Like a starved sentinel upon his post,
At watch and ward, till I am shrunk to nothing.

(A pause of some duration.)

Socrates

How are you now? Have you sprung a thought?

Strepsiades

Yes, yes, so help me Neptune!

Socrates

Ha! what is it?

Strepsiades

Why I am thinking if these cursed vermin
Will leave one fragment of my carcass free.

Socrates

A plague upon you!

Strepsiades

Spare yourself that prayer;
I'm plagued already to your heart's content.

523

SOCRATES

Please don't be so tender of your skin;
Tuck yourself up and buff it like a man:
Keep your skull under cover, and depend on it
It will make your brain bring forth some precious project
For furthering your good fortune at the expense
Of little else but honesty and justice.

STREPSIADES

Ah! would to Heaven some friendly soul would help me
To cheat the bugs
With a sleek lambskin!   (*A long pause.*)

SOCRATES

Well, how are you now?
What ails you? are you dozing?

STREPSIADES

Not I, by Heaven!

SOCRATES

Can you start nothing yet?

STREPSIADES

Nothing, so help me.

SOCRATES

Will your head breed no project,
Though nursed so daintily?

STREPSIADES

What should it breed?
Tell me, sweet Socrates; give me some hint.

SOCRATES

Say first what it is you wish.

STREPSIADES

A thousand times,
Ten thousand times I've said it over and over—

524

THE CLOUDS

My creditors, my creditors—It's them
I want to bilk.

SOCRATES

Go to! get under cover,
Keep your head warm, and rarify your wits
Till they shall sprout into some fine conceit,
Some scheme of happy promise: sift it well,
Divide, abstract, compound, and when it's ready,
Out with it boldly.

STREPSIADES

Miserable me!
I wish I were out!

SOCRATES

Lie still, and if you strike
Upon a thought that baffles you, break off
From that entanglement and try another.
So shall your wits be fresh to start again.

STREPSIADES (*not listening to what Socrates is saying*)

Ha! my dear boy! My precious Socrates!

SOCRATES

What do you want, old man?

STREPSIADES

I've sprung a thought,
A plot upon my creditors.

SOCRATES

Tell me!

STREPSIADES

Answer me this—Suppose that I should hire
A witch, who some fair night shall raise a spell,
Whereby I'll snap the moon out of her sphere
And bag her.

SOCRATES

What for?

STREPSIADES

To hold her fast,
And never let her run her courses any more;
That way I'll escape my creditors.

SOCRATES

How so?

STREPSIADES

Because the calculations of their usury
Are made from month to month.

SOCRATES

A gallant scheme;
And yet I think I could suggest a hint
As practicable and no less ingenious—
Suppose you are arrested for a debt,
We'll say five talents, how will you contrive
To cancel at a stroke both debt and writ?

STREPSIADES

Mercy! I can't tell you how offhand;
It needs some cogitation.

SOCRATES

If you were apt,
Such cogitations would not be hard;
They would be present at your fingers' ends,
Buzzing alive, like beetles on a string,
Ready to slip and fly.

STREPSIADES

I've hit the nail
That does the deed!

SOCRATES

Out with it!

526

THE CLOUDS

STREPSIADES

Probably you've noted
A pretty toy, a trinket in the shops,
Which being rightly held produces fire
From things combustible—

SOCRATES

A burning glass,
Vulgarly called—

STREPSIADES

You're right; that's so.

SOCRATES

Proceed!

STREPSIADES

Imagine now your whoreson baliff comes,
Shows me his writ—I, standing thus, do you hear me,
In the sun's stream, measuring my distance, guide
My focus to a point upon his writ,
And up it goes in smoke!

SOCRATES

By the Graces!
It's wittingly devised.

STREPSIADES

The very thought
Of his five talents canceled at a stroke
Makes my heart dance for joy.

SOCRATES

But now again—

STREPSIADES

What next?

527

SOCRATES

Suppose yourself at bar, surprised
Into a suit, no witnesses at hand,
The judge prepared to pass decree against you—
How will you parry that?

STREPSIADES

As quick as thought—

SOCRATES

But how?

STREPSIADES

Incontinently hang myself,
And balk the suitor—

SOCRATES

Come, you're joking.

STREPSIADES

Serious, by all the gods! A man that's dead
Is out of the law's reach.

SOCRATES

I'm through with you—
Instruction's lost upon you; your vile jests
Put me out of all patience.

STREPSIADES

No, but tell me,
What is it, my good fellow, that offends you?

SOCRATES

Your execrable lack of memory.
Why, what was the first rule I taught you?

STREPSIADES

You say the first? the very first—what was it?
Why, let me see; it was something, wasn't it,
About the grain—Oh blast! I have lost it.

528

THE CLOUDS

SOCRATES

Oh you incorrigible, old doting blockhead,
Can hanging be too bad for you?

STREPSIADES

Why there now,
Was ever a man so ill-used? If I can't make
My tongue keep pace with yours, teach it the quirks
And quibbles of your sophistry at once,
I may go hang—I am a fool indeed—
Where shall I turn? Oh gracious Clouds, befriend me,
Give me your counsel.

CHORUS

This is it, old man—
If your son at home is apt and docile,
Choose him in your place, and send him here.

STREPSIADES

My son is well endowed with nature's gifts,
But obstinately bent against instruction.

CHORUS

And do you suffer it?

STREPSIADES

What can I do?
He's a fine full-grown youth, a dashing fellow,
And, by the mother's side, of noble blood:
I'll feel my way with him—but if he kicks,
Whatever happens, nothing shall hinder me
But I will kick him headlong out of doors,
And let him graze wherever he will for me—
Wait only my return; I'll soon be here.   (*Exit* STREPSIADES.)

CHORUS

Highly favored shall you be,
    With gifts and graces kept in store
For those who our divinities adore,
And to no other altars bend the knee:

529

And well we know the obedience shown
  By this old clown derived alone
  From lessons taught by you.
  Wherefore to swell your lawful gains,
  You soon shall skin this silly cur,
  Whom you have put in such a stir,
  And take his plunder for your pains:
For look how often dupes like him devise
Projects that only serve to enrich the wise.
    (*Exit* SOCRATES. STREPSIADES *comes out of his house and speaks
to* PHEIDIPPIDES, *who stands at the door.*)

STREPSIADES

Out of my house! I call the Clouds to witness
You shall not set a foot within my doors.
Go to your Lord Megacles! Go there,
And gnaw his posts for hunger.

PHEIDIPPIDES

Ah, poor man!
I see how it is with you. You are mad,
Stark mad, by Jupiter!

STREPSIADES

You swear by Jupiter!
Why then, I swear by Jove there's no such god—
Now who is mad but you?

PHEIDIPPIDES

Why do you turn
Such solemn truths to ridicule?

STREPSIADES

I laugh
To hear a child prattle of such old men's fables;
But listen to what I'll tell you, learn from me,
And from a child you shall become a man—
But keep the secret close, do you hear me, close;
Beware of babbling.

530

THE CLOUDS

Hey! what's coming?

STREPSIADES

You swore just now by Jupiter—

PHEIDIPPIDES

I did.

STREPSIADES

See now what it is to have a friend like me—
I tell you in a word there is no Jupiter.

PHEIDIPPIDES

How so?

STREPSIADES

He's through; I tell you it's the truth;
He's out of place, and Vortex reigns instead.

PHEIDIPPIDES

Vortex indeed! What freak has caught you now?

STREPSIADES

No freak, it's fact.

PHEIDIPPIDES

Who tells you this?

STREPSIADES

Even Socrates the Melian,
And Chaerephon, the flea philosopher.

PHEIDIPPIDES

And are you so far gone in dotage, sir,
As to be duped by men like them, fellows
Whose bile has overflowed them?

531

STREPSIADES

Keep a good tongue;
Watch you don't slander such worthy men,
So wise and learned—men so pure
And clean in their morals, that no razor
Ever profaned their beards; their unwashed hides
Never dabbled in a bath, nor wafted scent
Of odorous unguent as they passed along.
But you, a prodigal fine spark, make waste
And havoc of my means, as if I were dead
And out of thought—but come and learn.

PHEIDIPPIDES

What can I learn or profit from such teachers?

STREPSIADES

You can learn everything that turns to profit;
But first and foremost you can learn to know
How totally unlearned you are;
How much a blockhead, and how dull of brain—
But wait awhile with patience—   (*Enters the house hastily.*)

PHEIDIPPIDES

Woe is me!
How shall I deal with this crazy old father?
What course pursue with one whose reason wanders
Out of all course? Shall I take out the statute,
And cite him for a lunatic; or wait
Till nature and his frenzy, with the help
Of the undertaker, shall provide a cure?
     (STREPSIADES *returns, with a cock in one hand and a hen in the other.*)

STREPSIADES

Now we shall see! Lo! what have I got here?

PHEIDIPPIDES

A chicken—

532

THE CLOUDS

STREPSIADES

Well and this?

PHEIDIPPIDES

A chicken also.

STREPSIADES

Are they the same then? Take care, good boy,
How you expose yourself, and for the future
Describe them cock and hen-chick severally.

PHEIDIPPIDES

Ridiculous! Is this the grand discovery
You have just borrowed from these sons of the dunghill?

STREPSIADES

This, and a thousand others—but being old
And lax of memory, I lose it all
As fast as it comes in.

PHEIDIPPIDES

Yes, and I think
By the same token you've lost your cloak.

STREPSIADES

No, I've not lost it; I have laid it out
Upon the arts and sciences.

PHEIDIPPIDES

Your shoes—
They've vanished too. Where have you laid them out?

STREPSIADES

Upon the commonwealth—Like Pericles
I'm a barefooted patriot—Now no more;
Do as you want as long as you but conform
And humor me this once, as in times past
I humored you, and in your playful age
Brought you a penny go-cart from the fair,

533

Purchased with what my legal labors earned,
The fee for my attendance.

(going toward the house of SOCRATES)

PHEIDIPPIDES

You'll repent,
My life upon it; you will repent of this.   (*following reluctantly*)

STREPSIADES

No matter, if you'll humor me—What, ho!
Why Socrates, I say, come forth, behold,
Here is my son!
I've brought him, though in faith
Sorely against the grain.

(Enter SOCRATES.)

SOCRATES

Yes, he's a novice,
And doesn't know how the baskets hang as yet.

PHEIDIPPIDES

I wish you'd hang yourself there in their place.

STREPSIADES

Oh monstrous impudence! this to your master!

SOCRATES

Look how the idiot quibbles upon *hanging*.
Driveling and making mouths—Can he be taught
The loopholes of the law: how to escape,
How to evade, and when to press a suit;
Or tune his lips to that soft rhetoric,
Which steals upon the ear, and melts to pity
The heart of the stern judge?

STREPSIADES

Come, don't doubt him;
He is a fine kid, and from a child
Took wondrously to dabbling in the mud,
With which he'd build you up a house so natural

534

The Clouds

It would amaze you, trace you out a ship,
Make you a little cart out of the sole
Of an old shoe maybe, and from the rind
Of a pomegranate cut you out a frog,
You'd swear it was alive. Now what do you think?
Hasn't he wit enough to comprehend
Each rule both right and wrong? Or if not both,
The latter way at least—There he'll be perfect.

Socrates

Let him prepare: his lecturers are ready.

Strepsiades

I will retire—When next we meet, remember
I hope to find him able to contend
Against right and reason, and outwit them both.
(*Exit* Socrates. *Enter* Dicaeologos [*right logic*] *and* Adicae-
ologos [*wrong logic*].)

Dicaeologos

Come on; come on, you bold audacious man,
And face this company.

Adicaeologos

Most willingly:
I desire no better: take your ground.
Before this audience, I am sure to triumph.

Dicaeologos

And who are you that vapor in this fashion?

Adicaeologos

Fashion itself—the very style of the times.

Dicaeologos

Yes, of the modern times, and them and you
I consider worthless.

Adicaeologos

I shall bring down your pride.

535

DICAEOLOGOS

By what witty weapon?

ADICAEOLOGOS

By the gift
Of apt invention.

DICAEOLOGOS

Then I see
You have your fools to back you.

ADICAEOLOGOS

No, the wise
Are those I deal with.

DICAEOLOGOS

I shall spoil your market.

ADICAEOLOGOS

And how, indeed?

DICAEOLOGOS

By speaking such plain truths
As may appeal to justice.

ADICAEOLOGOS

What is justice?
There's no such thing—I traverse your appeal.

DICAEOLOGOS

How? No such thing as justice?

ADICAEOLOGOS

No; where is it?

DICAEOLOGOS

With the immortal gods.

The Clouds

ADICAEOLOGOS

If it's there,
How did Jupiter himself escape
For his unnatural deeds to his own father?

DICAEOLOGOS

For shame, irreverent wretch,
I sicken at impiety so gross,
My stomach kicks against it.

ADICAEOLOGOS

You are crazed;
Your wits, old gentleman, are off the hinges.

DICAEOLOGOS

You are a vile blasphemer and buffoon.

ADICAEOLOGOS

Go on! you pelt me—but it is with roses.

DICAEOLOGOS

A scoffer!

ADICAEOLOGOS

Every word your malice vents
Weaves a fresh wreath of triumph for my brows.

DICAEOLOGOS

A parricide!

ADICAEOLOGOS

Proceed, and don't spare me—
You shower down gold upon me.

DICAEOLOGOS

Lead, not gold,
Would have been your retribution in times past.

ADICAEOLOGOS

Yes, but times present cover me with glory.

537

Aristophanes

DICAEOLOGOS

You are too wicked.

ADICAEOLOGOS

You are too weak.

DICAEOLOGOS

Thank your own self, if our Athenian fathers
Coop up their sons at home, and fear to trust them
Within your schools, conscious that nothing else
But vice and folly can be learned from you.

ADICAEOLOGOS

I think, friend, yours is but a ragged trade.

DICAEOLOGOS

And yours, oh shame! a thriving one, though late,
A perfect scamp, you tramped the street
With beggar's wallet crammed with hungry scraps.

ADICAEOLOGOS

Oh! what rare wisdom you remind me of!

DICAEOLOGOS

Oh, what rank folly theirs, who rule this city,
And let it nourish such a pest as you,
To sap the morals of the rising age.

ADICAEOLOGOS

You'll not inspire your pupil with these notions,
Old hoary-headed time!

DICAEOLOGOS

I will inspire him,
If he has grace to shun the malady
Of your eternal clack.

ADICAEOLOGOS

Turn to me, youth!
And let him rail at leisure.

538

THE CLOUDS

DICAEOLOGOS

Keep your distance,
And lay your hands upon him at your peril.

CHORUS (*interposing*)

Come, no more wrangling. Let us hear you both;
You of the former time, produce your rules
Of ancient discipline—of modern, you—
So that, both weighed, the candidate may judge
Who offers fairer, and choose between you.

DICAEOLOGOS

I close with the proposal.

ADICAEOLOGOS

It's agreed.

CHORUS

But which of you shall open?

ADICAEOLOGOS

That shall be he:
I yield him that point; and in reply,
My words, like arrows leveled at a butt,
Shall pierce him through and through; then, if he rallies,
If he comes on again with a rejoinder,
I'll launch a swarm of syllogisms at him,
That, like a nest of hornets, shall belabor him,
Till they have left him not an eye to see with.

CHORUS

Now, sirs, exert your utmost care,
And gravely for the charge prepare;
The well-ranged hoard of thought explore,
Where sage experience keeps her store;
All the resources of the mind
Employment in this cause will find,
And he, who gives the best display
Of argument, shall win the day:

Wisdom this hour at issue stands,
And gives her fate into your hands;
Yours is a question that divides
And draws out friends on different sides:
Therefore on you, who, with such zealous praise,
Applaud the discipline of former days,
On you I call; now is your time to show
You merit no less praise than you bestow.

DICAEOLOGOS

Thus summoned, I prepare myself to speak
Of manners primitive, and that good time,
Which I have seen, when discipline prevailed,
And modesty was sanctioned by the laws,
No babbling then was suffered in our schools;
The scholar's test was silence. The whole group
In orderly procession sallied forth
Right onward, without straggling, to attend
Their classes in harmonics; though the snow
Fell on them thick as grain, the hardy brood
Breasted the storm uncloaked: their harps were strummed
Not to ignoble strains, for they were taught
A loftier key, whether to chant the name
Of Pallas, terrible amid the blaze
Of cities overthrown, or wide and far
To spread, as custom was, the echoing peal.
There let no low buffoon intrude his tricks,
Let no capricious quavering on a note,
No running of divisions high and low
Break the pure stream of harmony; no scholar
Practicing wanton warblings out of place—
Woe to his back that so was found offending!
Hard stripes and heavy would reform his taste.
Decent and chaste their postures in the school
Of their gymnastic exercises; none
Exposed an attitude that might provoke
Irregular desire; their lips never moved
In love-inspiring whispers, and their walks
From eyes obscene were sacred and secure,
Hot herbs, the old man's diet, were proscribed;

540

THE CLOUDS

No radish, anise, parsley decked their board;
No rioting, no reveling was there
At feast or frolic, no unseemly touch
Or signal that inspires the hint impure.

ADICAEOLOGOS

Why these are maxims obsolete and stale.

DICAEOLOGOS

Yet so were trained the heroes, who imbrued
The field of Marathon with hostile blood;
This discipline it was that braced their nerves
And fitted them for conquest. You, indeed,
At great Athena's festival produce
Your martial dancers, not as they once were,
But smothered underneath the tawdry load
Of cumbrous armor, till I sweat to see them
Dangling their shields in such an unseemly way
As mars the sacred measure of the dance.
Be wise, therefore, young man, and turn to me.
Turn to the better guide, so you shall learn
To scorn the noisy market place, shun the bath,
And turn with blushes from the impure scene:
Then conscious innocence shall make you bold
To spurn the injurious, but to reverend age
Meek and submissive, rising from your seat
To pay the homage due, nor shall you ever
Wring a parent's soul, or stain your own.
In purity of manners you shall live
A bright example; vain shall be the lures
Of the stage-wanton floating in her dance,
Vain all her arts to snare you in her arms,
And strip you of your virtue and good name.
No petulant reply shall you oppose
To fatherly commands, nor taunting vent
Irreverent mockery on his hoary head,
Poor thanks for all his fond parental care.

ADICAEOLOGOS

Yes, my brave youth, follow his fine rules,
And learn by them to be a mere swine,

541

Driveler and dolt—I swear by Bacchus,
Folly and foul contempt shall be your doom.

DICAEOLOGOS

Not so, but fair and fresh in youthful bloom
Among our young athletes you shall shine;
Not in the market place loitering time away
In gossip, like our gang of idlers,
Nor in some vexatious paltry suit
Wrangling and quibbling in our petty courts.
But in the solemn academic grove,
Crowned with the modest reed, fit converse hold
With your collegiate equals; there serene,
Calm as the scene around you, underneath
The fragrant foliage where the ilex spreads,
Where the deciduous poplar strews her leaves,
Where the tall elm tree and wide-stretching plane
Sigh to the fanning breeze, you shall inhale
Sweet odors wafted in the breath of spring.
This is the regimen that will insure
A healthful body and a vigorous mind,
A countenance serene, expanded chest,
Heroic stature and a temperate tongue;
But take these modern masters, and behold
These blessings all reversed; a pallid cheek,
Shrunk shoulders, chest contracted, sapless limbs,
A tongue that never rests, and mind debased,
By their vile sophistry perversely taught
To call good evil, evil good, and be
That thing, which nature spurns at, that disease,
A mere Antimachus, the sink of vice.

CHORUS

Oh sage instructor, how sublime
These maxims of the former time!
How sweet this unpolluted stream
Of eloquence, how pure the theme!
Thrice happy they, whose lot was cast
Among the generation past,

542

THE CLOUDS

When virtuous morals were displayed
And these grave institutes obeyed.
Now you, who vaunt yourself so high,
Prepare; we wait for your reply,
And recollect, before you start,
You take in hand no easy part;
Well did he speak, and reasons good
By better only are withstood;
Sharpen your wits then, or you'll meet
Contempt as certain as defeat.

ADICAEOLOGOS

I'm ready, full up to the throat
And almost choked with plethora of words,
Impatient to discharge them. I know
The mighty masters of the modern school
Call me the Lower Logic, so distinguished
From the old practice of the ancient time,
By him personified; which name of honor
I gained as the projector of that method,
Which can confute and puzzle all the courts
Of law and justice—An invention worth
Thousands to them who practice it, whereas
It nonsuits all opponents—Let that pass.
Now take a sample of it in the ease,
With which I'll baffle this old vaunting pedant
With his warm baths, that he indeed forbids.
Listen, old man, discuss, if you please,
Your excellent good reason for this rule,
That interdicts warm bathing.

DICAEOLOGOS

Simply this—
I hold it a relaxer, rendering men
Effeminate and feeble.

ADICAEOLOGOS

Wait awhile—
I have you on the hook. Answer me this—
Of all the heroes Jupiter has fathered,

543

Which is for strength, for courage, and a course
Of labors most renowned?

DICAEOLOGOS

I know of none
Superior in those qualities to Hercules.

ADICAEOLOGOS

And who ever heard Herculean baths were cold?
Yet Hercules himself, you admit, was strong.

DICAEOLOGOS

Yes, this is in the very style of the times;
These are the dialectics now in fashion
With our young sophists, who frequent the baths,
While the gymnasium starves.

ADICAEOLOGOS

I grant you this;
It is the style of the times, by you condemned,
By me approved, and not without good cause;
For how else does ancient Nestor talk?
Can Homer err? Were all his wise men fools?
They are my witnesses.—Now for this tongue,
This member out of use by his decree,
Not so by mine.—His scholar must be silent
And chaste—damping prescriptions both—
For what good fortune ever did befall
The mute and modest? give me a case.

DICAEOLOGOS

Many—Chaste Peleus obtained his sword so.

ADICAEOLOGOS

His sword! and what did Peleus gain by that?
Battle and blows this modest Peleus gained;
While mean Hyperbolus, whose wretched craft
Was lamp-making, by craft of viler sort
Collected thousands of solid coins, not swords.

544

THE CLOUDS

But continence befriended Peleus so,
He won the goddess Thetis to his bed.

And drove her out of it—for he was cold,
Languid and listless: she was brisk and stirring,
And sought the sport elsewhere. Now are you answered?
Indeed, you're in your dotage. Look, young sir,
These are the fruits of continence: you see
What pleasure you must forfeit to preserve it—
All the delights that woman can bestow;
No amorous sports to catch the fair one's smile,
No luscious dainties shall you then partake,
No gay convivial revels, where the glass
With peals of laughter circulates around;
These you must sacrifice, and without these
What is your life? So much for your delights.
Now let us see how your score stands with nature—
You're in some scrape we'll say—intrigue—adultery—
You're caught, convicted, crushed—for what can save you?
You have no powers of speech—but armed by me,
You're up to all occasions: fear nothing;
Even give your genius scope; laugh, frolic, sport,
And flout at shame; for should a cuckold
Detect you in the fact, you shall so pose him
In his appeal, that nothing shall stick to you;
For Jove shall take the blame from off your shoulders,
Being himself a cuckold-making god,
And you a poor frail mortal—Why should you
Be wiser, stronger, purer than a god?

But what if this other scholar should incur
The adulterer's correction, pilled and sanded,
And garnished with a radish in his crupper,
The scoff of all beholders—What fine quirk
Will clear him at that pinch, but he must pass
For a most perfect Ganymede?

545

ADICAEOLOGOS

What then?
Where is the harm?

DICAEOLOGOS

Can greater harm befall him?

ADICAEOLOGOS

What will you say if I can confute you here?

DICAEOLOGOS

Nothing—my silence shall confess your triumph.

ADICAEOLOGOS

Come on then—answer what I ask.
Our advocates—what are they?

DICAEOLOGOS

Catamites.

ADICAEOLOGOS

Our tragic poets—what are they?

DICAEOLOGOS

The same.

ADICAEOLOGOS

Good, very good!—our demagogues—

DICAEOLOGOS

No better.

ADICAEOLOGOS

See there! Don't you see that you are foiled?
Cast your eyes around this company!

DICAEOLOGOS

I do.

ADICAEOLOGOS

And what do you discover?

546

The Clouds

Dicaeologos

Numerous birds
Of the same filthy feather, so Heaven help me!
This man I see; and this, and this fine fop
With his curled locks. To all these I can swear.

Adicaeologos

What do you say then?

Dicaeologos

I say I am confuted—
Here, wagtails, catch my cloak—I'll be among you.

Socrates (*to* Strepsiades, *just returned*)

Now, friend, what do you say?
Who shall school your son?

Strepsiades

School him and scourge him, take him to yourself.
And mind you whet him to an edge on both sides,
This for slight skirmish, that for stronger work.

Socrates

Don't be afraid; we'll finish him to your content
A perfect sophist.

Pheidippides

Perfect skin and bone—
That I can well believe.

Socrates

No more—Away! (*Exit* Strepsiades.)

Pheidippides

Trust me you've made a rod for your own back.
(*Follows* Socrates *into the house*.)

Chorus (*addressing the Spectators*)

Now to our candid judges we shall tell
What recompense they may expect from us,

547

If they indeed are studious to deserve it:
First, on your new-sown grounds in kindly showers,
Postponing other calls, we will descend.
The bearing branches of your vines shall sprout,
Nor scorched with summer heats nor chilled with rain.
This to our friends who serve us—but to him,
Who dares to slight us, let that mortal hear,
And tremble at the vengeance which awaits him:
Nor wine nor oil shall that man's farm produce;
For when his olive trees shall yield their fruit,
And his ripe vineyard tempts the gatherer's hand,
We'll batter him to ruin, lay him bare;
And if we catch him with his roof untiled,
Heavens! how we'll drench him with a pelting storm
Of hail and rain incessant! above all,
Let him beware upon the wedding night;
When he brings home his own or kinsman's bride,
Let him look to it! Then we'll come down in torrents,
So that he shall rather take his chance in Egypt,
Than stand the vengeful soaking we will give him.

(*Enter* STREPSIADES *with a sack of meal on his shoulder, talking to himself.*)

STREPSIADES

Lo! here's the fifth day gone—the fourth—the third—
The second too—day of all days to me
Most hateful and accursed—the dreadful eve,
Ushering the new moon, that lets in the tide
Of happy creditors, all sworn against me,
To rack and ruin me beyond redemption.
I, like a courteous debtor, who would
Soften their flinty bosoms, thus accost them—
"Ah, my good sir, this payment comes upon me
At a bad time, excuse me—That bill's due,
But you'll extend your grace—This you will cancel,
And totally acquit me."—By no means;
All with one voice cry out, they will be paid,
And I must be hounded in the bargain,
And threatened with a writ to mend the matter—
Well, let it come! They may do their worst;

THE CLOUDS

I don't care if my son has learned the trick
Of this new rhetoric, as will appear
When I have beaten on this door—(*knocks at the door*)—Boy,
    boy! come out!   (*Enter* SOCRATES.)

SOCRATES

Hail to Strepsiades!

STREPSIADES

Thrice hail to Socrates!
But first I beg you (*setting down the meal against the door*) to take
    this dole of meal
In token of the reverence I bear you;
And now, if you please, tell me of my son,
Your late novitiate. Is he making progress?

SOCRATES

He apprehends acutely.

STREPSIADES

Oh brave news!
Oh the transcendent excellence of fraud!

SOCRATES

Yes, you may forget your creditors—

STREPSIADES

And their vouchers too?

SOCRATES

Even if they had a thousand.

STREPSIADES (*singing and dancing*)

Then I'll sing out my song, and sing aloud,
And it shall be—Woe, woe to all your gang,
You money-jobbing caitiffs, usurers, sharks!
Away with your registers, your cents-per-cent;
I fear you no more; you cannot hook me now.
Oh! such a son I have in training for you,
Armed with a two-edged tongue that cuts both sides,

549

The stay, support and pillar of my house,
The scourge of my tormentors, the redeemer
Of a most wretched father—Call him out,
Call him, I say, and let my eyes feast on him—
What ho! My son, my boy—Your father calls;
Come and show yourself.   (*Enter* PHEIDIPPIDES.)

SOCRATES

Look at him!

STREPSIADES

My dear—my darling—

SOCRATES

There! you have your darling.

STREPSIADES

Joy, joy, my son! all joy—for now you wear
A face of a right character and cast,
A wrangling, quibbling, contradicting face;
Now you have it neatly on the tongue—
The very quirk of the time—"What's that you say?
What is it?"—Shifting from yourself the wrong
To him who suffers it—an arch conceit
To make a transfer of iniquity,
When it has served your turn—Yes, you will pass;
You've the right Attic stamp upon your forehead.
Now let me see a sample of your service,
For indeed you owe me a good turn.

PHEIDIPPIDES

What vexes you, my father?

STREPSIADES

What! the moon,
This day both new and old.

PHEIDIPPIDES

Both in one day?
Ridiculous!

550

THE CLOUDS

STREPSIADES

No matter—It's the day that
Will bring my creditors upon my back
All in a swarm together.

PHEIDIPPIDES

Let them swarm!
We'll smother 'em if they dare to call
One day two days.

STREPSIADES

What should hinder them?

PHEIDIPPIDES

What, do you ask? Can the same woman be
Both young and old at once?

STREPSIADES

They speak by law:
The statute bears them out.

PHEIDIPPIDES

But they misconstrue
The spirit of the statute.

STREPSIADES

What's that?

PHEIDIPPIDES

Time-honored Solon was the people's friend—

STREPSIADES

This has no bearing on the case of new or old.

PHEIDIPPIDES

And he appointed two days for the process,
The old and new day—the one for citation
The other for payment—

Aristophanes

STREPSIADES

Why did he name two days?

PHEIDIPPIDES

Why, so one might warn men of their debts,
The other serve them to escape the payment;
Otherwise they would be caught by the heels, as sure as fate,
On the new moon ensuing.

STREPSIADES

And so then
Upon the former day they commence
Their doles of first fruits
And not at the new moon?

PHEIDIPPIDES

Yes, because
They're hungry feeders, and make haste to thrust
Their greedy fingers in the public dish.

STREPSIADES

Away then, you witless creditors, away!
We are the wise ones, we are the true sort;
You are but blocks, mob, cattle, empty casks—
  Therefore with ecstasy I'll raise
  My jocund voice in fortune's praise,
  And, oh rare son!—Oh happy me!
  The burden of my song shall be;
  For hear! each passing neighbor cries—
  All hail, Strepsiades the wise!
  Across the market place as I walk,
  I and my son the public talk,
  All striving who shall have to boast
  He praised me first, or praised me most—
  And now, my son, my welcome guest,
  Enter my house and grace my feast.
  (*Exeunt* STREPSIADES *and* PHEIDIPPIDES. *Enter* PASIAS *and a*
  WITNESS.)

552

PASIAS

Should this man be permitted to go on
At such a desperate rate? It must not be.
Better for him to have broken up at once
Than to be so beset. Therefore
I am forced upon this hostile course,
Empowering you to summon my debtor
For the recovery of my property—
I will not make my country blush,
But I must rouse Strepsiades—   (*Enter* STREPSIADES.)

STREPSIADES

Who's this?

PASIAS

The old and new day call upon you, sir.

STREPSIADES (*to the spectators*)

Notice that this man has named two days—
And for what debt do you assail me?

PASIAS

For the many good dollars that you took up at interest
To pay for your son's racer.

STREPSIADES

I a racer?
Do you hear him? Can you not all witness
How mortally and from my soul I hate
All the whole racing calendar?

PASIAS

What then?
You swore to the gods you would pay me.

STREPSIADES

I grant you, in my folly I did swear,
But then my son had not attained the art
Of the new unconfutable logic.

553

PASIAS

And have you now the face to stand
Against all evidence?

STREPSIADES

Assuredly—
Otherwise, what's the good of my schooling?

PASIAS

And do you dare, knowing it's a falsehood,
To call the great gods to witness your oath,
When I shall put it to you?

STREPSIADES

What great gods?

PASIAS (*starting at the question*)
Mercury, Neptune, Jupiter himself—

STREPSIADES

To Jupiter, sure!
Paying half a dollar for the honor.

PASIAS

Insolent wretch, you'll perish in your folly!

STREPSIADES

Oh! that this madman were well scrubbed with salt
To save his brains from addling!

PASIAS

Down with you!
Do you make sport of me?

STREPSIADES

—I warrant
He'll take at least six gallons for a dressing.

THE CLOUDS

PASIAS

May great Jove and all the gods deal with me
As I will handle you for this buffoonery!

STREPSIADES

I thank you for your gods—They're pleasant fellows—
But as for your Jupiter, the learned and wise
Consider him a very silly thing to swear by.

PASIAS

Very well, you rash man! The time will come
When you'll wish you'd never said these words:
But will you pay the debt or won't you?
Tell me, and dismiss me.

STREPSIADES

Set your mind at rest;
You shall have satisfaction in a twinkling—   (*Steps aside.*)

PASIAS

What do you think of this fellow?

WITNESS

He will pay you.

STREPSIADES (*returning*)

Where is this dun of mine? Come here, friend,
How do you call this thing?

PASIAS

A kneading trough,
Or, as we say, a cardopus—

STREPSIADES

Go to!
Do you think I'll pay my money to a blockhead,
Who calls this kneading trough a *cardopus*?
I tell you, man, it's a *cardopa*—
Go, go, you won't get a cent from me,
You and your *cardopus*.

555

PASIAS

Won't you pay me?

STREPSIADES

Assure yourself I will not—Away! away!
Won't you get out of here, and quit my doors?

PASIAS

I'm going, but take this with you: if I live,
I'll sue you before night.

STREPSIADES

You'll lose your suit, and your fifty dollars besides.
I'm sorry for your loss, but who can help it?
You may thank your cardopus for that.
(*Exit* PASIAS *and* WITNESS. *Enter* AMYNIAS, *followed by a* WIT-
NESS.)

AMYNIAS

Ah me, ah me!

STREPSIADES

Who's that with his Ah me?
Whom has Carcinus * sent among us now—
Which of his doleful deities?

AMYNIAS

Alas!
Do you know who I am? I am
A wretch made up of woes—

STREPSIADES

A woeful wretch—
Granted! go on.

AMYNIAS

Oh inauspicious chance!
Oh you hardhearted, chariot-breaking fates!
Oh! Athena my destroyer, what a crash
You have given me!
* Inferior tragic poet noted for his doleful scenes

STREPSIADES

Ha! what ails you?

AMYNIAS

Do not mock my miseries, but bid your son
Repay what he has borrowed.

STREPSIADES

What do you mean?
What should my son repay?

AMYNIAS

The sum I lent him.

STREPSIADES

Is that it? Then your case is desperate;
Truly you're out of luck.

AMYNIAS

I'm out of everything—
I overthrew my chariot—By the gods,
That's being *out,* with a vengeance.

STREPSIADES

Bah—a trifle!

AMYNIAS

But, sir, my lawful money is no trifle;
I'll not be kicked out of that.

STREPSIADES

I'll tell you what you are—Out of your wits.

AMYNIAS

How so?

STREPSIADES

Because your brain seems leaky.

557

AMYNIAS

By Mercury, I'll lock you up,
If you don't pay me.

STREPSIADES

Wait, one short question—
When Jove rains on us, does he rain fresh water,
Or only vapors that the sun exhales?
Answer me that.

AMYNIAS

I don't care what he rains;
I don't bother myself with such conceits.

STREPSIADES

And do you think a man who has no wit
To argue upon these rare points will argue me
Out of my money?

AMYNIAS

Let your debt go on,
And pay me the interest.

STREPSIADES

What's that?
What kind of thing is interest?

AMYNIAS

A thing that grows from day to day,
And month to month, swelling as time rolls on
To a round sum of money.

STREPSIADES

Well defined!
One question more—What do you think of the sea?
Isn't it fuller now than ever before?

AMYNIAS

No, by the Gods! not fuller, but as full:
That's my judgment of it.

558

THE CLOUDS

STREPSIADES

Oh you miser!
You'd stint the ocean, and yet cram
Your swelling coffers till they overflow—
Get me a whip, that I may lash him hence:
Take to your heels—away!

AMYNIAS

I'll gather
My witnesses against you.

STREPSIADES

Get out! get out!
Away! you ass, you!

AMYNIAS (*to the spectators*)

Isn't this an outrage?

STREPSIADES (*smacking his whip*)

Will you not bolt? will you not buckle kindly
Into your geers, or must I mount and goad you
Under the crupper, till you kick and wince
For very madness? Oho! Are you off?
A welcome riddance—All the devils drive
You and your cursed chariot away from here!

(*Exit* STREPSIADES.)

CHORUS

Mark here how rarely it succeeds
To build our trust on guilty deeds:
Mark how this old cajoling elf,
Who sets a trap to catch himself,
Falsely believes he has found the way
To hold his creditors at bay.
Too late he'll curse the Sophists' school,
That taught his son to cheat by rule,
And trained the modest lips of youth
In the vile art of torturing truth;
A modern logic much in use,
Invented for the law's abuse;

559

A subtle knack of spying flaws
To cast in doubt the clearest cause,
Whereby, in honesty's despite,
The wrong side triumphs over the right—
Alas! short triumph he must have,
Who glories that his son's a knave:
Ah foolish father, the time will come
You'll wish that son of yours were dumb.

    (STREPSIADES *rushes out of the house in great confusion, followed by* PHEIDIPPIDES.)

STREPSIADES

Ho there! Ho! for pity's sake some help!
Friends, kinsmen, countrymen! turn out and help!
Oh! my poor head, my cheeks are bruised to jelly—
Help by all means!—Oh, you ungracious cub,
Would you beat your father?

PHEIDIPPIDES

I would!

STREPSIADES

There, there! he admits he would beat his father.

PHEIDIPPIDES

I admit it, good father!

STREPSIADES

Parricide!
Impious assassin! Sacrilegious wretch!

PHEIDIPPIDES

All, all, and more—You can't please me better;
I glory in these attributes. Go on!

STREPSIADES

Monster of turpitude!

PHEIDIPPIDES

Crown me with roses!

560

The Clouds

STREPSIADES

Wretch, will you strike your parent?

PHEIDIPPIDES

Piously,
And will maintain the right by which I do it.

STREPSIADES

Oh shameless villain! can there be a right
Against all nature to treat a father so?

PHEIDIPPIDES

That I shall soon make clear to your conviction.

STREPSIADES

You, you convince me?

PHEIDIPPIDES

With the greatest ease:
And I can work the proof two ways;
Therefore choose between them.

STREPSIADES

What do you mean?

PHEIDIPPIDES

I mean to say we argue up or down—
Take which you like. It comes to the same end.

STREPSIADES

Yes, and a precious end you've brought it to,
If all my care of you must end like this,
That I have brought you up to beat me,
(Which is a thing unnatural and profane)
And after justify it.

PHEIDIPPIDES

That I'll do.
By process clear and categorical,
So that you'll admit you're a convert
To a most wholesome beating.

STREPSIADES

Come on!
Give me your arguments—but spare your blows.

CHORUS

How to restrain this headstrong son of yours
Concerns you now, old man, to find the means,
For surely he could not be so confident
Without some cause; something there must be,
Some strong possession within himself,
That buoys him up to this high pitch of daring,
This bold assumption; that we may know this,
Give us distinctively the whole detail
From first to last how this contention sprang,
So we shall hear, and hearing, judge between you.

STREPSIADES

If it pleases you, I'll unfold the cause
Of this base treatment to your patient ears,
And thus it stands—When we had supped together,
As you all know, in a friendly way, I asked him
To take up his lute and give me the good song
Of old Simonides—"the ram was shorn"—
But he directly scoffed at my request—
It was a fashion out of date indeed—
He would not sit twanging the lute, not he;
It was not for him to cackle over his wine,
As if he were some wench working the hand-mill—
It was vulgar and unseemly—

PHEIDIPPIDES

Grossly so;
And wasn't it high time that I should beat you,
Who had no better manners than to make
Your guest chirp like a grasshopper?

STREPSIADES

These were his very words, and more than these;
For by and by he told me that Simonides

562

THE CLOUDS

Was a paltry poet. This you'll admit
Was a tough morsel, yet I gulped it down,
And passed it off by asking him to recite
Some passage out of Aeschylus, meanwhile
Fingering a myrtle wreath, as is the custom,
To grace the recitation—He indeed,
Flouting my offer, instantly replied—
"I judge your Aeschylus, of all our poets,
First of the spouters, incoherent, harsh,
Precipitous and turgid."—Oh my friends,
Wasn't this more than flesh and blood should bear?
Still, still I smothered rage within my heart,
And calmly said—"Call something else to mind
More to your taste and from some modern bard,
As long as it's good and worth the hearing—"
And then, would you believe it? he began
Reciting from Euripides—Great Jove,
Guard my chaste ears from such another dose!
A perilous long-winded tale of incest
Between son and daughter of the same sad mother.
Sick to the soul I spurned at such declaiming,
Adding, as well I might, all that my scorn
Of such vile trash could add! till, to be short,
Words led to words, and blows too, as it proved,
For leaping from his seat he sprung upon me,
Struck, buffeted, and banged me out of measure,
Throttled me, pounded me almost to dust—

PHEIDIPPIDES

And what less does that heretic deserve,
Who won't praise Euripides, the first
In wisdom of all poets?

STREPSIADES

He the first!
How my tongue itches!—but the rogue is ready;
He'll beat me if I answer.

PHEIDIPPIDES

And with reason.

STREPSIADES

What reason, graceless cub, will bear you out
For beating me, who in your baby age
Caressed you, dandled you upon my knee,
Watched every motion, humored all your wants?
Then if you lisped a syllable I caught it—
Bryn cried the infant—at once I gave you drink:
Mamman it mewed—and that indeed was bread:
Yes, I performed the nurse's dirtiest task,
And held you out before me at your needs;
And now in my necessity you showed
No mercy to the pressing calls of nature,
But having pummeled me till my poor bowels
Could hold no longer, kept me fast imprisoned
To struggle with occasion as I could.

CHORUS

Now every young man's heart beats an alarm,
Anxious to hear his advocate's appeal;
Which if he can establish, the same right,
Asserted by him, will devolve on all,
And beating then will be so much in vogue
That old men's skins will be reduced to cobwebs—
Now you, who hold up this new paradox,
See that you defend it well, for it asks
No trivial reasons to enforce persuasion.

PHEIDIPPIDES

Now gratefully the mind receives new lights,
Emerging from the shades of prejudice,
And casting old establishments aside!
Time was, till now, when every thought of mine
Was centered on the stable; then I had not
Three words upon my tongue without a stumble;
But now, since I've been put into the way
Of knowing better things, and the fine art
Of subtle disputation, I am bold
To meet this question, and convince my hearers
How right it is to punish this old sinner.

The Clouds

STREPSIADES

Mount, mount your chariot! Oh, if I could see you
Seated again behind your favorite horses,
Even though with four in hand, so that you kept
From driving me at such a pelting rate.

PHEIDIPPIDES

Now then I ask you, gathering up my thread
Where it was broken off, if you, my father,
When I was just a lad, spared my back?

STREPSIADES

No, for I studied all things for your good,
And therefore I corrected you.

PHEIDIPPIDES

Agreed.
I also am studious of your good,
And therefore I most lovingly correct you;
If beating is a proof of love, you have
Plenty of it, for by what exemption
Is your most sacred carcass freed from stripes
And mine made subject to them? Am I not
Freeborn as you? Tell me, if the son's in tears,
Should not the father weep?

STREPSIADES

By what rule
Of equity?

PHEIDIPPIDES

What equity is there
If none but children are to be chastised?
And grant they are, the proverb's in your teeth,
Which says old age is but a second childhood.
Again, if tears are seen to follow blows,
Shouldn't old men expiate faults with tears
Rather than children, who have more to plead
In favor of their failings?

565

STREPSIADES

Where's the law
That warrants this proceeding? There's none like that.

PHEIDIPPIDES

And what was your lawmaker but a man,
Mortal as you and I are? And though time
Has sanctified his statutes, may I not
Take up the cause of youth, as he of age,
And publish a new ordinance giving
Sons the right to correct their fathers,
Remitting and consigning to oblivion
All *ex post facto* beating? Look at instinct—
Ask nature how her brute creatures
Kick at their parents, which in no way differ
From lordly man, except that they compile
No laws, and hold their rights without a statute.

STREPSIADES

If you peck at your poor father
Like a young fighting cock, why don't you peck
Your dinner from the dunghill, and at night
Roost on a perch?

PHEIDIPPIDES

The cases aren't the same,
Nor does my master Socrates endorse
Rules so absurd.

STREPSIADES

Stop beating me then,
Or you'll preclude yourself.

PHEIDIPPIDES

What do you mean preclude?

STREPSIADES

Because the right I have of beating you
Will be your right in time over your son,
When you shall have one.

The Clouds

But if I have none,
All my sad hours are lost, and you die laughing.

STREPSIADES

There's no denying that.—What do you say, sirs?
I think there is something in his plea;
And as for us old sinners, to tell the truth,
If we deserve a beating we must bear it.

PHEIDIPPIDES

Hear me—there's more to come—

STREPSIADES

Then I am lost,
For I can bear no more.

PHEIDIPPIDES

Oh fear not,
But believe what I now have to tell you
Will cause you to make light of what is past,
For it will bring much comfort to you.

STREPSIADES

Let me have it:
If it is comfort, give it to me.

PHEIDIPPIDES

Then know,
From now on, I'm resolved to beat my mother
As I have beaten you.

STREPSIADES

What do you say? How?
Why this would outdo all you've done.

PHEIDIPPIDES

But what if I have not a proof
To excuse this beating?

STREPSIADES

Show me a proof that you have hanged yourself,
And, with your tutor Socrates besides you,
Gone to the devil together on a string;
Those excuses I'll thank you for—
Oh inauspicious goddesses, O Clouds!
By trusting you, these woes have come to me.

CHORUS

Evil events from evil causes spring,
And what you suffer flows from what you've done.

STREPSIADES

Why wasn't I forewarned? You saw that I was old,
And played upon my weak simplicity.

CHORUS

It's not for us to warn a willful sinner;
We do not stay him, but let him run his course,
Till roused by misfortunes, his conscience wakes,
And prompts him to appease the offended gods.

STREPSIADES

I feel my sorrows, but I own they're just:
Yes, you reforming Clouds, I'm duly punished
For my intended fraud.—And now, my son,
Join hands with me and let us go together
To work our vengeance on those base deceivers,
That Chaerephon and Socrates,
Who have duped us both.

PHEIDIPPIDES

Grace forbid
I should lift up my hand against my masters!

STREPSIADES

Yes, but fear avenging Jove,
God of your ancestors, and revere him.

THE CLOUDS

PHEIDIPPIDES

You're mad to talk to me of Jove—
Is there a god with such a name?

STREPSIADES

There is! there is!

PHEIDIPPIDES

There is no Jupiter, I tell you so;
Vortex has whirled him from his throne, and reigns
By right of conquest in the Thunderer's place.

STREPSIADES

It's false, no Vortex reigns but in my brain.

PHEIDIPPIDES

Laugh at your own dull joke and be a fool!

(*Exit* PHEIDIPPIDES.)

STREPSIADES (*striking his breast*)

Insufferable blockhead that I was;
What ailed me to court this Socrates,
Even to the exclusion of the immortal gods?
O Mercury, forgive me; don't be angry,
Dear tutelary god, but spare me still,
And cast a pitying eye upon my follies,
For I have been intemperate of tongue,
And dearly rue it—Oh my better genius,
Inspire me with your counsel how to act,
Whether by legal process to assail them,
Or by such apter means as you may tell.
I have it! Now you've inspired a thought;
Away with the lazy law; you are not for it.
With fire and torch I will fall upon them,
And send their school in smoke up to the Clouds.
Ho, Xanthias (*calling one of his slaves*), ho! bring me without delay
Your ladder and your ax, mount the roof,
Break up the rafters, drop the house upon them,
And bury the whole hive beneath the ruins.

569

(XANTHIAS *mounts the roof and begins working with his ax.*)
Hurry! if you love me, hurry! Oh, for a torch,
A blazing torch new lighted, to set fire
To the infernal edifice.—I vow
I'll soon unhouse the rascals, who now carry
Their heads so high, and roll them in the dust.

(*Enter a* DISCIPLE.)

FIRST DISCIPLE

Woe! mischief! misery!

STREPSIADES (*mounts the roof and fixes a torch to the joists*)
Torch, play your part:
And we shall muster up a conflagration.

FIRST DISCIPLE

What are you doing, fellow?

STREPSIADES

Chopping logic;
Arguing a knotty point with your house-beams.

SECOND DISCIPLE

Oh horror! Who has set our house on fire?

STREPSIADES

The very man whose cloak you nabbed so neatly.

SECOND DISCIPLE

Undone and ruined—!

STREPSIADES

Oh, how I hope so!
And so you'll be if this ax
Does not deceive my hopes, and I escape
With a whole neck.

(*Enter* SOCRATES.)

SOCRATES

Ho there! Who is that?
You there upon the roof—what are you doing?

570

THE CLOUDS

STREPSIADES

"Treading on air—contemplating the sun—"

SOCRATES

Ah me! I'm suffocated, smothered, lost—

(*Enter* CHAEREPHON.)

CHAEREPHON

Poor me, I'm melted, scorched, consumed—

STREPSIADES

Blasphemers, why did you insult the gods?
Dash, drive, demolish them! Their crimes are many,
But their contemptuous treatment of the gods,
Their impious blasphemies, exceed them all.

CHORUS

That is all!—The Chorus has fulfilled its part.

Further Reading

THE THREE MUSKETEERS by Alexandre Dumas

BELL, A. C. *Alexandre Dumas*. London: CASSELL, 1950.

DAVIDSON, A. F. *Alexandre Dumas*. Philadelphia: J. B. LIPPINCOTT CO., 1902.

MAUROIS, A. *Alexandre Dumas*. New York: ALFRED A. KNOPF, 1955.

SAUNDERS, E. *The Prodigal Father*. New York: LONGMANS, GREEN AND CO., 1951.

SPURR, H. A. *The Life and Writings of Alexandre Dumas*. New York: FREDERICK A. STOKES COMPANY, 1902.

LIVES OF THE ENGLISH POETS by Samuel Johnson

BOSWELL, JAMES. *The Life of Samuel Johnson, LL.D.* Edited by George Birkbeck Hill; revised and enlarged edition by L. F. Powell. In six volumes. Oxford: THE CLARENDON PRESS, 1934–1950.

REYNOLDS, SIR JOSHUA. *Portraits;* Character Sketches of Oliver Goldsmith, Samuel Johnson, and David Garrick. Edited by Frederick W. Hilles New York: MCGRAW-HILL, 1952.

KRUTCH, JOSEPH WOOD. *Samuel Johnson*. New York: HENRY HOLT AND COMPANY, 1944.

CLIFFORD, JAMES. *Young Sam Johnson*. New York: MCGRAW-HILL, 1955.

ETHICS by Baruch Spinoza

HAMPSHIRE, S. *Spinoza*. (Pelican Philosophy Series.) Harmondsworth, Eng.: PENGUIN BOOKS, 1951.

JOACHIM, H. H. *Study in the Ethics of Spinoza*. Oxford: CLARENDON PRESS, 1901.

KAYSER, R. *Spinoza, Portrait of a Spiritual Hero*. Introduction by Albert Einstein. New York: PHILOSOPHICAL LIBRARY, 1946.

POLLOCK, F. *Spinoza, His Life and Philosophy*. 2nd ed. New York: THE MACMILLAN COMPANY, 1899.

WOLFSON, H. A. *The Philosophy of Spinoza*. 2 vols, Cambridge: HARVARD UNIVERSITY PRESS, 1934.

THE CLOUDS by Aristophanes

CORNFORD, F. M. *The Origin of Attic Comedy*. New York: LONGMANS, GREEN AND COMPANY, 1914.

CROISET, M. *Aristophanes and the Political Parties at Athens*. Translated by James Loeb. New York: G. P. PUTNAM'S SONS, 1909.

EHRENBERG, V. *The People of Aristophanes*. Cambridge: HARVARD UNIVERSITY PRESS, 1951.

JAEGER, W. "The Comic Poetry of Aristophanes," in *Paideia: The Ideals of Greek Culture*. vol. 1. Translated by G. Highet. New York: OXFORD UNIVERSITY PRESS, 1939.

LORD, L. E. *Aristophanes, His Plays and His Influence*. New York: LONGMANS, GREEN AND COMPANY, 1925.